Ants,
Indians,
and Little
Dinosaurs

Ants,
Indians,
and Little
Dinosaurs

SELECTED FROM *NATURAL HISTORY*

AND EDITED BY ALAN TERNES

THE AMERICAN MUSEUM
OF NATURAL HISTORY

CHARLES SCRIBNER'S SONS

New York

Contents

Ants,
Indians,
and Little
Dinosaurs

Introduction

ALAN TERNES

This book might never have come into being if the offices of *Natural History* Magazine were in one of those monolithic buildings that rise above midtown Manhattan. Then the trips to and from work would be a mindless routine, from subway tunnel to Muzak-coddled elevator, to numbered floor and numbered door of a rectangular office. If my colleagues and I occupied such a precisely defined office niche, I might be able to give you a straightforward description of *Natural History,* the magazine from which all the articles in this book were selected.

Somewhere above the Hall of Man and below Margaret Mead's office, the magazine occupies a floor of the tower furthermost from the main entrance of The American Museum of Natural History. The Museum, at Central Park West and Seventy-ninth Street in New York City, is a gigantic baroque assemblage of halls and passageways that would frighten the hunchback of Notre Dame. With switchbacks, detours, stairs, and a couple of meanders to look at displays, the distance from the entrance to my desk is about four city blocks.

Carved out of a round tower, my office has one curved and two fairly straight walls, and one point and several oblique corners. It sometimes seems like a small, misshapen schooner heading generally southeast toward the Caribbean, or the coast of South America, or Africa—depending on the currents in my mind and the manuscripts on my desk.

Every day, depending on the route of my four-block walk, I travel to distant places and times. Often I go through the huge Akeley Hall of African Mammals, around the rushing herd of elephants, past burning Sudanese plains, deep into the Congo to stand with Mbuti pygmies beside a glowing fire and listen to them sing to their forest gods. Or go by way of the Hall of Ocean Life, pausing to gaze up at the ever-awesome blue whale, and then pass through the Hall of North American Forests, crawling on the litter with giant caterpillars, lounging in the shade of redwoods.

And there are the seemingly infinite passageways and rooms behind the scenes, where the 200-odd scientists and researchers pursue their wonders. Although I walk to work along Central Park, on stormy days I sometimes hitch a ride home with one of my suburb-dwelling colleagues. We have found a semi-secret route through subterranean passages that enables us to reach the parking lot on the opposite side of the Museum without going outside. Treading through that labyrinth, time seems suspended. We squeeze past dusty dioramas that drew crowds a half-century ago, step over unopened boxes with labels from distant continents, climb over a giant clamshell, dinosaur bones, and a meteorite. When we step out into the parking lot, the return to our time and culture always gives me a jolt.

From its conception more than a century ago, The American Museum of Natural History has been a national museum with an international scope—and *Natural History* Magazine, since its beginnings in 1900, has had the same domain. One pleasant perquisite of working for such a magazine is that its editors occasionally travel to Africa, the Amazon, and other exotic regions of the earth. To clear my desk before each trip, I sometimes pass a lonely night stint at my office. If the Museum seems weird in general, you should experience it at 3 a.m. With most of the lights off, the four-block walk becomes much longer. The murky artifacts loom much larger. Many of the objects, to their original owners, had magical powers—and late at night I begin to believe in magic. I am not alone in having these feelings.

The night guards prefer to walk in pairs on their rounds through the deserted halls.

After my first year of uncertain wanderings to and from work, I decided to visit every nook and cranny of the Museum, starting with the public areas and then taking in all the private areas that my key would open, as well as any area where I could inveigle a guard or a curator to let me enter. After four years, I have seen only about one-third of the Museum.

The point of all this rambling is that I am certain all the editors of *Natural History* during its seventy-five-year history have been profoundly affected by their environment. In many ways, the magazine and this book are a product of The American Museum of Natural History, in all its bewildering, glorious diversity. The articles appear here in substantially the form in which they were first published in the magazine.

Time Magazine once referred to *Natural History* as the "offbeat" nature magazine. After a great deal of thought, I have concluded that the writer meant that *Natural History* is not in step with *Time,* or *Newsweek,* or daily newspapers and television. I like that thought. A monthly magazine about man and the natural world should not compete with the news media.

With its peculiar ecological perspective, *Natural History* is often a couple of beats ahead, as witnessed by its articles over the years on energy, food, and population. Admittedly, things go in cycles, and the difference between being a couple of beats ahead or behind is a moot point. Still, my colleagues and I would rather, like Thoreau, listen to the beat of our own drum.

Offbeat *Natural History* marches with vigor—and with gratitude to its 350,000 loyal subscribers—into its seventy-fifth year. And the offbeat goes on.

PART ONE

On Fauna and
a Stone Age Friend

Naturalists may attempt to achieve a scientific objectivity toward the creatures they study, but fortunately for editors they invariably fail. Some, such as observant J. Frank Dobie, make no attempt to hide their emotional feelings toward an animal; Alan M. Beck, gathering data for his doctorate at Johns Hopkins University, carefully recorded for days the feeding times and places of a stray dog but admits he selected the dog and named him "Shag," because "I had become fond of him." Affection and compassion pervade most of these articles —even the annoying mosquito wins Marston Bates's admiration for its ingenuity in finding breeding sites.

These scientists, as they observe and begin to understand the lives of animals, develop a sense of stewardship. They become eloquent spokesmen for the species. Where can the elk live in the winter, asks Olaus J. Murie. "How much *good* land have we given to wildlife? Are we, after all, giving the elk a 'dirty deal'?" Victor B. Scheffer urges the establishment of "non-hunting preserves in scenic waterways" for the killer whale. The "gentle and elegant" cheetah will surely become extinct

7

unless it "is more strictly protected" in Africa, concludes George B. Schaller.

Finally, the study of other creatures can lead to a better understanding of our own species. T. C. Schneirla's studies of ants, Nikolaas Tinbergen's observations of gulls, and Maximilian Renner's analysis of internal clocks in bees are all avenues for insights into human social behavior. Psychologist Frank A. Beach shows the changing attitudes toward animals by tracing their treatment in the courts. Archie Carr, despite his personal terror, takes advantage of a snake bite to analyze the reasoning underlying folk medicine. And ornithologist E. Thomas Gilliard in the remote mountains of New Guinea transcends the cultural gap between himself and a contemporary Neolithic man through their common interest in birds.

The Smart Coyote

J. FRANK DOBIE

[1942]

"Next to God," the Mexican country people say, "the coyote is the most astute animal on earth." Rangemen will sometimes admit that he is as smart as a cutting horse—and a cutting horse can "do everything but talk Mexican." He's at times even smarter than a steel trap, some trappers have conceded. He is so smart that centuries and centuries before the history of the native peoples of North America began to be recorded he had burned himself upon their imaginations and come to be both hero and clown of more tales than all the other animals of the continent combined have inspired.

The trouble—from the standpoint of the scientific mind—is that evidence of the coyote's smartness so often edges off into pure folklore. I have been a long time taking down evidence from many witnesses and sifting it. I am going to start out with cold facts; if I run into the yarns, I'll make a sign and swear that I don't know whether I am telling the truth or not.

Like the rattlesnake and the droll little burrowing owl, the coyote will be associated with prairie dogs as long as a prairie dog is left in coyote country. The coyote is very fond of prairie dog meat, and the prairie dogs, always on guard—except when they are safe in their underground forts—and always alarming each other at the faintest suggestion of danger, are probably the most difficult of all small animals for beasts of prey to catch. But really smart people are various in their ingenuity.

One of the best observers and the most richly informed homemade naturalist I have ever known was

9

Don Alberto Guajardo, whose many years of ranching, soldiering, surveying, mining, hunting, and gathering medicinal plants for exportation had taken him over most of northern Mexico. He compiled history from ancient documents, read Latin, and spoke two other languages besides his native Spanish, but he always asserted that the best contributor to his education had been an old Lipan Indian.

One time during his boyhood, he told me, he went out hunting with this Lipan. This was back in the days when Apaches and Comanches still raided, and, suspecting danger, the old Indian and the boy hid in brush overlooking a valley well populated by prairie dogs. The sky was dark and threatening rain. Before long the boy saw a coyote come out among the prairie dogs on the edge of the "town," close to the base of the big hill on which the two hunters were hidden. The coyote was not aware of them. He went to scratching, scratching at a dog hole into which his approach had sent the owner, followed by neighbors into their respective holes.

"Surely," said Don Alberto to the old Lipan Indian, "that coyote does not think he can dig down to the bottom of a prairie dog hole."

"No, no," replied the old one. "He knows what he is doing. Wait with patience and you shall see."

By now thunder was rolling up, and the coyote was digging more energetically. This animal seems always to feel the approach of changing weather. The plan of the digger began to be apparent. He was merely pulling down the crater-like, encircling mounds of two or three prairie dog holes and using the dirt to throw up a rough V-shaped dam, the flanges pointing uphill, so that they would catch the water as it flowed down, thus directing it into the now unprotected holes enclosed by the V.

Presently the heavens turned loose. The rain was a regular gully-washer and fence-lifter. The water scooted down the hillsides in sheets. That caught by the coyote's dam poured into the holes. Meantime the coyote had placed himself back of the dam, at its apex, where he awaited results. The typical prairie dog hole has a roomy side-tunnel, or station, not far from its mouth, where the owner, with his family, can remain clear of the water at the bottom of his burrow. Sometimes the burrows are connected. Water will not reach the prairie dog and his store of food until the hole is filled from the bottom. Many a boy has failed to drown out a prairie dog by pouring buckets of water after him. But here a stream of water was being diverted into the holes. Before long the watching Indian and Mexican boy on the hillside saw a prairie dog emerge, only to be nabbed by the ingenious coyote.

Not long ago I spent a day and a night with H. C. (Pete) Gamison at his cabin overlooking Eagle Nest Lake in northern New Mexico. For nearly fifty years he has been hunting, poisoning, trapping lobo wolves and coyotes. He has enough education to give perspective to his natural intelligence and observations. Not many men alive know at first hand as much about the wolf family as he knows.

One time, he told me, he watched a pair of hungry coyotes out to catch a prairie dog. They tracked leisurely along, one right behind the other, toward the edge of a prairie dog town. Presently there was a great chattering at them. But the prairie dog they were headed for could see only the lead coyote, the one behind keeping his head down and his body hidden by that of the first. When near the mound on which the prairie dog stood nervously scolding, the lead coyote made a rush, and, of course, the prairie dog ducked. The sun was shining from a clear sky, and when the coyote leaped over the hole he darkened it with his shadow. He went on, other prairie dogs chattering and ducking, the noise growing dimmer as he passed.

But the second coyote had stopped when the first one leaped, and while the play was going on, he flattened himself out as flat as he could behind the dog mound. There he waited until the prairie dog should come up. Before long he reappeared, looking with intentness toward the enemy that had threatened and passed but was still in sight. It is the nature of a prairie dog to look for what has scared him. While this one was indulging his nature, expressing his displeasure at the same time, the accomplice of the first actor made a leap and caught him. Then there was a tussle over the morsel, the two coyotes soon tearing it to pieces and devouring it.

By coincidence, three or four days after Pete Gamison had enriched me with his coyote lore, I paid a visit to the veteran naturalist and teller of animal tales Ernest Thompson Seton, at Seton Village, near Santa Fe. After hearing talk on wolf sagacity, I came away with a copy of Mr. Seton's autobiography, *Trail of An Artist-Naturalist*. A few hours later, I read this passage:

"One coyote crouched behind a thick greasewood; the other walked openly toward a prairie dog that was yapping on its mound. He made a half-hearted rush as the prairie dog dived. The coyote far back behind the greasebush now rushed forward and crouched behind a bush that was only six feet from the prairie dog hole. Meanwhile Coyote No. 1 sauntered slowly forward. Presently the prairie dog peeped out. He saw that Coyote No. 1 was at a safe distance, and that he was going still farther away. The yapper became bold; he stepped right out and yapped at Coyote No. 1. Coyote No. 2 rushed forward and almost got him. In this case the trick failed, but obviously it must often be successful."

An old trail driver and cowman, J. H. Maltsberger, of Cotulla, Texas, not at all given to the fanciful tales he has often heard, told me that early one morning he saw a coyote closing up prairie dog holes in a certain part of a town. Later he got a prairie dog cut off from its own hole. Naturally it made for the next nearest hole—one that the coyote had with malice aforethought plugged. The hesitation at the closed door cost this prairie dog his life.

After bringing sheep and goats to America, the Spanish *conquistadores* soon came to recognize the coyote as the chief enemy of these small animals, though one encounters no record of its interfering with the spread of cattle and horses. The early Spanish historian

Clavigero describes the coyote as using its tail as a whip. Having picked out a fat sheep and seized it by the neck, the coyote was said to lash its victim in the rump to urge it to a convenient place for eating. This cunningly fantastic way of leading a sheep to its own slaughter may be doubted by some naturalists, but many shepherd people both in Mexico and the United States aver that it is true. The coyote is not strong enough to move a carcass in the manner of the mountain lion, and so if he moves it at all, he must use his wits.

In the old days before coyotes had been killed off sheep ranges and before wolf-proof fences had been put up to keep them out, dogs were essential to every shepherd guarding his flock, especially at night. Then it was common for one or more coyotes to make a feint attack in the darkness on one side of a flock, drawing all the dogs after them; meanwhile other coyotes cut in from an unprotected direction, getting their meat in such a hurry that they would be gone before the guards reappeared.

It is the neck of a chicken, as with goats or sheep, that the coyote aims to seize. His hold on the neck is not invariable, but whereas a coon will seize a chicken by the leg or wing, making off while the chicken's squawk arouses dog or man, the coyote is likely to kill the chicken immediately by biting it through the neck or head. He is a noisy fellow, but he will not be heard barking or howling while on the hunt, and he seems to recognize the value of silence in his victim as well as in himself.

Dogs may learn better than to attack porcupines, but few which do attack achieve a strategy that will save their faces from being quilled. Nat Straw, famous hunter and trapper of New Mexico, told me that examination of the stomachs of dead coyotes had frequently revealed porcupine quills as well as flesh, though he never found quills in the coyote's head. He was puzzled until a forest ranger described seeing a coyote root a porcupine over, seize it in the breast, which is spineless, and in this fashion gain his entrance.

Of all predatory animals, wolves are undoubtedly the most cooperative. Coyotes go beyond timber wolves in cooperation, for they relay and otherwise assist each other not only in running down game but in eluding their own pursuers. A mother coyote whose not-yet-grown offspring is being run by a pack of hounds will actually, after running a while with the young one, turn back and make right through the dogs, trying to lead them off the trail. It takes a great deal of training to prevent most dogs from switching on such a trail.

For ways that are dark and tricks that are effectual, followers of hounds in the vast brush country of southwestern Texas will tell you that the coyote is several laps ahead of the fox. One summer night while I was out with a group of these brush country hunters, we heard the dogs running for hours in an area hardly two miles square. The dogs were having a wonderful time; they were giving us wonderful hope and expectation; and I believe that at least one coyote—maybe more than one—was having a wonderful time.

An hour or so before daylight a man named Wright dropped out of the race, saying that he was going to take a nap on a nice bed of mesquite grass he had spied close to a mesquite tree and that he would rejoin us when we came back his way. Upon our return after sunup he told how, at daybreak, he had heard the dogs making eager music fully a half mile off, seemingly coming his way, when two coyotes trotted into sight. One of them looked mighty hot and tuckered out; the other appeared to be entirely fresh. They did not sense him, apparently, and presently the tired coyote disappeared in a direction leading away from the hounds while the fresh one tore out in their direction. It is certain that the dogs did not run down a thing on that hunt.

Coyote teamwork after jack rabbits, antelopes, and an occasional deer has been observed many times. It is the nature of these animals to circle when pursued. Coyotes will take stands—pretty much as mustang hunters used to in running down the great-circling mustangs. As a fagged pursuer comes up behind the game, he is relieved and drops out for a rest until it is his turn to run again.

Riding one day over a divide in Montana with another rangeman, Malcolm S. Mackay, in *Cow Range and Hunting Trail,* tells how he noticed a coyote sitting on a hillside and intently watching something in the valley below. Looking in the same direction, the men soon saw another coyote coming behind a jack rabbit. After a circle that covered perhaps a mile, the rabbit passed near the waiting coyote, which now dashed in while the first coyote dropped out.

"Going downhill, the coyote would almost catch Mr. Jack Rabbit. He would have caught him if Mr. Jack had not done some real dodging. Going uphill, the long springy legs of Mr. Jack gave him a distinct advantage, but in that country there are as many valleys as there are hills, and so what the jack gained going up the coyotes gained going down. The race went on for three complete laps. Then, after having saved his bacon numerous times by flattened-out dodges, the jack quit circling and ran straight up a ridge toward a mountain. The last we saw of him he was doing well, with both coyotes far behind."

An old rangeman and hunter named George Bigford told me that he had seen as many as eight or ten coyotes round up a number of jack rabbits and keep circling them while one coyote would run in and catch himself a mouthful. At this the rabbits all scattered, coming out so thick, however, that nearly every coyote in the round-up caught one.

One winter while I was deer-hunting in the brush country, I tied my horse on a hill and began slowly walking along a dim trail that wound down a brushy draw. Before long I saw in a sparse opening ahead of me a coyote haunched down on the left-hand side of the trail. He was looking very intently, though in a manner altogether patient, to the right. I stopped to watch him. I did not wish to shoot him. For maybe two minutes he remained absolutely motionless; then he sensed me and disappeared.

When I stepped to the spot he had occupied and looked where he had been looking, I saw a badger digging into an enormous rat's nest of cactus leaves and thorned sticks built in and around a clump of prickly pear. The badger is obtuse in his senses. This one was not in the least disturbed by my nearness. Directly he got down to the fur lining in the nest, and a big fat wood rat darted out, coming my way. Had I been a coyote, or had the displaced coyote been in his selected position, that rat would certainly have become a juicy morsel. A Mexican goat herder told me he had seen as many as three coyotes hanging around a badger, waiting for him to scare out wood rats. Of course, the badger sometimes catches a rat himself. A well-established nest usually has more than one runway into it. A coyote can dig very well indeed in soft ground himself. He knows where he can dig in a sandy arroyo down to water, and he knows when to let the badger dig for him.

Perhaps there is a kind of understanding between the coyote and the badger. The Mexican name for badger (Indian in origin) is *talcoyote*—"like a coyote." Suggestive of the relation between the two animals, a pot that I have, 2,000 years old perhaps, excavated from ruins in Mexico, shows a coyote head on one side and a badger head on the other. A badger has been observed following—as best he could, for he is not a swift runner—a coyote that chased a cottontail into a hole. The presumption is that the badger expected to dig the rabbit out, not for the coyote's benefit, however. The coyote sometimes gets a gopher excavated by a badger, just as he does a rat. If a female coyote can find no better place, she will den and pup in a badger hole.

Mary Austin, who made many acute observations on the wildlife of the Southwest, says that the coyote watches crows and buzzards—"tracks in the sky," as the Indians call these birds—for guidance to carrion. The coyote that will touch a carcass left by a mountain lion, no matter how many signs point to it, is the exception, however. He is afraid of the mountain lion, which occasionally eats coyote flesh.

Over and over, in ways endlessly various, the coyote has proved himself extraordinarily adept at taking advantage of the situation. If he can't get meat one way, he'll get it another. If he can't get meat at all, he'll thrive on berries, acorns, watermelons, any vegetable food that any other animal eats. He can fish like a coon. He is as omnivorous as human beings or hogs. No other creature of the wild has so well adapted itself to the changes wrought by encroaching civilization. Chased off of sheep-grazed and chicken-pecked plains, he is now found in high mountains, away up on the Yukon River, far east of the Mississippi River—places that a generation ago were unknown to the species.

Truly, he lives by his wits. May his shadow never grow less!

The Life and Times of Shag

❖❖❖❖❖❖

ALAN M. BECK

[1971]

It was still dark enough to see stars when I arrived at the Amalgamated Clothing Workers of America (ACWA) building near downtown Baltimore. I saw and heard nothing. I left the car, walked around the building, returned, checked the air temperature, and reported my findings into a tape recorder I always kept with me:

2 September 1970, 64 degrees F., clear and slightly windy, 4:20 a.m. No signs, garbage behind homesite from previous day now gone—probably collected. I will now wait for Shag, who I suspect is still in the shrubbery, left side of ACWA, Eutaw and McMechen.

Studying the stray dogs of Baltimore is my thesis project for a doctorate in ecology, and for the next few weeks I would be concentrating on Shag, a large, white, shaggy-haired male with black markings. I chose him from the study population because he was a truly ownerless stray. Ordinarily, owned and ownerless strays are indistinguishable, except at moments of owner-dog interaction, and both types serve as the feral dogs of the city environment.

Lately, Shag had been spending his nights in the shrubbery, although earlier in the summer he had found shelter in a house hallway. He would push the front door open to gain access and wait for someone leaving to help him get back to the streets, but his habit of "marking" the inside hall had led to his ouster by the building's residents. During the past two years, I dis-

18

covered other stray dog den sites—in vacant buildings and garages, under porches and cars, and in garbage dumps. All provide protection against weather and people.

4:50 a.m. Barking now becoming apparent. The area is coming alive, but still no sign of Shag.

Waiting is a very real part of wildlife study. I welcome it, however, as it gives me time to plan future approaches and reflect on aspects just completed. I spent the first part of the summer of 1970 sampling the dog populations of selected areas around the city, mainly by photographing each stray dog and plotting the sighting on maps. One advantage of working in the urban ecosystem is the ability to locate the subject with remarkable precision by using street crossings and house numbers.

Another advantage of studying feral dogs is that their mixed heritage leads to wide variations in morphology and behavior, which enabled me to recognize individuals. I seldom encountered the monotony of pedigree breeds. As part of my studies, I photographed every stray dog I saw while traveling through a neighborhood. A dog photographed more than once is, in the terms of wildlife study, a recapture. Therefore, just as a wild bird population can be calculated from the number of banded birds recaptured, I was able to compute the city's stray dog population from the number of dogs rephotographed. Photographic recapture and other methods revealed a total population of 100,000 dogs, both owned and ownerless, in Baltimore, which is an increase of 25,000 animals over the city's dog population as estimated ten years ago by Dr. Kenneth Crawford, the state veterinarian.

Cities throughout the world are encountering such dog population explosions, including the half-million dogs each in New York, Mexico City, and Buenos Aires. In many cities, dogs appear to be increasing more rapidly than humans. Such populations have many ecological implications for a city. A study by New York's Environmental Protection Administration noted that the owners of dogs permit them to leave from 5,000 to 20,000 tons of excrement and from 600,000 to over 1 million gallons of urine on the streets each year. Even if Baltimore has only one-fifth of those estimates, what does it mean for this or any city? While my original objective was to establish the life history of the feral urban dog, I had to include such implications, for they are part of the ecology of the animal.

Ever-growing fecal depositions are a potential health hazard as well as an insult to the senses. There is the possibility of visceral larva migrans (VLM), a syndrome caused in humans when the eggs of *Toxocara canis* (dog worms) are ingested, usually by children playing in or eating infected dirt, often from under street trees where dogs may have defecated days earlier. Severe cases of VLM, characterized by enlargement of the liver and spleen, convulsions, and blindness, are very rare. One symptom, which often goes undetected, is a marked increase in the number of eosinophil cells in the blood. Milder symptoms, such as coughing and fever, are so like other childhood diseases that VLM goes undiagnosed most of the time. Although there have been six child blindness cases reported at Baltimore's Johns Hopkins Hospital in the past ten years, there has been no record of VLM frequency in its less debilitating form.

Dog feces is a major factor in the breeding of house flies, which then possibly transmit such bacteria as *Salmonella* from dogs to man. In addition, rat eradication officials and residents of my study area have observed rats feeding on dog feces and, indeed, rats are most common in alleys with high fecal residues. Garbage, from cans knocked over by dogs, and dog feces are probably important components of the rat food chain.

At 5:22 a collie bolts out of an open doorway, which

is then closed. Other dogs are now apparent, but still no sign of Shag.

This kind of pet release, before and after the usual workday, is one reason why dog activity is greatest in the mornings and evenings. Ownerless strays are also active during these periods, possibly because dogs are gregarious animals, initiating each other's activity, or because all dogs avoid activity during the heat of the day.

6:00 a.m. The sky is light blue and church bells are ringing. Shag and a male Doberman, Shag's constant companion, appear in the rear view mirror. Where in the hell did they come from?

Waiting was over, and I left the car to follow at a distance with tape recorder and camera. Because feral urban dogs are accustomed to the presence of man, their normal activities may be studied more easily than those of most wild animals. If the dogs gave any indication that I was altering their behavior by following them, I turned away or "tied" my shoelace, which was all that was necessary for them to lose interest in me. Anyone observing my behavior must have assumed that I was an unemployed photographer with particularly obstinate shoelaces.

Shag and Dobe headed for their usual feeding alley, where they were joined by several other dogs in going from garbage can to garbage can, sniffing and occasion- ally lifting off bags from the tops. Some of the cans had already been knocked over. It was 6:09 and still dark enough to observe rat activity. Dogs, cats, and rats all seemed to ignore each other, sometimes eating garbage within a foot of each other. But my presence chased away the rats. Garbage collection was on Mondays and Thursdays. As this was Wednesday, there was ample food. But even after collection on the following day, there would be enough residue left on the ground to attract dogs before the street sweepers removed it, so

garbage collection day was not an environmental catastrophe. The residue persists to the evening and undoubtedly feeds the nocturnal rats, mice, and roaches. Subtle
changes in canine presence and behavior do occur with
food availability, so dogs can be used as indicators of
urban environmental deterioration and can be correlated
with trash and pest species.

*By 6:20 Shag and Dobe returned to the alley beside
the ACWA building, where, as usual, they found water
under the air conditioner unit. They lay down in the
median green, facing east. It is 59 degrees F. At 6:34
Dobe rose and left.*

This was my day to be with Shag, so I waited, watching him as he slept. Five minutes later he stood,
stretched, looked and sniffed in all directions, then immediately took off in the same direction as Dobe had.
They were a true pack of two.

One-half of the dogs I observed were in the company
of other dogs (as many as 17 in one pack), but few
packs are stable in size and membership. Instead the
packs form and dissolve over a period of minutes or
hours, giving the impression of a loose social structure,
more like that of people in the streets than wolves in
the wild.

I followed Shag through several alleys, and at 6:45
we caught up with Dobe, who was feeding at the base of
an overflowing apartment house dumpster. Children,
unable to open its heavy door, had left garbage bags at
the base. The dogs left to continue their tour of the
alleys and streets. Being large dogs they could often lift
bags of garbage out of the cans without knocking them
over. They would rip open paper and plastic bags by
shaking them or running with them in their teeth. I am
not sure whether they could smell the food through
the plastic bags or had learned what they contained
from previous encounters with open plastic bags.

At 7:00 a.m., the dogs are back on Madison and meet

*two small pet dogs that have just emerged from a door-
way. Shag attempts a typical nose-anus greeting but is
rebuffed by barks and snaps. No fight. Shag and Dobe
cut across recently cleared field.*

The new dogs, although considerably smaller, had a
territorial advantage. The interaction between pet and
nonpet stray has many implications for the pet owner
concerned about disease and dog fights.

*At 7:10 Shag found a garbage can on its side and
pulled out wrappings frequently used for food take-out
orders. He ate what appeared to be a portion of spa-
ghetti with bread.*

At 7:13 both dogs left the can, and I surveyed what
remained of the "kill." Shag had finished all the spa-
ghetti, bread, and sauce but had left prunes, raisins, and
tobacco.

After more travel, through alleys and a playground,
both dogs came to rest on the median strip a block
away from the homesite. While on their stomachs they
both stared intently at a building diagonally across the
street. Fortunately, the median had benches and I could
rest too. They were not sleeping but were waiting for
something to happen, although I could not figure out
what.

*At 7:52 we all heard a human whistle. The dogs im-
mediately ran to the building they were watching, where
a woman dropped food to them from a second-floor
window: hot dogs to Dobe and chopped meat to Shag.*

This was yet another food source. (In interviewing
residents of my study areas, I now include a question
about feeding strays. About 20 percent have answered
affirmatively. Usually food is just put out for any dog
that finds it.) This feeding stop, while not daily, was
somewhat regular for Shag and Dobe.

After another short walk around the area, the dogs

returned to the homesite for more water; by 8:43 they entered the shrubbery, which was 3 degrees cooler than the air temperature of 67 degrees F. They rustled around in the bushes, often changing positions, but settled down to sleep by 10:20 a.m.

In 4.3 hours, Shag and Dobe had spent 124 minutes resting and 137 minutes moving about. Even during their activity period, much time was spent resting, possibly because food and water were so readily available. Another sign of the availability of food was the relatively small home range for a carnivore. By plotting all sightings and connecting the outermost points, I judged their home range to be not more than 0.1 square mile.

During their morning's activity, they spent 29 minutes feeding and 2 minutes in social contact with other dogs, which was below average. From my observations of Shag and Dobe on previous days, I knew that they would not leave their homesite in the shrubs during the heat of the day, so I went home for some food and rest. In the evening, I picked them up again as they made a similar, slightly shorter round of their territory.

During the summer and early fall I observed Shag's and Dobe's routine for many days and nights. The morning just described was a typical one for a feral urban dog. I had selected Shag for this intense study partly because I could identify him easily, but also because—like the woman who threw the preferred tidbits to Shag—I had become fond of him. So when both Shag and Dobe disappeared late in the fall, I was concerned and curious. And their fate was important for my study, because the causes and rates of mortality are important information for an understanding of the ecology of an animal population.

Shag could have been killed by a car, for he had had many close calls. Often, as an auto approaches, dogs appear to act submissively—whimpering, crouching with ears back, and holding their ground. They do not necessarily jump back reflexively as humans do. This behavior, together with their propensity for chasing fast-moving objects, may be why many dogs are injured by cars. In a review of veterinary hospital records, Tom Large, a freelance writer, found the car to be the most common source of dog injury, and Edward C. Harmon, Jr., superintendent of Baltimore's Animal Shelter, estimates that some 17,000 dead dogs are collected from the streets yearly by his scavenger service. I suspect most are car kills. The high annual mortality of about one-fifth of Baltimore's dogs (a conservative estimate, since not all dead dogs are found) means that few feral dogs live to an old age. Therefore, a younger population is maintained. Younger animals are more susceptible than older ones to diseases such as rabies, distemper, and *Toxocara* infection.

As he was a stray on the streets, Shag could have been collected alive by the Animal Shelter. Captured dogs are held for some time so they can be retrieved by owners or adopted. Eventually, dogs that are not claimed are humanely killed (more than 6,000 dogs a year are too many for continuous boarding) and rendered into animal proteins for hog food supplement or low-phosphate grease for soap. This recycling is consistent with ecology and a sensible and safe solution to the problem. But this was not Shag's fate, because I visited the shelter many times and did not find him.

Man is very much a part of the ecology of the stray dog in the city. Born beneath the porch of an empty house or in the trunk of a junked car, or released as an unwanted pet, the feral dog's life cycle is continually involved with the works and actions of man. His food supply comes from the handouts and the garbage of man. And most often his death, beneath the wheels of a car (as I feared for Shag) or in the vacuum chamber of the S.P.C.A., comes at the hand of man.

The dog, in turn, is part of the ecology of urban man. Baltimore city veterinarian Dr. David R. Berzon handles reports of some 7,000 dog bites yearly (there are probably at least twice that many). Children under 15 years of age are the usual victims (60 percent of all bites) and up to 30 percent of the biting dogs are strays that are never retrieved for examination. Fortunately rabies is not yet a problem in the area.

Not only do dogs bite, they also disrupt garbage, defecate, chase cyclists, and bark: all impingements on the quality of life of the urban dweller. In many ways dogs compete for, as well as share, the urban environment with man. But these sources of conflict are solvable with responsible ownership, leash laws, health codes for in-house toileting or fecal retrieval ("scoop law"), city planning to include dog areas, and education to include an understanding of dog behavior (teaching children how to avoid being bitten). Some regulation of dog numbers will undoubtedly be necessary.

My concentration on the stray dogs of Baltimore has blurred the real advantages of the interrelationship of man and dog in the city. At times of great social stress, of fear and loneliness, the well-cared-for dog is a source of companionship and pleasure. The dog owner develops a view of another species, of a type of wildlife that is all too often missing in the urban ecosystem.

This last point became evident to me about six weeks after I lost track of the two dogs. One day I observed Shag being walked on a leash by a man. Shag was still quite shy, but he appeared to be enjoying his new domestic life. I interviewed the man, who told me he had taken in both Shag and Dobe, who was living with a relative in the suburbs. He reported that the veterinarian felt that although Shag did have worms, he was generally healthy and at normal weight. This was further proof of the ample food supply for Baltimore's feral dogs.

Occasionally his new master lets Shag out unattended in the mornings, and I have since observed him checking out the garbage cans along some of his old rounds. But Shag's range is much smaller now, he rarely eats anything, and he quickly returns to his new homesite.

The Elk of Jackson Hole

❖❖❖❖❖❖

OLAUS J. MURIE

[1935]

As the 1934 hunting season opened in Jackson Hole, Wyoming, great concern was expressed by many people over the elk situation, particularly because a portion of the Teton State Game Preserve, for many years kept an inviolate sanctuary, was this year opened to hunting. The gist of opinion, both local and elsewhere, appeared to be that the elk were getting "a dirty deal."

At the risk of adding unduly to the already voluminous literature on the elk, I should like to discuss them once more and state frankly my impressions of the present situation.

First, why do we want the elk? Why all this furor over an animal? Is our interest selfish? Commercial? Altruistic? It may be worth while to examine our motives, for they underlie our actions. I should like to review our various viewpoints, how different ones of us make use of wildlife and enjoy wildlife. To do so, and before discussing the present hunting season, let me go back and relate some personal experiences.

One day in July I had climbed to the summit of a high, bare ridge, and sat down on a prominent point to rest and to sweep the landscape with my glasses. Below me, in rolling undulations, stretched the forest, with numerous open parks. At one side the ribbon of Pacific Creek wound its way toward the valley, the upper Jackson Hole, the distant parts dimmed in the haze of a quiet summer day. And before me, emerging from the mist of the valley, rose the Tetons.

At first there was little sign of active life. A Clark's

nutcracker flew by me with strident wing beats, high over the treetops, and disappeared in a grove of white-barked pine. There was a clatter of pebbles as a fat marmot scrambled up the slope nearby, then squatted in the entrance to his rocky den and looked over the world with infinite patience.

Then a movement in a green meadow just below me caught my eye, and I stiffened to alert attention as an elk came out of the shadow of a pine and began grazing. I caught other small movements, then discerned other shapes obscured in the shadow of the forest edge, and to my amazement I became aware of a whole herd of elk resting in the shade. They were mostly cows and calves, although I made out the outlines of a spike bull, with velvet antlers, in among the trees. It was the season of plenty and the animals lay about in green vegetation in all attitudes of relaxation and comfort.

Another cow arose and slowly wandered out in the meadow, where she picked daintily at the grass. Presently several more joined her, until the meadow was dotted with feeding elk. A calf, getting into the spirit of the occasion, trotted up to its mother and nudging her boisterously, readily found the well-known fountain of good things for calves, while its mother nonchalantly went on chewing. Soon the lazy animals began to lie down again, the calves almost disappearing in the tall grass.

It was a satisfying picture, a green wilderness meadow, dotted with sleek, red-coated elk, oblivious of danger, only concerned with their utter well-being in the season of plenty. A bright spot in the memories of the wilderness traveler.

I could mention numerous such occasions, the bright side of elk life, and incidentally a high type of human enjoyment of wildlife.

The winter presents another aspect. But lest we get the notion that winter is all hardship, let me refer to another incident.

I was snowshoeing in the foothills of southern Jackson Hole, tracking a coyote to see what it had been up to during the night. On one slope I found an exciting snow record of its chase of a jack rabbit, the long leaps, the desperate dodging of the quarry, the violent turmoil of bloody snow, then the long, orderly line of coyote tracks, with an occasional red spot in the snow.

Topping a rise, I came suddenly in view of a group of elk on another slope before me. Some were feeding, but most of them were lying down in a picturesque clump of aspens. The entire hillside was pitted with the elk diggings, where, as I later found, they had pawed down through the snow to a depth of at least thirty inches. Here they must dig for every mouthful, a miserable existence, one would think. Yet this, too, was a picture of contentment. Possibly the elk were not fully aware of the beauty of the winter landscape, the delicate tracery of aspen shadows on the snow, the ghostlike, snowy Tetons across the valley, but certainly they were a part of this picture of well-being. It was not an occasion of misery. One must judge the situation from the standpoint of elk hardihood and ability and ecological fitness. The elk did not mind digging for their dinner provided the dinner was there, under the snow, and had not previously been grazed off or cut for hay.

Yet another incident. It was nearing the end of the hunting season, about the middle of November as I recall it. Two of my friends had waited until that time to go elk hunting, with the idea that the colder weather would insure keeping the meat in good condition. I was invited to go along, and as I could combine the task of supplying the larder with the opportunity of obtaining a specimen for study, I went. As there were many hunters in the field, I was urged to appear at the ranch home of one of my friends at some outlandish hour before daylight in order that we might have a chance. I do not recall just what the alarm clock complication was, but when I arrived at the ranch all was dark and silent; but my saddle horse was there, tied to the fence, all saddled and ready to go, a mute invitation: "Go and hunt if you wish, we couldn't wait and lose our last chance for an elk this year."

I got on the horse and went, heading for the murky foothills showing in the darkness. A fine snow was falling. Presently the gray light of dawn pervaded the snowy atmosphere, and I could see horse tracks in the road I was following. As I entered the rolling hills, I saw more tracks. I passed a tent or two, where hunters were busy at breakfast—someone rising even later than I. By this time there were many tracks—evidently many others realized that only two more days of the elk season remained.

It was daylight by now, with intermittent flurries of snow. Two horse tracks led off across an opening in the woods, and I followed, idly wondering if my friends had gone there.

As I worked my way through the woods, seeking the open meadows, I had glimpses of elk, shadowy shapes disappearing in the timber. Occasionally I heard distant shooting. I came out on an open knoll and spied two horsemen below me, wearing flaming red caps. Just to pass the time of day, I turned in their direction, and as I came nearer I recognized my two friends, who stared in surprise at seeing me.

It is not my purpose to describe the details of the hunt, least of all the dying struggles of the elk. We did get elk, after a delightful roaming over snowy hills and through pine woods and aspens. We had fleeting glimpses of brown bodies through the trees, heard calves squealing in the distance. Then, on the top of a wooded hill, we came on a band of them. One of my companions left us to follow doggedly the trail of a wounded animal, which took him the rest of the day, while the other two of us fastened ropes to the necks of the elk we had shot. With a half hitch over the muzzle, and with a loop at the other end thrown over the saddle horn, we "snaked" them out over the snow, all the way down into the valley.

I wish to point out that the killing of the elk did not measure our enjoyment of the hunt. We were after elk, to be sure, and wanted to get them—meat hunters, if you please. But none of us get a thrill from shooting game, it is too easy. Our enjoyment of this hunt consisted of the exhilarating sting of flying snow, the slow flush of dawn, snowy woods, the creak of saddle leather, glimpses of fleeing elk, something of the excitement of seeking, of *wanting* a wild animal. In short, we enjoyed a little of the flavor of *wilderness.*

Space does not permit recounting the numerous experiences with elk that are enjoyed in the Jackson Hole country. Each summer eastern vacationists come into the valley, and some of these procure pack trains and wander into the mountains, enjoying the wilderness landscapes, the elk, moose, deer, and lesser wood folk, and the exquisite sense of seclusion and primitiveness. Naturalists come in to enjoy the fauna and the flora, which is still largely unmodified by artificial conditions. Local dude ranches send their guests into the mountains, and residents of Jackson Hole enjoy the various phases of the out-of-doors as opportunity and inclination permit.

In the fall the hunters come. In the earliest part of the season, chiefly, come the trophy hunters, who generally go back in the mountains for more or less extended camping trips. Later when the weather is colder and when the elk come down and are more available, meat hunters are more numerous, although even then many hunters seek a trophy as well as the meat.

During the fall of 1934 a special effort was made to effect a large kill of elk. With that end in view, a portion of the Teton Game Preserve, that part lying east of Pacific Creek, where hunting of elk is easy and where they can be obtained before leaving their summer range, was opened to hunting. In view of the interest aroused over this action and the comment that has ensued, it may be worth while to enumerate some of the facts and their implications.

When the season opened, hunters flocked to the hunting grounds. Various hunting camps were established by outfitters, with guides available, some of these within easy reach of the highway. As the season advanced and the elk came lower, hunting could be done from a car, by driving to the vicinity of elk crossings. As the elk came south through the mountains along the east side of Jackson Hole, other areas became favorite hunting grounds.

Efficient checking stations where hunters are required to report their kill have been maintained by the Forest Service and State Game and Fish Commission on the various highways leading out of Jackson Hole. Preliminary figures indicated that the total kill of elk in Jackson Hole would be well over 3,000.

Many who witnessed the progress of the hunt are dissatisfied. Some complain that the hunting was too easy. Along a certain stretch of country paralleling the highway along Buffalo Fork, it was reported that 50 or more elk carcasses were found, some entire, others with the hindquarters removed, or in various degrees of abandonment. And of course there were the usual number of cripples that escaped.

One observer told me, in disgust, that a hunter drove in with a moose permit, got his moose the same day, and either that night or next day was on his way. Another complained that 150 bull moose will have been taken out of this general area this year—too many, he thought, and these include some which have in the past delighted tourists along the highway. It is claimed that the hunting on the game preserve drove the elk from very favorable summer and fall range north of the Buffalo Fork and hastened their migration southward to winter range which is already short because of the drought and which should have been saved until as late a date as possible. This was a possibility that I pointed out when the opening of the preserve was discussed. Yet in all fairness it should be mentioned that in 1934 there was an unusually early migration, or "shifting" of the elk, many appearing at low elevations even in the summer, possibly owing to the premature drying up of portions of the high summer ranges. This tendency toward an early migration may well be a factor in the partial abandonment of fall ranges coincident with the hunting. It is a situation, nevertheless, well worth considering in the future.

Apparently there has been comparatively little law violation. Some cow moose were shot, mistaken for elk, and some elk were shot illegally. The warden service is excellent and in game cases convictions are usually obtained. It is my opinion that poaching is no longer a major problem in Jackson Hole.

No doubt there have been abuses of the hunting privilege. Unethical practices probably have occurred. While some of the law violations have been in the nature of mistakes, inexcusable of course, but still mistakes, others almost certainly were vicious in character. Probably some mistakes have been made by the game authorities, although it is my opinion that in spite of certain mistakes, the hunting in recent years has been well handled. It is not my purpose to gloss over abuses. But if we view the situation in a broad way, and with an eye to the future, it takes on a different aspect. Let us examine some of the features.

It may be objected that we are killing too many elk this year. I do not fully agree with some of the estimates of the present number of elk in the herd. Some estimates seem too high as a basis for management plans. I prefer to rely chiefly on the organized counts made from time to time. But after all, in the present instance this matter seems unimportant. We have a large herd, whatever the number may be. Even if the herd were temporarily cut in half, it would not be serious, in my opinion. Numbers can be controlled by controlling hunting, as the situation demands. We have had a series of drought years, and this summer even parts of the summer range became very dry, and the feed is short everywhere. Far better to reduce the herd temporarily, in whatever degree that may be attained in an orderly manner, than to injure the range further, and permit the suffering due to food shortage in winter.

The meat hunter is often derided. He is only after *meat,* not after *sport.*

Let us examine this question for a moment. No doubt each hunter thinks he is getting sport in getting his elk, whether he be a hunter who spends much money and time on a lengthy pack trip, or one who merely steps out of his car to shoot his elk.

I was standing on a rocky ridge one day, taking motion pictures of a band of elk. They filed past me and disappeared down the slope. A moment later I heard a shot down below. Going over to a point, I looked down and saw a car on the road that wound up this narrow valley, and on the slope above the car a group of people, apparently a family, with several children, was busy dressing out an elk. Easy hunting, to be sure.

I must admit that a hunt from an automobile does not appeal to me as much as a long wilderness experience, and I believe we should strive for the highest type of hunting, weaving into the event all the esthetic elements we can achieve. Yet we have the practical matter of disposing of a given number of animals in a limited area. Most hunting areas today are limited, considering the number of hunters. It is useless to argue that we should so manage the areas that all hunters are forced to go into the back country with pack horses to hunt. In the first place, many times this is unfair to the man of moderate means. It means that he cannot hunt. Then, too, such a procedure would probably destroy the very thing we are striving for. A crowded wilderness is no longer a wilderness—it has magically vanished.

After all, can we legislate or "manage" sportsmanship into the hunters? Impossible. Even the trophy hunter who spends much money on a long trip, perhaps making it an excuse for an outdoor debauch, may be infinitely less a sportsman than he who buys his local license and modestly drives out in his car to get his winter's meat.

After all, when local residents take some of the surplus game and use the meat, that is a legitimate use, and the meat becomes a local economic asset.

The values of wildlife have been stressed so much in recent years and have become so well known that it seems trite even to mention them. The commercial value of wildlife no longer needs advertising. Indeed, in true American style, we may be overdoing it. In our zeal to capitalize on the financial values, we are in danger of killing the goose that lays the golden egg, by too much development and resulting destruction of primitive charm of sport. Aside from the financial aspect, the recreational values, from the human standpoint, which I consider the greatest of all, include such activities as hunting in the fall, wilderness camping summer and fall, the sport of outdoor photography, and observation by nature enthusiasts. Not the least of its values, by any means, are the scientific aspects. We should be willing to admit that we have not solved all problems of natural history in this generation, but should pass on to other generations an unimpaired field for study. Finally, and I think we are inclined to forget this important aspect, we have in the domineering human a trace of generosity toward wild creatures, a growing desire to save them *for their own sake*. From the purely human standpoint, this is admirable, and it deserves encouragement.

I have here been speaking of *wildlife*. After all, the elk are only an item in the larger, greater picture before us. I submit, that the elk, stripped of its environment, its associated flora and fauna, its wilderness, so to speak, has lost most of its value for us.

I have reserved for the last the most important problem confronting us. This is not how many elk shall we kill this year, but where can they live? Snows are piling up in the mountains. The elk are down once more, to find the foothills and valley devastated by drought, overgrazed, or with the vegetation harvested and stacked. Even the swamp could be partly harvested and grazed in the past dry summer. Only limited areas are left for elk grazing. The inevitable conflict with harassed ranchers has begun, and the overworked wardens are busy trying to adjust difficulties.

I shall depart from Jackson Hole for a moment and take a countrywide viewpoint. As a matter of fact, Jackson Hole is in the lead in many respects. We have here become aware of the great value of primitiveness, the frontier. Thanks to the Forest Service, Teton National Forest has in the past been administered so as to preserve the wilderness to a great extent. State authorities and local sentiment have contributed their share toward this end. Nevertheless, we have our serious game-range problem. And it is a general problem throughout the country. What will we do about it?

From the standpoint of community welfare, recreation and hunting, if viewed only from the commercial angle, represent an industry involving millions of dollars annually. This probably ranks with any other local industry, in the majority of communities, or could be made to do so. It is no longer a minor by-product.

We used to feel, "Well, if there is any land left over, we'll let it be for the game." And we have set aside the rough, high country, which can't be used for anything else. Then we find a winter range problem.

Do we expect to carry this enormous national business without any investment whatever? How much *good* land have we given to wildlife? We give them the leavings, then wonder and worry over our game problems of malnutrition and diseases, and try to patch and fuss. Are we, after all, giving the elk a "dirty deal"?

We have public domain, we have submarginal lands. I think we have the opportunities. Also, I think we have a better understanding. We have already awakened to the needs of the waterfowl, and the Biological Survey is energetically pushing a hopeful program of marsh restoration and possibilities for our big game. The vital thing to remember is that our herbivores require lowland winter ranges, wilderness recreation requires a wilderness, and wilderness requires space.

This Gentle and Elegant Cat

❖❖❖❖❖❖

GEORGE B. SCHALLER

[1970]

With its small round head, trim waist, and long, slender legs, the cheetah is the most atypical of the cats, an animal built for speed, a greyhound with the coat of a leopard. A delicate and aristocratic animal, it seems to belong with royalty; indeed, trained cheetahs were used as early as 865 B.C. by King Hashing of Persia to hunt antelope. In the sixteenth century the Mogul emperor Akbar the Great of India is said to have kept 1,000 cheetahs. A hooded cat would be transported in a bullock cart to within 300 feet of a herd of blackbuck antelope. With the hood removed, the cheetah slipped off the cart, crept closer, and finally sprinted after the prey. If it missed, the keeper came up, chanting, "Oh, great King, do not be angry, you will kill the next one," as he slipped the hood over the cat's eyes. But if it captured an adult male, as it was taught to do, success was rewarded by a cup of blood from the slain animal.

Today this sport is extinct in India and so is the cheetah—the last one was shot there in 1952. A few survive in southwestern Iran and some possibly in Turkmenistan and in one or two localities in the Near East. Strays occur only occasionally in North Africa. Fortunately cheetahs are still widespread in the open woodlands and plains south of the Sahara where suitable prey survive. But they are nowhere abundant, not even in the national parks. The 5,000 square miles of the Serengeti in Tanzania contain perhaps 150 cheetahs, one per 33 square miles; the large Kruger National Park in South Africa has about one per 27 square miles.

Considering the long contact that man has had with the cheetah, remarkably little was known of its habits until recently. Aloof and self-contained, it remained an enigma, even refusing to breed in captivity. Among Emperor Akbar's 1,000 cheetahs, only one had young, a litter of three. No other captive births were reported until 1956, and since then only seven litters have been born in zoos. When I joined the Serengeti Research Institute in 1966 to study predators, particularly the lion, in the Serengeti National Park, I became intrigued by the cheetah, not only by its mystery but also by its delicate beauty and lithe grace.

Most Serengeti cheetahs are migratory, following the movements of their principal prey, the Thomson's gazelle. During the rains early in the year, when the gazelles are on the plains, the cheetahs are there too, but when the grass dries up in July, both move 25 and more miles to the edge of the acacia woodlands that cover much of the park. There some cheetahs remain for several months. Occasionally one stays within a 3- to 4-square-mile area for a month, but usually each uses some 20 to 25 square miles of terrain in the course of a season. The same cheetah tends to return yearly to the same locality, and one of my pleasures was to recognize an individual after a long absence.

Cheetahs do not establish territories in the sense of defending a locality against other cheetahs. Several animals commonly range over the same area, but they avoid contact. When two see each other, they veer apart without associating. Cheetahs also squirt a mixture of scent and urine against tree trunks and often deposit their feces on prominent locations such as termite mounds. A cheetah that smells a fresh marker knows that the area has been visited recently and can then plot its movements to avoid a meeting. Cheetahs do not advertise their presence by roaring in the manner of lions. Their calls are a birdlike chirp and a sedate, staccato chirr used mainly to keep mother and cubs in contact with each other.

It has often been said that adult cheetahs are sociable

and travel mainly in groups. I found this infrequently in the Serengeti. Excluding mothers with cubs, 52 percent of my sightings were of solitary individuals, 31 percent of the cheetahs were in pairs, and the rest in groups of three to four. Two or three adult males sometimes became companions for months, but I never saw two adult females in a group. Adult males and females associated mainly during courtship. Although I frequently saw groups of two to four males and females, these were with few exceptions litters of grown cubs that had not yet split up. The extent to which female cheetahs are asocial was shown well by a mother and her two grown daughters. Although all three wandered over the same area and sometimes saw each other, to my knowledge, they never met.

This particular family provided me with some of my most interesting observations on cheetah life history. The mother gave birth to at least three cubs in July, 1967, in a jumble of granite boulders and brush. By September she had only two cubs left. Most cheetahs lose about half of their cubs as a result of illness, predation, and abandonment, but a few manage to raise their whole litters of four to five. Her cubs, like those of all cheetahs, were black with a long blue-gray mantle of hair on their heads and backs, a striking natal coat that is lost at about three months. The cubs began to follow her around when they were about six weeks old; at three months they ceased to suckle. They were a close-knit family and shared kills without fighting. After a meal they licked each other's faces, purring loudly. Yet somehow their social existence seemed constrained; it lacked that intense quality of contact found among lions and even leopards. Perhaps it was because cheetahs do not rub their cheeks and bodies sinuously together in greeting, as lions and other cats do. Perhaps their tenuous social contacts as adults make an intimate bond between mother and offspring irrelevant. In fact, one observation suggests that mothers cannot recognize their young when they are small.

Once two mothers, each with two cubs about three

months old, met inadvertently at a kill, then parted after briefly threatening each other. But one cub followed the wrong mother. She noticed the addition but could not distinguish the newcomer from her own. She cuffed any cub that approached her until all three cringed, and she refused to associate with them for at least eight hours. I was afraid that she would abandon all of them. Somehow the extra cub was reunited with its mother that night.

How to hunt was perhaps the most important lesson these cubs had to learn while still with their mother. At first they played around her while she stalked, sometimes alerting the prey by running ahead. But later, at about three months of age, a change occurred. They followed discretely or watched while she hunted. A female may even provide her cubs with the opportunity to learn the techniques of killing. My wife, Kay, watched a cheetah carry a live gazelle fawn to her five-month-old cubs and release it. They tried to capture it, and once they knocked it down but were unable to kill it. Finally the mother did so. At the age of about one year cubs themselves will initiate some hunts. For example, in August, 1968, when she was 13 months old, a cub of the litter I had observed for over a year bowled over a gazelle fawn several times with a swat of her paw. But she was so inept at grabbing it that finally the mother ran up and killed it. In three subsequent hunts the mother took the initiative. On October 1, when they were almost 15 months old, the cubs bungled yet another hunt, only to be helped again by their mother.

Some two weeks later, on October 17, the family was still together, but on the following day the cubs separated permanently from their mother. It was a sudden and dramatic break, especially considering the cubs' inability to hunt well. There was no gradual severing of the social bonds, no tentative, solitary excursions, just an abrupt transition from dependence to complete independence. These cubs never again associated with their mother. Other litters behaved similarly. In contrast, the leopard, another solitary cat, behaves in a more typical manner.

One female cub whose history I traced from birth began occasionally to roam on her own at the age of 13 months but continued to meet and share kills with her mother until she was 22 months old. Three months later her mother conceived again.

The two cheetah sisters lost weight after separating from their mother, but they survived, and with the onset of the rains they moved to the plains. By February, 1969, they too had split up, for I met one as I was walking across the plains. She lay on her side, looking around with raised head in the curiously detached manner of cheetahs. I sat down 100 feet from her and fifteen minutes later heard a gazelle fawn bleat. Then over a rise came two jackals in pursuit of the fawn. The cheetah sprinted past me, knocked the fawn down, and grabbed it by the neck. She had obviously learned to hunt. As she ate I moved slowly toward her, finally reclining 15 feet away. She stared at me with guileless, amber eyes but did not flee. We stayed together for over half an hour, once only 10 feet apart, one of my most memorable experiences with a wild animal.

One of these young females conceived in April, 1969, when 21 months old, and her sister courted in May. A tame but free-living cheetah raised by Joy Adamson bred at the age of 22 months for the first time. On July 12, I found the litter of the first young female: four cubs only a day or two old, with eyes still closed, weighing a mere 12 ounces each. They lay in a patch of grass six miles from the place where their mother was born two years earlier. She was just moving the cubs to a thicket 900 feet away, carrying them one at a time by the back or a leg. After all had been moved, she returned twice more and searched the site, seemingly unable to count with precision. At the age of three weeks the cubs could walk unsteadily. On August 19, the photographer Simon Trevor saw her take the cubs to their first kill. The gazelle was not dead and the cubs were obviously frightened, jumping back each time it kicked. Another generation had to learn to become predators.

The hunt of a cheetah is surely one of the most exciting spectacles in Africa—the slow stalk, the tense period of waiting until the prey is inattentive, and finally the explosive rush at speeds of at least 60 miles per hour, making the cheetah the fastest of all land mammals. Cheetahs may hunt at any time during the day, and on moonlit nights as well, but usually they do so between 7:00 and 10:00 a.m. and 4:00 and 6:00 p.m. They seldom work hard for their meals but lie in the shade, seemingly waiting for prey to drift into the vicinity. Or from a termite hill, they scan the horizon for prey and then slowly walk in its direction. At some time between spotting a possible quarry and chasing it, the cheetah selects one, and I was particularly interested to find out what determined that choice.

Size of prey was obviously one factor. In the parts of the Serengeti where I observed cheetahs, Thomson's gazelle was the preferred prey (91 percent), followed by Grant's gazelle, wildebeest, impala, and hare in that order. A Thomson's gazelle weighs some 35 to 40 pounds, just one large meal for a cheetah weighing 110 to 130 pounds. Adult Grant's gazelle, impala, and reedbuck were also killed, but of the wildebeest only the calves were captured. Similarly, some 68 percent of the cheetah kills reported from Kruger National Park consisted of impala, and most of the other prey was relatively small too. A cheetah hunting alone seldom preys on anything weighing much more than itself, and this limits it to the small antelopes and the young of the large ones. But several cheetahs together may attack a large animal, as in Nairobi National Park where four males killed kongoni and zebra.

Prey selection can operate in two ways. In one, the predator chooses a particular animal out of a herd—a sick one, a newborn one—and pursues it, ignoring all others. In the other, the prey selects against itself, so to speak, by becoming vulnerable in some way. Leopards, for example, catch nearly twice as many adult male Thomson's gazelles as would be expected from their number in the population. These seem to be mostly non-territorial males that roam through high grass and along river courses where leopards hunt, in contrast to females and territorial males that remain in areas of short grass where they are not so vulnerable to leopards.

Cheetahs hunt mainly in the open plains. There they catch about 30 percent fewer adult males than expected, possibly because cheetahs prefer to select prey that is fleeing rather than standing around alertly as territorial males do. I collected and aged the jaws of 163 gazelle kills. The cheetahs had captured many fawns less than six months old, whereas yearlings, some 9 to 24 months old, were almost immune to predation. The cheetahs took many adults, but no age class was particularly selected. Most of the adult prey taken were presumably healthy, although the cats may have been able to detect slight disabilities, which I could not. Gazelles sometimes suffer from heavy infestations of lungworm or sarcoptic mange and such animals possibly respond less briskly to the cheetah. However, when the ages of gazelles killed by cheetahs are compared with those killed by lions, it is obvious that the two cats select very similarly. A lion captures its prey by surprise in a short fast rush, during which there is little or no time to test for weakness in an individual. In contrast, the cheetah may take its prey with a long run. Despite their different hunting techniques the adult gazelles killed by these two cats had a similar age structure, except that lions kill fewer small young and more yearlings. Possibly cheetahs catch the sick, and lions, the healthy, but I am inclined to think that most prey selected by both species was in reasonably good condition.

When observing a cheetah hunt, the selection for fawns is obvious—any fawn in a herd is immediately pursued. This is not surprising when hunting success is considered. Although cheetahs can attain tremendous speed, they are unable to keep it up for more than about 900 feet. If the gazelle dodges several times, the cheetah, exhausted, may have to give up the chase, and 23 out of 26 unsuccessful hunts that I observed failed for that reason. A fawn can run neither fast nor far, and in 31 chases after them, the cheetah was successful every time after an average run of 600 feet. On the other hand, of 56 pursuits after large young and adults only 54 percent resulted in a kill after a chase up to some 900 feet. Cheetahs are pragmatists: better a small meal than none at all.

Cheetahs prefer to hunt a solitary individual or one in a small herd, because they have difficulty selecting a gazelle and keeping it in sight in a large, milling herd. Individuals that enter tall grass, graze behind some bushes, or otherwise enable the cheetah to stalk undetected are chosen. With endless patience the cat may wait for a gazelle to lower its head and graze while briefly facing away from the danger, thus giving the cheetah an undetected second during the rush—often the difference between success and failure. The selection process is not always an easy one. Cheetahs sometimes bound toward a herd, then give up for no obvious reason, probably because they are unable to find a suitable quarry. Or they first pursue a herd at moderate speed before suddenly making a selection. Here are two typical hunts:

A female cheetah climbs 10 feet up a tree and spots ten gazelles about 700 feet away. She approaches the herd slowly, with head held low, until she is some 300 feet from the animals. She sits and watches for five minutes. One gazelle grazes somewhat apart from the herd. The cheetah rushes and is within 100 feet before the gazelle flees. After a chase of about 480 feet, which includes a sharp 180-degree turn, the gazelle flips forward, tripped by the cheetah, which lunges in and grabs the throat. After five minutes, the gazelle dies from strangulation.

A female cheetah spots a dozen gazelles on a burned stubble 800 feet away. She slowly walks 300 feet toward them; then, at a moderate speed, bounds about 500 feet before selecting the smallest individual in the fleeing herd. She sprints after it, follows three zigzags closely, and after 400 feet, catches it in a cloud of dust. She emerges holding it by the throat.

After knocking a gazelle down by hitting its flank or rump with a paw, the cheetah typically grabs it by the throat and throttles it, a task that requires four and a half minutes on the average. The carcass is often dragged to a shady spot. Cheetahs usually eat the meat off one thigh first; after that they cut the meat from the abdomen and rib cage, sometimes stopping to lap up any blood that collects in the body cavity. Finally they strip the rest of the meat from the inside. All that generally remains is the articulated skeleton with much of the skin and the whole digestive tract. The cats eat rapidly, glancing nervously around at intervals. This is not surprising, for lions, hyenas, and other predators often arrive at the kill, having been alerted by the descending vultures that a meal is in the offing. Cheetahs are timid creatures, low in the predator hierarchy, and 12 percent of their kills end in someone else's stomach. Twice I saw a cheetah driven from its kill by a solid phalanx of vultures. The cheetahs did little to retaliate when their kill was scavenged except to hiss and moan in a peculiar manner, although one bold hyena was slapped in the face.

To find out how often a cheetah kills, several persons with the Serengeti Research Institute and I watched a female with two small cubs for 26 days. There is a primitive pleasure in spending a day with a predator. Nothing happens for hours. The plains shimmer with heat waves. Yet there is a tension in the air, a feeling of impending violence. During these 26 days the cheetah killed 24 Thomson's gazelles, ranging from small fawns to adults, and one hare. At this rate she would kill 337 gazelles per year. She caught nothing on three days, although she tried, but on two days she captured 2 gazelles each. She captured an average of 22 pounds of animal per day, but she lost two kills to lions and one to hyenas. About 40 percent of the weight of a carcass was not eaten, mainly the digestive tract and bones. This left about 11½ pounds of meat for the mother and two cubs, almost twice as much as she actually needed, judging by the amount fed to cheetahs in zoos. Other mothers killed equally often, but solitary cheetahs captured prey probably only once every two to three days. Taking into account the size of the cheetah population, the percent of gazelle in their diet, and other factors, it seems likely that the Serengeti cheetahs kill 15,000–20,000 gazelles a year, only a small percentage of the several hundred thousand gazelles in the park.

Given such a large amount of prey and their success in catching it, there were surprisingly few cheetahs in the park. The Nairobi National Park, only 44 square miles in size, usually had some 10 to 15 resident cheetahs, showing that the species can tolerate quite high densities. Adult females outnumbered males by a ratio of 2:1 and one-third of the females were accompanied by cubs, often large ones. Females that lose their litter may come into estrus again within a week, and the gestation period is only 90 to 95 days. The Serengeti cheetahs have a high reproductive potential, a satisfactory number of cubs are raised, and food seems to be no problem. Yet something keeps the population depressed at a low level. A leopard killed and stored a cheetah in a tree, several lions captured and strangled one, and a litter burned in a grass fire, but such deaths were insignificant to the total cheetah population.

The wild dog, an equally rare predator in the park, provided a hint. These pack-living predators raised large litters, but canine distemper killed over half the members of one pack and undoubtedly affected other packs as well. During my stay in the Serengeti the wild dog population did not increase. It had failed to increase since at least 1956, the period for which there is information. The dog population seems to be controlled by disease, not by the food supply. Possibly cheetahs are also affected by disease, although I have no evidence to show this. The basic question of just what factors operate on the dog and cheetah populations to keep them stable at such a low level remains unanswered. Disease can cause a decrease but something else must finally determine that level at which the population stabilizes.

The cheetah is uncommon to rare everywhere, and the species balances itself delicately between security and extinction in an area. Any additional mortality, such as shooting by man, may well have a serious effect on a population. Yet in 1966 75 cheetah coats were sold in New York alone to satisfy the vanity of a few women. A total of 3,168 cheetah skins were imported into the United States in 1968–69, as many as would normally be found in 98,525 square miles of Africa, given the densities in Kruger and Serengeti national parks. Unless the cheetah is more strictly protected, this gentle and elegant cat will surely follow its Indian cousin into extinction over much of Africa.

Beasts Before the Bar

❖❖❖❖❖❖❖

FRANK A. BEACH

[1950]

A five-year-old boy was murdered on March 27 in Sarasota, Florida. Perhaps "murder" is not the right word, for Edward Schooley was killed by a circus elephant. "Dolly" had been one of the most docile members of the Ringling Brothers, Barnum and Bailey elephant herd for more than twenty years. But for some inexplicable reason she suddenly turned vicious and trampled to death the child who was offering her a peanut. The president of the circus publicly announced that Dolly would be destroyed, and this was done within three days after the tragedy.

According to radio reports, circus officials received many letters and telegrams from people all over the country complaining that Dolly's execution was unjustified. They apparently felt that a moral issue was involved and that an animal could not be held responsible for its actions. This point of view implies some interesting assumptions concerning animal psychology, but one thing is quite clear. If such an event had happened one or two centuries ago, the animal involved would have received quite different treatment. The law today states merely that dangerous or vicious animals must be destroyed. This represents a fairly recent simplification of older legal codes.

Ancient Hebraic law decreed that the goring ox be stoned to death. Plato's "Laws" directed that if any animal killed a man, except in combat authorized by the State, the nearest kinsman of the victim should prosecute the murderer. The case was tried by a public official,

48

and if the verdict was against the accused, the guilty animal was banished from Greece. Citizens of Rome used to celebrate the anniversary of the preservation of the capitol from night attack by the Gauls. On this occasion homage was paid to descendants of the sacred geese whose cries had given warning of the enemy's approach. On the same day a dog was crucified for the failure of its forefathers to give the alarm.

During the Middle Ages the practice of trying and condemning animals was common in Europe and the British Isles and later even in the New World. It was not confined to small villages and backward regions. In 1546 the French Parliament, the highest court in the land, ordered the execution of a cow, which was first hanged and then burned at the stake. Similar legal trials survived until fairly recent times. In 1906 in a small Swiss village a man and his son, accompanied by their dog, robbed a householder, and in the course of the crime the victim was killed. The two men were sentenced to life terms, but the dog was condemned to death because, the court decreed, it was the chief culprit, without whose complicity the crime would have been impossible.

Between A.D. 824 and 1845, there were at least 144 formal prosecutions resulting in the execution or excommunication of animal criminals. When a domesticated animal injured or killed a human being, it was formally arrested and thrown into jail. Then the judge or ruling nobleman of the district appointed one or several attorneys, who were charged with the duty of defending the accused. Public prosecutors and defense lawyers argued each case before the bar, and the evidence was weighed carefully by the judge before he rendered his verdict.

Mass indictments were not uncommon. On September 5, 1379, the village swineherd of Saint-Marcelle-Jenssey left the communal herd in the care of his son. Before his father was out of sight, the boy began to tease some nursling piglets, which promptly burst into a cacophony of terrified squeals. Three old sows charged the tormentor, knocked him to the ground, and killed him before his father could intervene. All the pigs were hurried off to jail, and after due process of law, Philip the Bold, Duke of Burgundy, condemned the three murderers to death. Their guilt was so plain that no one protested the decision, but the legal position of the remaining animals was less clear. The prosecutor insisted that they should be punished as accomplices. He called several witnesses, who testified that all of the swine had hastened to the scene of the murder and shown by their gruntings and aggressive actions that they thoroughly approved of the assault. A wholesale execution was narrowly averted when the attorney for the defense pointed out that the punishment of the convicted pigs would doubtless serve as an effective object lesson to the other swine and would deter them from committing any more offenses against men. The Duke found this argument convincing, and when the three murderers went to the gallows, the rest received a severe warning and were then released.

It was commonly assumed that lower animals possess a moral sense and could reasonably be expected to understand and obey man-made laws. But there were some jurists who held that the animal's owner was at least partially responsible for its actions. On January 10, 1457, a sow was convicted of "murder flagrantly committed" and was sentenced to be hanged. Her six sucklings were originally included in the indictment as accomplices. Positive proof was lacking, however, and they were released to their owner after he had furnished bail for their reappearance in the event that new evidence was uncovered. The man apparently believed in the inheritance of criminal tendencies, because after worrying about the matter for three weeks, he brought the piglets back to court, openly repudiated them, and refused to be answerable for their conduct in the future.

Swine were not the only animals guilty of criminal offenses. Cattle and horses occasionally ran afoul of the law and received precisely the same treatment as human criminals. Not only was the court procedure the same in each type of case; the same methods of execution were employed. The more common forms of capital punishment were hanging, beheading, or burning at the stake. Whenever possible, the animals were dressed in human clothes before the sentence was carried out.

Homicide was not the only crime for which animals were tried and punished. Jail sentences ranging from a few weeks to several years were not uncommon in cases of the willful injury of a human being by dogs, horses, cows, or other animals. In one Russian village a "he-goat" butted an important official while he was fastening his shoe, and as punishment the goat was banished to Siberia.

A German innkeeper's dog showed such poor judgment as to bite the leg of a village councilman. The animal's master was jailed at once, but he complained so vigorously against this miscarriage of justice that the judge ordered his release. After all, the innkeeper argued, why should he languish behind bars while the real culprit went free? Appreciating the logic of this approach, the court arranged for the incarceration of the dog for a period of one year. The sentence was duly served, and the animal shared its cell with two human prisoners.

Medieval methods of dealing with *wild* animals were, of necessity, more complicated. It was often impossible to capture and keep in jail the untamed creatures that sometimes brought harm to men. Nevertheless, the death sentence was occasionally imposed. In 864, the Council of Worms decreed death by suffocation to a swarm of wild bees that had stung a citizen to death. When animal culprits were not available for physical retribution, action of a different sort was possible. Insects and other pests that indirectly harmed a man by destroying his property could, with appropriate assistance from the clergy, be excommunicated. This extreme measure was not usually resorted to until milder alternatives had been exhausted.

It was customary, for example, to implore a swarm of locusts or a colony of rats to depart and cease whatever depredations they may have been committing. In some cases formal provisions for sanctuary were arranged, and the animals were notified by a Crier that they could take and maintain possession of a particular plot of land which had been set aside for their use. Usually the threat of excommunication was employed in an attempt to force the undesirable visitors to move away.

After the Middle Ages the Church grew less willing to participate in such animistic rituals as the excommunication of animals, but laymen continued to rely upon the efficacy of direct appeal to the presumed intellectual and emotional natures of lower animals. Sometimes the approach was informal and persuasive. In an old issue of the *Journal of American Folk Lore* there appears a copy of a letter dated October 30, 1888. It is addressed very correctly to "Messrs. Rat and Co." The writer begins with fervent expressions of his esteem for the rats and mentions his fear that they must find their present quarters at No. 3, Pine Street quite unsuitable for winter occupancy. He points out that the building was intended only as a summer residence and therefore is draughty and poorly supplied with food. By fortunate coincidence there is at No. 36, Sea Avenue a large, well-built house where the rats "can live snug and happy." The cellar is well stocked and a nearby barn contains large stores of grain. (Directions for reaching the address are included.) Having thus demonstrated his good intentions, the author of the published letter politely suggests that the rats take advantage of his well-meant advice. If they fail to do so, the letter concludes, "the undersigned, who owns the property at No. 3, Pine St., will be forced to use Rough on Rats."

The ethical propriety of adjuring the vermin to move to a neighbor's house seems not to have concerned this gentleman. At that, he was only repeating, with minor modifications, the medieval offer of sanctuary. The more attractive the new abode, the better the chances of acceptance. Peasants in some parts of Europe followed a similar practice in attempting to get rid of cabbage worms. It was customary to go out into the garden and invite the worms to depart, calling out, "In yonder village is church-ale." Church-ale signified a festival which, the peasants must have assumed, no lively cabbage worm could possibly resist.

These historical accounts illustrate the universal human tendency to recognize certain similarities between ourselves and lower animals. In scientific jargon the tendency is termed anthropomorphism. It rests upon an implicit belief that other living creatures have the same kinds of psychological experiences as men and women. Probably many of the people who protested the killing of the circus elephant, Dolly, rationalized their objections by thinking of the precipitating event as an "accident." They may have felt that the animal did not "mean" to injure the boy. Regardless of their reasoning, these individuals were reacting precisely as human beings have reacted for many centuries.

Basic human attitudes and beliefs do not change rapidly. The notions that permitted our forefathers to try, convict, and execute animals as though they were criminals are not completely lacking from our own psychology in this modern and supposedly scientific age.

The difference is that our ancestors assumed that animals had a moral sense and that they either lived up to it or not. If an animal was guilty, it must be punished according to the same law that applied to man. Today, we know a great deal more about the psychology of animals than our ancestors did and are in a position to know much better how a given animal should be treated. We should ask whether the offender is naturally vicious or whether it was goaded to violence by somebody's cruelty or carelessness.

The emphasis today is on proper precautions and laws to ensure public safety. Society demands that a dangerous animal be put where it can do no harm; but it also demands that the animal be treated humanely.

The Cliché of the Killer

❖❖❖❖❖❖

VICTOR B. SCHEFFER

[1970]

Along the shores of the Puget Sound of Washington, the Norwegian fishermen call the killer whale "*spekkhog-geren*," or fat-chopper. They see it in action. They watch it go rushing through a school of seals, porpoises, or fish, tearing out great chunks of meat, then circling to pick up the pieces. And when a fisherman has a chance to photograph a killer—perhaps one found dead on the beach or tangled in a net—he focuses on the teeth, the awful weapons of destruction, strong and yellow, evenly spaced, up to fifty in number. The photographer can be expected to stress this feature, which perpetuates the cliché of the killer whale as a vicious and bloodthirsty beast. The killer (*Orcinus orca*) has had a very bad press.

In the lore of the killer, two stories are often recounted as evidence of its fierceness. The first is that of Ponting, the photographer who traveled with Robert Scott to the Antarctic in 1911. Ponting was standing on an ice floe, camera in hand, waiting for a group of eight killers to reappear. Suddenly the animals rose beneath the ice, breaking it into bits and forcing him to dance from one bit to another to gain the safety of the shore.

"And not a moment too soon," he wrote. "As I looked back, a huge black and tawny head was pushed out of the water at the spot, and rested on the ice, looking round with its little pig-like eyes to see what had become of me. The brute opened his jaws wide, and I saw the terrible teeth which I had so narrowly escaped." Ponting came to no harm, and down to the present day there is no authentic record of a human attacked by a killer whale. Frightened, indeed, but not attacked.

The second story, Professor Eschricht's, was published in 1866. From the stomach of a stranded killer he recovered thirteen porpoises and fourteen seals; a fifteenth seal was stuck in the animal's throat. But reading his story with a critical eye, you find that this impressive meal was, in fact, only fragments representing food eaten over an uncertain period of time.

A more recent story is told by John Prescott, curator of Marineland of the Pacific, in southern California. Among the Channel Islands he saw a killer whale leap clear of the water while holding an adult male sea lion crosswise in its jaws. "The whale then played with the sea lion for about twenty minutes, sometimes throwing the carcass high into the air." No mean trick, when a bull sea lion may weigh 600 pounds!

Although today we know a great deal about the killer whale, we continue to marvel at what we learn. The largest of the dolphin family (up to nine tons), it can outswim any other marine mammal (up to thirty knots), and it lives in all the seas of the world to the limits of polar ice. In the course of evolution it has become a predator supreme. If you were to select a counterpart among the sea mammals to match the lion or the wolf, or any other large, active, pack-hunting animal of the land, the killer whale would uniquely be your choice. Among the eighty kinds of cetaceans, only the killer whale feeds extensively on warm-blooded prey.

The marine waters near my home in the Pacific Northwest have become famous as the birthplace of the idea that the dread killer whale can be tamed. In captivity it proves to be docile, "friendly," articulate, and responsive to individual trainers whom it learns to identify. Having no enemies in the sea, it looks upon man without fear. We are just beginning to realize the value of the killer whale to entertainment, education, and research. And we are beginning to realize that certain ethical problems in the chase and capture of this magnificent creature will have to be solved. But more about this in a moment.

To the best of my knowledge, no killer whale has ever been taken alive and unharmed anywhere in the world outside the sheltered waters of Washington State and British Columbia. (A dying individual was once held in southern California for less than two days.) A biologist who studies whales for the United States government believes that in Puget Sound "the killer whale population is probably denser than anywhere else in the world," while two local whale hunters claim that "as many as 200 or more at a time may swim into this inland area of water."

New light on the killer whale can be dated precisely from July 16, 1964, when collectors from the Vancouver Public Aquarium fired a harpoon into a surprised young male near Saturna Island, British Columbia. They were after a fresh carcass to be used as a model for a museum replica. But the victim was only stunned, and in a flash of serendipity, the collectors decided to tow him alive to Vancouver, forty miles away. This they did, and there they kept him in a makeshift pen for eighty-seven days. Thousands of visitors came to see the world's first captive killer whale. On a special radio program his voice was heard by millions across Canada, while the Canadian National Film Board released a movie about him in forty-four countries. The name Moby Doll, chosen in a radio contest, proved embarrassing to the aquarium staff when they finally learned his sex.

Public interest in killer whales was still running high when, six months after the death of Moby Doll, another killer was accidentally trapped behind a fishnet near the village of Namu, British Columbia. This was a big one, twenty-one and a half feet long, weighing 7,520 pounds. Seattle promoters purchased him for $8,000 and towed him to a pen on the Seattle waterfront. Here Namu, as he was called, became very tame and eventually allowed men to ride on his back. He lived for a year in the polluted waters at the edge of the city, then died of a bacterial infection.

The first killer whale deliberately chased and taken alive was the young female Shamu, who was surrounded in a purse seine near Puget Sound in 1965. She lived peaceably for several months in the pen with Namu, then achieved distinction as the first killer whale to fly. She was sent in a turboprop plane to Sea World, in San Diego, California.

Still there, Shamu has learned an amazing repertoire of tricks, one of which is to leap vertically to clear the water with the length of her graceful seventeen-foot body. Another trick is to open her jaws wide to admit the head of her trainer, who plays the role of doctor examining her tonsils.

Thirty to forty killer whales have been captured in the Pacific Northwest and held for sale or display since the summer Moby Doll made the headlines of the world. Reliable figures are hard to obtain, for the hunting of small whales and dolphins is unregulated in Washington State. In one spectacular catch in 1967 in Puget Sound, fifteen killers were netted; of these, seven were released, three died of injuries, and five were held for sale.

In the spring of 1968, fishermen of Pender Harbour, British Columbia, perfected a method of netting killers inside a narrow inlet. They captured eight that year. Pender Harbour has proved to be an ideal place to hold killer whales. It is sheltered, clean, and close to a fish dock where food for the whales can be easily obtained. Since 1968 the Vancouver Public Aquarium has maintained a research station there. Scientists come throughout the year to study killer whales under semiwild conditions. The animals often "talk" to their companions outside the fence.

At one time or another, killer whales have been exhibited in at least seventeen oceanariums: in Australia (1), Canada (3), England (2), France (1), the Netherlands (1), and the United States (9).

The killer whale is the largest marine mammal ever held in captivity and is therefore of interest to scientists who plot animal functions on the so-called shrew-to-elephant curve, or the curve illustrating the physiology of mammals from the smallest in weight to the largest. Actually, a bat may be the smallest mammal and the blue whale is certainly the largest. For example: a shrew weighing less than an ounce will eat food equal to 150 percent of its body weight per day, while a killer whale the size of Namu, weighing 7,520 pounds, will eat only 5 percent.

Other zoologists study the killer whale's adaptations to swimming and diving. A killer was found tangled in a submarine cable off Vancouver Island at a depth of 3,378 feet. A killer in Puget Sound, carrying a harpoon, line, and floats, remained under water for 21 minutes.

The Vancouver Public Aquarium has a splendid female killer whale named Skana. I recently watched as a team of physiologists put a modified "plumber's friend," or suction cup, over her blowhole to collect respiratory gases. Others took blood samples from her tail for study of the oxygen content. Still others took electrocardiograms. Skana, who has known only kindness in captivity, was remarkably patient during the four-hour probing of her life processes. She had learned to accept the periodic "letting down of Skana," when her pool is drained and scrubbed and she herself is stranded on a foam-rubber cushion, surrounded by eager investigators.

I will never forget that scene as the water slowly drained away and six men in black rubber suits stood on the floor of the pool beside the black-and-white beast. By gently tugging her tail or flipper now and then they persuaded her to settle on the cushion, like a mother hen on the nest. Once, in what might have been apprehension, she jerked her tail and baptised a man by total immersion. Had she released the full power of that tail, she would have broken his neck.

On an ordinary day when Skana is loafing in her pool, she may be visited by a zoologist intent on listening to the songs she sings underwater and out. Her clicks are useful for echolocation; her whistles and squeaks for communication with the killer whales of the open sea who now live only in her memory.

It took more than 1,600 trials to test the sharpness of Skana's vision underwater. Surprisingly, her eyesight is equal to that of a cat in air. She occasionally slips into periods of deep sleep like that of men and other terrestrial mammals. In scientific language, one expert has written that Skana gives off "low intensity aperiodic vocalizations" during sleep. (That is to say, she snores.)

A spin-off result of holding killer whales in captivity is new light on their husbandry, or care. How does one wean a toothless, 800-pound suckling baby? In one report, a veterinarian force-fed a baby whale three times daily, using a formula made up of one gallon of fresh whipping cream mixed with human-baby food, some fish, warm water, and vitamins—until the animal began eating independently.

And towering above the scientific value of captive killer whales is the knowledge that millions of people are now being led to a new experience—a combination of entertainment and education—that surely leaves them with a warmer and closer feeling for animals.

The distressing fact remains, however, that the pursuit, capture, and even killing of this splendid species of wildlife is unregulated in the United States. Killer whales belong to all of us, yet any amateur with a spear, gun, or net can now legally chase them.

I recall one Sunday when a killer whale created the worst traffic jam in the history of the Columbia River Bridge near Portland. A female killer had wandered 110 miles up the river from the ocean. She sported for several days off Jantzen Beach, where thousands came to see her from the shore. One night, she was harpooned and killed by two men, the Lessard brothers. Arrested for taking a "fish" with illegal tackle, they were later released when the difference between a whale and a fish was made clear to the prosecutor.

Several years ago, an editorial on Seattle's radio station KIRO announced that "the real purpose of the whale-catching [in Puget Sound] is abundantly clear. It's to make music on the cash register, whether as entertainment . . . or to sell whales to other marine shows." As I write today, the price of a live killer whale is about $20,000.

In closing this narrative of the gentle whale and what

it has done for men, I suggest what men can do for the whale. I endorse the enactment of a law for the regulation of killer whale hunting in Washington State.

The whale populations should be monitored to insure against overkilling. A hunting license would bring revenue to support population research.

There have been unintended cruelties in the hunting of whales. Shrouded in secrecy, at least six whales have been killed by Seattle showmen. One disappeared when a drug syringe was fired into its back from a helicopter. But zoologists know that you cannot immobilize a marine mammal in the water; it will drown. Another whale, a five-ton bull, died of infection. The hunters had thrust a 16-inch harpoon into its back and to the harpoon had tied a 1,000-foot line with floats. Their intention had been to mark the largest male of a family—the group leader, or "pod bull"—so that they could track the family and eventually surround it with nets. A whale law would allow an observer with no financial interest in the operations to be present during the chasing and handling of whales.

Hunting should be banned from waters where many people now thrill at the sight of whales in the wild and free. At present there are more than 186,000 pleasure boats operating in Puget Sound. The thought has often been expressed that persistent hunting will drive the whales away from their usual haunts. I have enough respect for the intelligence and social instinct of *Orcinus* to believe that this may be so. A whale law would establish no-hunting preserves in scenic waterways and within sight of urbanized shores.

Whether the whales of Washington State should be managed at the state or federal level is not altogether clear. Little is known about the movements of any American dolphin, porpoise, or small whale, with the exception of the Alaskan beluga, or white whale. One could argue that by its very nature a marine mammal is free to travel across state and national boundaries and is thus a proper subject for national and international regulation. In my opinion, however, it would be more practical to regard as resident species those that are commonly seen feeding—and perhaps even breeding—within state waters. Rather than quibble about jurisdiction, we should take the first step: regulate by license the hunting, holding, and killing of killer whales in Washington State.

To those who believe that nothing is worth doing unless we can beat the Communists at it, I offer no encouragement. The Russians have already banned the hunting of dolphins in the Black and Azov seas for a ten-year period that started in 1966.

Of Love in Infants

❖❖❖❖❖❖

HARRY F. HARLOW

[1960]

The use of infant monkeys in many laboratory experiments is perhaps dictated by necessity, but few scientists would deny that it is also remarkably convenient. Monkeys are far better coordinated at birth than human infants; their reactions can be evaluated with confidence at an age of ten days or earlier, yet their development follows the same general line as that of humans.

The monkeys' well-being and even survival pose a number of problems, however—particularly if they must, in the course of experimentation, be separated from their mothers only a few hours after birth. Nonetheless, at the University of Wisconsin's Primate Laboratory we were able, using techniques developed by Dr. Gertrude van Wagenen of Yale, to rear infant monkeys on the bottle with a far lower mortality than is found among monkeys nursed by their mothers. Now one of the components of our technique involved the use of a gauze diaper folded on the floor of the infant monkeys' cages, following Dr. van Wagenen's observations that monkeys would maintain contact with soft, pliant surfaces during nursing. We were struck by the deep attachment our monkeys formed for these diaper pads and by the distress they showed when, once a day, the pads were removed for reasons of sanitation. This observation led us into quite a new series of experiments—research into the importance of bodily contact in infant love.

Love of infants for their mothers is often regarded as a sacred or mystical force, and perhaps this is why it has received so little objective study. But if facts are

62

lacking, theory on this subject is abundant. Psychologists, sociologists, and anthropologists usually hold that the infant's love is learned through the association of the mother's face and body with the alleviation of such physical tensions as hunger and thirst. Psychoanalysts specially emphasize the importance to emotional development of attaining and sucking at the breast. Our experiments suggest something else is involved.

We contrived two substitute "mothers." One was a bare cylinder made of welded wire and surmounted by a wooden head. In the other, the wire framework was covered by a layer of terry cloth. We put eight newborn monkeys in individual cages, each with equal access to a cloth and to a wire mother. Four received their milk from one type of mother, four from the other—the milk being obtained from nursing bottles fixed in the mothers' "breasts."

Physiologically, the two mothers proved to be equivalent—the monkeys in both groups drank as much milk and gained weight at the same rate. But psychologically, the two mothers were not at all equivalent. Both groups of monkeys spent far more time climbing over and embracing their cloth mothers than they did their plain wire ones; they even left their electric heating pads to climb on the unheated cloth mother. Those that suckled from the wire mother spent no more time than feeding required.

The theory that infant love is related to satisfaction of hunger or thirst was thus contradicted, and the importance of bodily contact in forming affection underscored. This finding was supported by the next phase of our investigation. The time that monkey infants spent cuddling their surrogate mothers was a strong indication of emotional attachment, but it was perhaps not conclusive. Would they also turn to their inanimate mothers for comfort when they were subjected to emotional stress?

With this question in mind, we exposed our infant monkeys to strange objects likely to frighten them, such as a mechanical teddy bear that moved forward, beating a drum. It was found that, whether the infants had nursed on the wire mother or the cloth one, they overwhelmingly sought comfort in stress from the cloth one. The infant would cling to it, rubbing its body against the toweling. With its fears thus assuaged, it would turn to look at the previously terrifying bear without the slightest sign of alarm. It might even leave the comfort of its substitute mother to approach the object that had frightened it only a minute before.

It is obvious that such behavior is analogous to that of human infants, and we found that the analogy held in situations that less obviously involved stress. If a human child is taken to an unfamiliar place, for example, he will usually remain calm and happy so long as his mother is nearby, but if she leaves him, fear and panic may result. Our experiments showed a similar effect in infant monkeys. We put the monkeys in a room that was much larger than their usual cages, and in the room we placed a number of unfamiliar objects—a crumpled piece of newspaper, blocks of wood, a metal plate, and a doorknob mounted on a box. If a cloth mother was present, the monkey, at the sight of these objects, would rush wildly to her and, rubbing against the toweling, cling to her tightly. Its fear would then diminish greatly or else vanish altogether, as in the previous experiment. Soon the monkey would leave its mother to explore its new world. It now regarded the objects as playthings. Returning from time to time to the mother for reassurance, it followed an outgoing pattern of behavior.

If, on the other hand, the cloth mother were absent, the infant would rush across the room and throw itself head down on the floor, clutching its head and body and screaming in distress. The bare wire mother afforded no more reassurance than no mother at all—even monkeys that had known only the wire mother from birth showed no affection for her and got no comfort from her presence. Indeed, this group of monkeys showed the greatest distress of all.

In a final comparison of cloth and wire mothers, we

adapted an experiment originally devised by Robert A. Butler in this laboratory. Butler had found that monkeys enclosed in a dimly lighted box would press a lever to open and reopen a window for hours on end, with no other reward than the chance to look out. The rate of this action depended on what the monkeys saw: a glimpse of another monkey elicited far more activity than that of an empty room.

When we tested our infant monkeys in such a box, we found that those raised with both cloth and wire mothers showed as great an interest in the cloth mother as in another monkey but responded no more to a wire mother than to an empty room. In this test, as in all others, the monkeys that had been fed on a wire mother behaved in the same way as those that had been fed on a cloth-covered mother surrogate.

Thus, all objective tests we have been able to devise indicate that the infant monkey's relationship to its substitute mother is a full one. There are, of course, factors other than bodily contact involved. For example, the simple act of clinging, in itself, seems important: a newborn monkey has difficulty surviving in a bare wire cage unless provided with a cone to which it can cling.

Yet our experiments have clearly shown the importance of the comfort derived from bodily contact in the formation of an infant's love for its mother and revealed the role of breast-feeding to be negligible or nonexistent. They have also established an experimental approach to subtle and dramatic relationships.

In the Life of a Herring Gull

❖❖❖❖❖

NIKOLAAS TINBERGEN

[1939]

I wish I could show you the glorious scene of Dutch North Sea sand dunes in early spring. You certainly would have to use your legs, it is true, for it requires an hour's bicycle tour and a subsequent hour's walk through the sand, but I am sure you would enjoy it.

The bicycle ride takes us through the meadows and through the awaking bulb-fields. High in the pale blue sky the larks are singing, and brilliantly black-and-white lapwings are hurrying northward.

In the sand dunes the scenery is quite different. Pale yellow sandhills, dark valleys covered with birchwoods, irregular hummocks with yellowish green marram grass, and gentle slopes covered with "dune thorn" shrubbery. This is the home, and has been for centuries, of our herring gulls. When we watch the locality on this first warm day in March, we see the arrival of the gulls. In winter they live scattered along the coast, from Heligoland and the Danish-German coast down to northern France. Now they have gathered near the breeding places, have changed their plumage into the brilliantly white breeding dress.

When the tide is rising and they have finished their feeding on the beach, they rise into the air, forming an irregular chaotic flock. Soaring and calling they slowly climb higher and higher while traveling inland, and like a cloud-mass of whirling flakes they arrive above the colony-haunt. Their calls carry miles and miles over the desolate sand hills. They circle and circle, and we expect them to come down, but they stay high up in the air, and that is all we see of them on this day. After some hours, they leave again and collect on the seashore.

Returning some days later, we may watch them alight in the dunes before us. An enormous change occurs within the seemingly chaotic cloud; the individual birds scatter all over the colony, and before we realize it they have neatly arranged in pairs, each pair occupying a little dune or hummock. Chaos has changed into organization!

If we spend an hour or so in closely watching the individual pairs, the complexity of this organization becomes more and more obvious. Some pairs fight against other gulls, and it soon appears that the fights are strictly localized; the birds resent the presence of other birds only near their resting place. True border clashes result. They seem to know each other very well, for they never attack their own mates, even in the most entangled scrimmages. Sometimes they join the flock, indulging in a wild social flight high in the air; after which, descending again, they alight on the very same spots they occupied before. How do they find their way? How do they recognize each other? How do they communicate without having any "speech"? What is the meaning of their calls, their movements, their fighting? In other words: how is this community organized?

It takes some time and some trouble to answer these questions, but we don't need very elaborate equipment for our study. A small, cubical tent a yard or so on a side is our most important accessory. It is drably colored and has peepholes in different sides. Good field glasses are valuable, and we will have to use a net or trap to catch some birds for banding, for, as we will see later, our ability to recognize individuals by their natural peculiarities of posture, face expression, and the like is much too poor. The gulls recognize individuals at a glance without using our aluminum and colored bands; we humans don't have such splendid powers of discrimination.

Although I happened to do my watching in Holland, the same can be done in the United States, since the herring gull is abundant on the Atlantic Coast. We do best to start our study by patient watching, keeping two or three pairs under observation and neglecting all other birds. Each pair stands on its post. The birds are dull and spend their time in preening and sleeping. An instantaneous change, however, occurs in all birds when a strange gull alights in the neighborhood. One bird of each pair stretches its neck, at the same time pointing the head downward, and in this threatening attitude walks to the intruder. The change in the expression of such a threatening bird, brought about by a mere change in posture, is amazing. The intruder seems to think the same way and takes wing at once. This is firsthand proof of the value of this movement as a kind of "language": the birds "understand" what their colleagues' movements mean! Now it occurs often that an intruder, though he may be scared, does not flee, and then, after prolonged mutual threatening, a fight may result. One bird gets hold of the other, takes its bill, wing, tail, or neck in its own bill, and, having a good hold, pulls or shakes it furiously. Feathers may fly, wings may flap, and the struggle may continue for many minutes.

These fights occur only at the borders of the territories of the individual pairs. Watching the same birds day after day we will actually see that every bird only fights in defense of the territory, a piece of ground some 100 to 300 square yards around the post.

Often it is only one bird, usually the male, that does the fighting, while the partner walks around excitedly. Which is the male, which the female? In every pair the male is markedly stronger and bigger. Even a human observer can see this. But further than that we cannot go. It is impossible for us, in most cases, to identify a bird outside its territory. Yet the gulls do so without difficulty. A flying bird, upon returning, alights beside its mate among a flock of other gulls without showing any hesitation. How does it know? Sometimes the voice is the clue. We know this by observations like the following:

A gull is incubating before us and, not at all concerned about our tent, falls asleep. As long as he takes his nap, "traffic" in the colony goes on, numerous birds flying to and fro, some of them calling. Our bird remains asleep. Suddenly, promptly after the call of another flying bird, he wakes up and calls, and looks at the flying gull; the latter alights, and it appears to be the mate of the sitting bird. Nature made this fine experiment for us.

In other cases, however, we are sure that the partner was recognized in flight without having given any sound. Recognizing a gull in flight at a distance of 30 yards is beyond our abilities, but not beyond those of a herring gull!

When we watch the same part of the colony next year, we find that the same territories and the same posts are occupied again. But is it done by the same birds? Again we don't recognize them! Therefore, we have to band our birds. Catching a gull on its nest seems an easy thing, but it may take hours or even days before we get him. He gets a combination of colored bands and is released. The bands rattle as he flies off. Fortunately, he is not scared too much and does not desert his eggs. Now the mate must be caught. We wait till she relieves the banded bird in incubation, and our net traps her, too. In this way we mark several pairs. Next year, great surprise! We find the territories occupied, and we recognize our banded birds! Such moments of pure joy about a discovery are the highlights of biological research.

Some of these banded pairs returned year after year, and two of our seven pairs did so during four consecutive years. Sometimes, a banded bird moves to another part of the colony, but presumably this occurs only when its mate has died.

These bands may be useful in answering our other questions at the same time. Where do our gulls come from? Where were they born? We have eight colonies at different places on our coast. Are they populated by Dutch-born gulls, and does a bird born in one colony settle to breed in another colony or does it return to its own colony after the four years that elapse before it reaches maturity? Fortunately, many young were banded on former occasions by other field naturalists, and sometimes we caught on its nest a bird that bore a band which betrayed its birthplace. We started a regular hunt for banded birds. Every banded gull was watched, its nest located, and the bird caught when possible. Thus we caught eleven gulls in our colony at Wassenaar, ten of which appeared to be Wassenaar-born. Another colony on the famous bird island of Texel, about 65 miles from Wassenaar, yielded us fifteen banded birds, fourteen of which were Texel-born. This proved that herring gulls as a rule return to the colony where they were born, select a territory, and keep that territory during the rest of their lives. The life of a herring gull, by the way, may be very long: the oldest bird known is over 20 years old! Most of them, however, do not live longer than a few years and the greater number do not even reach maturity.

The mates of a pair remain together. Probably they separate in winter, but next spring they find and recognize each other somewhere on the seashore, before they return to the breeding haunt! We have still more evidence of the remarkable power of discrimination of these birds. A gull knows not only its mate, but also its neighbors. This appears in observations like this one: we once observed a pair that not only chased strangers from their own territory but also from their neighbors' territory. Only the neighbors themselves were allowed to stay. Whatever the neighbors did, however they behaved, they were always recognized and never attacked as long as they did not intrude on the first pair's territory.

When the season advances, nests are built and eggs are laid. Everywhere in the colony nests with eggs can be found. The eggs are very variable, and sometimes we find a very abnormally colored clutch. Next time we want to show it to some friends, and then we may have some trouble in finding it again—to their amusement. Yet the gull never has any trouble in finding and recognizing his nest.

How does he know his own eggs? We will have to arrange some experiments. Our hide is pitched at a distance of some 30 feet from a nest. Before hiding, we remove the eggs and put them a foot from the nest. In the nest itself we put the eggs of a neighbor. The returning bird walks to the nest, settles on the neighbor's eggs, and disregards its own clutch. We change conditions, leaving the bird's own clutch outside and removing the strange eggs. Now the bird returns and incubates in the empty nest! Next we destroy the nest. Two artificial nests are made, close to the original nest. In nest A we put the bird's own eggs, in nest B the abnormally colored eggs we found before. The gull returns, tries to sit down on the original nest spot, but hesitates, then steps to nest A, hesitates again, looks to nest B, steps into it, and settles down. Suddenly it sees A, rises, walks over to A, and sits down. In this way the bird goes to and fro several times, apparently equally stimulated by both clutches.

We extended these experiments and they showed that the color of the eggs did not make any difference at all. Blue and yellow eggs were brooded as greedily as normal eggs. Red eggs, however, though sometimes accepted, were often refused. Sometimes a gull first gave the red eggs some vigorous pecks, and then could not resist their form and brooded them. We also offered large wooden eggs that had a volume of eight times a normal egg. Some individuals seemed to prefer these "ostrich eggs" to eggs of normal size! They tried to sit on them, but fell down, forward, backward, or sideward, again and again! It was difficult for us not to burst into laughter at that sight. The gull apparently was so busy with this highly attractive egg that it did not notice our desperate struggle for self-control.

After these experiments we knew that a herring gull certainly does not recognize its own eggs but that it knows exactly where to look for them.

The hatching of the eggs brings a marked change over the colony's daily life. Everywhere the little downy chicks appear, and soon after birth they desire food. The old birds have taken care of this by swallowing great quantities of food on their last foraging trip. Strangely enough, the little chicks, which don't know—*cannot* know—anything about this world, do exactly the right thing to get food. They "know" what to do just as a newborn baby "knows" how to drink. The chicks walk to the parents, making faint, high sounds, and pick at the red spot on the parent's bill. If you take such a chick away and offer it a stuffed herring gull's head with the red spot on the base of the bill instead of at the end, the chick pecks at the base.

The real parent bird regurgitates food and takes tiny little parts of it in its bill. In this way the chick gets the food.

The chick "knows" still more. At the sound of the adult's danger cry it crouches and keeps quiet. We have our difficulties in locating it.

From now on, family life becomes more complicated. The old birds learn to recognize their own young. In the beginning we could change their young for their neighbors' young; they would feed and brood these strangers equally well. Repeat the same thing after a few days and they will refuse to feed every stranger, though these young may beg and harass them for food. Mostly they even kill strange young outright.

The young, on their part, are learning a great deal, too. They learn to know their territory, and each chick has its fixed hiding place, where it instantly goes when the old birds' danger calls give warning. Also, they have their "shadow rooms," special places where they hide from the sun during noon.

After some days, they know their own parents and do not beg food of strangers that happen to visit the territory. When they are very hungry, however, they may do so occasionally.

I should certainly like to tell you much more about the ways of the herring gulls, but space does not allow this. However, the story so far given will be sufficient to show the numerous relations that exist within this bird city, some based upon remarkable innate capacities to react to other individuals, others evolving from highly complicated learning processes. The birds have connections with territories, with their feeding grounds and nests, with mate, young, and neighbor, and certainly with other individuals as well. In numerous ways they influence each other's behavior: they threaten by posture and voice, they alarm each other in case of danger, they even have a red spot on their bills, the only function of which is to guide the feeding behavior of the newborn chick.

The herring gull is not the only bird that lives in such a complicated social relationship, nor is social organization confined to colonial birds. Every bird that associates with another bird, mate or young, is connected with its companion by numerous intricate relations. The study of these relations is only at its beginning. Yet it has already revealed striking similarities between human and bird communities, and we may certainly hope that a better understanding of the ways of birds will bring us a better understanding of human nature.

The Lady Lives on Blood

❖❖❖❖❖❖❖

MARSTON BATES

[1950]

Everyone is familiar with mosquitoes. Those poor people who have never been outside the region of Western civilization characterized by modern plumbing may plausibly deny acquaintance with bedbugs, lice, ticks, leeches, or even fleas; but they have all encountered mosquitoes either on picnics or, more intimately, in the bedroom.

Most of us have repeatedly gone through desperate nocturnal conflicts with a single mosquito that has somehow found a hole in the screening and come in to buzz triumphantly first in the left ear and then in the right before settling down to test the blood supply on an exposed shoulder. It is just a test, because the mosquito has already gone when you make the first swat.

I have spent many hours of my life inside large cages with mosquitoes, watching the intimate details of their life, including their individual and collective idiosyncrasies in biting. I have learned a lot about the character traits of *Anopheles maculipennis* and *Culex pipiens,* but none of this knowledge is of any avail during that midnight struggle. After that first swat, my body tenses in expectation of the next attack. I think I feel a bite and swat again, but a buzz in the ear tells me that the "bite" was probably one of those tricks of sense perception that the psychologists are always fussing with. I decide that the proper course is to let the mosquito settle down and fill up with blood, so that she will go off in a corner somewhere to start the digestive process and stop this silly braggart buzzing.

I try to relax and presently a series of sensations on

one side of the nose informs me that the mosquito has really settled down. I begin to think, why let the brute get away with this? The proboscis, I reflect, is surely well inserted by now and the mosquito sufficiently preoccupied with finding a capillary so that I'll be able to get in a really crushing swat.

I cautiously remove my arm from under the bedclothes and with infinite patience bring it into position for the blow, which is delivered with speed and precision. I feel my bruised nose to see whether I can detect the squashed mosquito. Nothing. Quite possibly the body fell off onto the sheet. But a minute later I hear that damned buzz again.

It is, of course, only the female of the species that bites. Not much is known about the food habits of the males, but they have been caught frequently on flowers, or sucking the easily got-at juices of things like fruits and manure. In Albania, I once tried baiting traps for male mosquitoes with all sorts of substances, and I found that I could catch a few with absorbent cotton moistened with perfume from my wife's dressing table. Cow manure was just about as attractive as the perfume, though.

Male mosquitoes are easily distinguished from females because of their conspicuous, feather-like antennae. There are a few records in the scientific literature of attempts at blood sucking on the part of male mosquitoes. When such misguided males have been caught and carefully examined, however, they have always turned out to be hermaphrodites—examples of a queer blending of male and female characters in a manner that is characteristic of insects. One side of the body may be male, the other side female, or the head male, the abdomen female, or something of that sort. These anomalies, called "mosaic gynandromorphs," are possible because sexual characters are determined directly by the hereditary materials of each particular cell, and not indirectly through the action of hormones, as is the case with us and other mammals.

It is the blood-sucking habit of the female mosquito

that gives these insects their peculiar importance for man. Not so much because of the annoyance caused to the human blood donor as because of the incidental possibility of transmitting disease. Many of the disease-causing parasites of man circulate in the bloodstream, and an insect picking up a sample of this infected blood and later probing some new victim for the next blood meal, provides a fine transportation arrangement—from the point of view of the parasite—for getting from one man to another.

The blood-sucking habit must be a very ancient one with mosquitoes. Fossil mosquitoes from the Oligocene, some 40 million years ago, look hardly any different from the mosquitoes of today, and presumably they had the same habits. There has thus been plenty of time for the mosquitoes and the parasites to work out mutually satisfactory arrangements for exploiting the vertebrate blood supply.

As long as mosquitoes were regarded merely as bedroom or picnic nuisances, they were given very little attention by scientists. But with the discovery, at the turn of the century, of their role in the spread of malaria and yellow fever, two of the most widespread and deadly of human diseases, they came in for a great deal of attention indeed. As a result of this study, yellow fever has been brought as completely under control as smallpox. Malaria is still public enemy number one for a large share of mankind, but in many parts of the world it has been eliminated as a health problem, and where it is still rampant, the difficulty is not so much a lack of knowledge as a lack of the funds and organization for the necessary public health measures. In the course of these 50 years of study, we have incidentally learned a great deal about mosquitoes.

The most recent complete list of the mosquitoes of the world was published in 1932, and at that time 1,400 different kinds were known. I once calculated that an average of 40 supposedly new kinds have been described every year since 1932, which would bring the total well above the 2,000 mark. But many of the "new" kinds

turn out to be mistakes, the new name becoming a syn-
onym of some older name, so that 2,000 is probably a
safe estimate for the known kinds of mosquitoes in the
world.

South America and the Orient have the largest variety,
with over 500 species each. About 400 species are
known from Africa, and 200 from Australia. North
America, with 121 species in the most recent catalogue,
and Europe, with 125 species, have less variety—but
they make up for this in number of individuals. As one
goes north in either hemisphere, there is a steady decrease in the number of different kinds of mosquitoes
liable to be encountered, but there is no corresponding
decrease in the number of bites. The world's highest mosquito content per cubic foot of air probably occurs
somewhere in Alaska or Siberia.

A man who gets caught in a place where there are millions of mosquitoes looking for a source of blood cannot help but wonder what all of these mosquitoes would
have done if he hadn't happened along. All of the evidence indicates that most kinds of mosquitoes cannot
develop eggs until after they have secured a meal of
blood. If a female fails to find a victim, she is doomed
to die childless, her function of reproducing the species
unfulfilled.

A French scientist, Emile Roubaud, discovered that
one variety of the common house mosquito, *Culex
pipiens,* can develop eggs without a blood meal. This discovery led to extensive investigations by many scientists,
resulting in dozens of learned papers and in the discovery of four other kinds of mosquitoes that can develop eggs without blood. Curiously these particular
species that really don't need blood are among the most
vicious and bloodthirsty of all mosquitoes. If they can
get a blood meal, they lay more eggs than if blood is
denied them, but they can be carried along very successfully in the laboratory for many generations with no
richer food than apples and raisins.

For the sake of completeness, I had better note here
that there are a few groups of mosquitoes in the tropical

forests that have taken up more pleasant habits—bright, metallic green and blue fellows that buzz about in the sunshine visiting flowers. A few have acquired very queer habits indeed, like the African and Malayan *Harpagomyia* that station themselves along ant runways and tease the passing ants into giving up honey. The *Harpagomyia* places itself directly in front of an advancing ant, sometimes even nipping the ant between its front legs, and not releasing it until it stops and opens its jaws, when the mosquito thrusts the swollen tip of its proboscis into the ant's mouth and rapidly absorbs the food offered.

But the basic food association of mosquitoes is with blood, and since disease transmission depends on biting habits, these have received particular attention from scientists. Work on biting habits, for instance, has been important in efforts to discover exactly which kinds of mosquitoes are responsible for disease transmission in different places. Laboratory studies show that any species of *Anopheles* can transmit malaria, but in a given place there may be a dozen or so different kinds of *Anopheles* breeding in different sorts of water. To control them all might be impossibly expensive, and it becomes necessary to determine the relative importance of the various species. It usually turns out that only one species is primarily responsible for malaria in a given region, and by learning the habits of this species, control work can be greatly simplified.

When a mosquito has filled up with blood, she goes off somewhere to digest the meal—a process that takes from two days to a week, depending on the kind of mosquito and on the temperature. She starts with the abdomen red and distended with blood and ends with it distended with eggs. The number of eggs depends on the kind of mosquito, on the amount of blood that she managed to get, and on the kind of blood. Human blood isn't necessarily the best; in one series of experiments, mosquitoes that fed on canaries, guinea pigs, and rabbits produced more eggs per milligram of blood than mosquitoes that fed on men or monkeys. In any case, the eggs are fairly numerous, 100 to 400 being developed per blood meal.

Digestion completed, the mosquito's next problem is egg laying. The larvae of all mosquitoes develop in water —one of the few statements I can make that needs no exceptions or qualifications—so the mosquito must put the eggs in some place where the larvae, when they hatch, will find suitable water. The common domestic *Culex* mosquito finds a rain barrel or puddle, sits on the water surface, and extrudes the eggs one by one, arranging them into a "raft." The eggs are held together by a sticky substance with which they are covered, and the form of the raft is determined by manipulations of the hind legs of the mosquito. Unless disturbed by a water beetle or an inquisitive scientist, the mosquito fixes its whole abdomenful of eggs into one raft; this finished, it flies off to look for another meal.

The *Anopheles* mosquitoes mostly lay their eggs in ponds, marshes, or areas of quiet water along the margins of lakes. The egg laying is carried out during a sort of hovering dance in which the mosquito bobs up and down over the water surface, dipping down every once in a while to "taste" the water by sticking in a leg (taste buds in insects are mostly on the legs), but otherwise dropping the eggs as she dances along several inches above the water.

Each kind of mosquito has its favored kind of water accumulation for breeding, and some kind of mosquito has learned to utilize almost every imaginable type of breeding place. For the most part, the larvae are closely associated with the water surface, hanging from the surface film and getting air through a tube that breaks the water surface at the tail end of the body. Because of this habit, mosquito larvae are never found in the open water of lakes, where they would merely serve as fish food, or in places where they would be damaged by wave action or water currents. In lakes or large streams, larvae are found in places where they are protected by vegetation, and while many species breed in small, swift streams, their adaptations are to keep out of the current, rather than to resist current action. In such streams, the larvae are found in seepage on gravel bars, in quiet side eddies behind boulders or under waterfalls, and in other places of the sort.

The queerest breeding places are in the tropical forests. In those regions, there are numerous unexpected places in which water accumulates, and every such place seems to have its peculiar species of mosquito larva. I have spent a deal of time in the South American rain forest trying to imagine places where water might occur; if I reasoned correctly and found water, I usually found also some new kind of mosquito.

A very common breeding place is the water that accumulates in rot holes in trees—and such tree holes are used by mosquitoes in the north as well as in the tropics. In South America, the bromeliads—the plants of the pineapple family—provide the habitat of dozens of species of mosquitoes. These plants are epiphytes, living perched on the branches of forest trees, and their long narrow leaves grow out of a watertight base that forms a structure called a "tank" by botanists. All sorts of debris accumulates in this base, forming a rich infusion that provides the plants with food. It also gives shelter to a whole special fauna of aquatic organisms, including dragonfly larvae and tadpoles as well as mosquitoes. The leaves of many tropical plants allow water to accumulate at their bases—this is true of banana plants, for instance—and even a thin film of water serves for certain specialized types of mosquitoes. The large upright flowers of some plants collect water, and such flowers also have their special mosquitoes.

The forest fauna that interested me most was that of bamboos. The hollow bamboo stems are often perforated by birds or by boring insects, and whenever a hole has been made into the stem, water accumulates in the internode. Some of these worm holes are very tiny indeed, so that one cannot imagine a mosquito squeezing through; yet when the bamboo is cut open, water and mosquito larvae will be found. These bamboo mosquitoes, we discovered, have very special habits. To breed out adults, we would put the larvae in test tubes plugged with absorbent cotton; but these bamboo mosquitoes, when they hatched in such a tube, would simply wriggle through the cotton plug and thus escape. We couldn't keep them in cages covered with ordinary mosquito-proof screen. A bamboo mosquito, coming across such a screen, would simply stick its head into the mesh and wriggle through, instead of futilely bumping against the screen like an ordinary mosquito.

The growth rate of a larval mosquito varies greatly according to the habits of the species. Those that breed in temporary rain pools sometimes grow very fast indeed, passing from egg to adult in the three or four days that elapse before the pool dries up. Others, that live in protected situations like tree holes, may take many months to grow up.

I have often been asked, "How long does a mosquito live?" Meaning, of course, an adult mosquito. The answer is, "It depends." In Europe and North America, many kinds of mosquitoes pass the winter as adults, hibernating in outbuildings, in caves, or in tree holes. With such mosquitoes, the last blood meal of the fall turns into a fat reserve instead of into eggs, and the adults live for many months in an inactive state.

The conditions of life for such a hibernating mosquito are very different from those for an active mosquito engaged in its proper business of annoying picnic parties. The hazards of existence for an active mosquito must be tremendous, and probably few of them manage to live for more than a few days. Yet to transmit malaria or yellow fever, we know that a mosquito must live for at least a week or two, to complete the incubation period of the parasite. Since these diseases are, or have been, very common, a great many mosquitoes must survive for this incubation period.

I have often wondered how it happens that anyone ever gets malaria, considering all of the hazards of the mosquito transmission cycle. Yet we are sure that we know all of the essential facts about malaria transmission; and millions of people get the disease every year, so the system of transmission would have to be called "successful."

In the United States, to be sure, this transmission system may already have met complete defeat. At a meeting of malaria experts held late in 1949, the specialists were asked how many new cases they had seen during the year among persons living in the United States. Only four new cases were described, although of course there were numerous cases of relapses, or of infections acquired abroad. Not many years ago there were millions of new cases of malaria in the United States every year.

Thus we seem to have the basic information that is necessary for the control of the disease, and in regions with well-developed public health services, malaria is on the way to becoming a medical curiosity. In India, Africa, and much of tropical America, it is still the major human disease, but the need is mostly for expanded public health organization. But even with malaria removed from the face of the earth, mosquitoes would still be valuable and interesting subjects for study, perhaps giving us clues to the general problems that seem to be just beyond our understanding: problems of the adaptations and mutual relations of our fellow organisms, and of the method and direction of the evolution of species.

Carpenter Ants

❖❖❖❖❖❖

T. C. SCHNEIRLA

[1951]

Ants of the genus *Camponotus* are popularly known as "carpenter ants" because they work in wood. It might be more fitting to call them "wood-carving ants," because they do not actually build of wood but gnaw out the soft or partly decayed interior of logs or stumps. When this wood-carving process is carried out extensively by a colony living in the forest or in a human habitation, the interior wood is virtually riddled. In the final stages, the chambers and galleries of the ant nest are separated only by thin partitions or narrow pillars.

You may have had opportunity to examine the extensive galleries of a colony of these ants in a felled tree, or you may have heard a neighbor express his anxiety at having carpenter ants in his house. It is easy to gain the impression that these ants are deadly enemies of trees in general and of people inhabiting wooden houses. Before attempting to assure you that the problem is not always as desperate as it may appear, I suggest that you acquaint yourself with some of the interesting habits of these creatures. A simple and effective artificial nest can be constructed by putting some of the ants and some wood from their home nest into a quart bottle. The bottle is then covered with a piece of cloth for the next few days, or long enough for the part-colony to become established. A rubber or glass tube may be used to connect the bottle with a smaller bottle or a glass-topped box that serves as a food place. In an artificial nest of this sort, the ants will thrive on a diet in which sugar-water, pieces of insect body or cooked meat, and boiled egg are given successively.

This setup may be used to carry out many interesting and instructive tests on the behavior of the ants. For example, a path may be complicated by a simple maze apparatus, and the learning of specially marked workers may be tested. Or orientation to visual stimuli may be investigated by shifting a light to the opposite side of the path after the workers have established their route. In this and similar tests, the disruptive effects of changes in the route or its landmarks should give useful clues as to how the habit of traversing the maze was established.

The ants are blind to red light, so it is possible to observe the colony with its brood and queen in one of these artificial nests without disturbing their activities. Thus the domestic affairs of the *Camponotus* colony can be worked out through careful observations. The manner in which workers feed one another, the queen, and the larvae by the regurgitation of the liquid contents of their crop merits detailed watching. As W. M. Wheeler demonstrated in his important book, *The Social Insects,* these exchanges among individuals, together with similar acts such as the licking of larvae and the queen's body surface by workers, and of worker by worker, provide the basis for the essential unity of the colony.

Another kind of interchange occurs when the colony is roughly disturbed, as by a sharp rapping on the artificial nest or on the shell of the log housing a colony in the open. Then the workers, and especially the largest (or major) workers, rush excitedly about, spreading the excitement and alerting the colony not only by the actual physical collision of antennae and bodies but by another and indirect means. This involves the rapping of the abdomen (and sometimes the head) against the wooden substratum, a procedure that sets up vibrations which reach other workers through the wood, exciting them at some distance. In an artificial nest provided with a floor of hard cardboard, the abdomen rapping of agitated workers gives rise to vibrations audible to the human ear as a rapid patter of faint drumbeats.

Ants of this genus are found almost throughout the

temperate and tropical zones around the world. Species such as our ubiquitous *C. pennsylvannicus* and its reddish subspecies *C. pennsylvannicus ferrugineus* of the north-temperate regions are characteristically found in shady woodlands, where they generally establish their nests in stumps and fallen trees. The excavations of many species like *C. pennsylvannicus* are made mainly in wood; the nests of others like the subspecies *C. pennsylvannicus ferrugineus* are tunneled extensively in the soil and only secondarily in the wood above; while the nests of other species like the yellow *C. castaneus* of our northern states are burrowed exclusively in the ground. Under propitious conditions, standing trees are frequently entered by some of the species; and among these species, *C. pennsylvannicus* often makes its nests in the wood of human dwellings. Perhaps the most specialized and curious of all *Camponotus* nests are those of species in the subgenus *Colobopsis,* mainly confined to the southern states. *Colobopsis* nests are found in hollow twigs or in galls; however, they are not very easily found, for their small entrances are plugged against come-what-may by the curiously flattened heads of the major workers, inserted like corks into the openings. The living door remains in place until a few short taps from the antennae of a returning worker on the outside, or a brush from an ant ready for exit on the inside, causes it to open and stand ajar briefly.

The colonies of the black species *C. pennsylvannicus* and its subspecies *C. ferrugineus* of the American temperate zone may grow to be fairly large. There may be as many as a few thousand workers, a single reproductive female (the queen), a brood of varying make-up, according to the season, and at certain times of year a considerable number of young winged males and queens. As with many other species of *Camponotus,* the workers (or neuter females) are polymorphic; that is, they range in size and type from the large and robust workers-major to the smallest, the workers-minor. The queen is readily distinguished from the workers by her great size, her large head and bulging thorax, and by the high polish she generally acquires from the almost incessant licking and stroking of her body by workers.

Colonies that have weathered the hazard of their first two or three years are usually able to produce reproductive individuals—the large winged males and females. The late summer brood of males and females, after emerging from their large cocoons, usually remain in their parent nests through the winter, huddled in clusters with the hibernating workers within the inner recesses of their catacomb-like shelter. They make their exodus early in the following warm season, in late spring or early summer as a rule. If the occupants of a house have been unaware of a flourishing *Camponotus* colony within the foundation beams, the discovery is likely to come on some warm day in late spring, when from some chink in the molding a whole host of males and numerous females may come out into the room.

In the open, the winged males and females spill out of their home nests on the warm and bright days from May into July and soon take to the air in a mating flight. This results in the fertilization of many of the females. In contrast to the large-eyed but tiny-headed males, which cannot survive long as solitary individuals after the flight, many of the inseminated queens return to some woody surface or to the earth and are able to establish themselves. Fascinating and unsolved problems are presented both by their behavior and their physiology, which seem to change markedly after fertilization has taken place.

When a fertilized queen descends from her flight, she drops or bites off her wings, then soon becomes photonegative. That is to say, she is markedly light-shy, whereas before fertilization she was light-positive, as indicated by upward spiraling toward light in the mating flight. As a result of this change, when the newly fertilized queen reaches a sheltered dark place, she settles down. If accidentally exposed to light, she again promptly disappears from view. In the northern states, if you pull strips of bark from logs and stumps in the late spring, you are likely to expose one or more newly established *Camponotus* queens. Each is in a little cell ringed around with a wall of wood fibers set up by the queen herself. Or she may find her way into the deserted burrow of a tunneling wood beetle in which she comes to rest at some turning. She may perish through seasonal vissicitudes or through the invasion of her cell by ants or other predatory insects. Otherwise, however, the young queen can survive by living on her own tissues and can found a colony through her own resources.

Her now degenerating wing muscles and the fat bodies with which she is abundantly equipped provide nourishment for her and her first brood. For, unlike the colony-founding queen of some Australian ants of primitive ponerine species, which leave their cells and forage about, thereby procuring food for themselves and for their first brood, the *Camponotus* queens remain sequestered and have no food except what is available from their own bodies. On this special "reducing diet," the queen soon begins to lay eggs, and with this substance she can feed the larvae which presently appear.

That the first brood is not lavishly fed by the queen is evident from the very small stature of the few workers that appear in the first lot. They are all of the worker-minor caste. However, these diminutive workers may succeed in consolidating the young colony by slowly extending the nest and by foraging in the environs, bringing in food that is used to replenish the queen's reserves and feed the additional brood. If the first pygmy workers do not carry out such work effectively, the colony is likely to perish. If they work well, the population grows and the nest is extended into wood and earth. As soon as the first workers have appeared and are busy in the nest, the queen turns to producing eggs as her exclusive task. Thereafter she labors no more except in this important capacity as egg-making machine.

Once a colony has gained its first good foothold, the larvae presently are sufficiently well fed and develop into workers of the larger type, the intermediates or majors. With a good food supply, a temperature near 75 degrees F., and not too much or too little moisture in the air, the workers of *C. pennsylvannicus* require a little more than two months for their complete development from newly laid eggs to the callow (or newly emerged adult) stage. This period is divided roughly as follows: 23 days from the laying of the egg to its hatching into a larva, 21 days for the growth and maturation of the grublike larva, and 21 days for the development of the mature larva within its cocoon into a prepupa and then into the adult-like pupa. Sunny and somewhat humid weather generally hastens development; cool, unusually variable, or very dry weather is likely to retard development. Although the workers require the larger part of a summer for their development, they are adults when the pupal stage is finished and grow no more after they emerge from their cocoons. In this they are very unlike the termites.

The hardiness of established colonies of carpenter ants is due not only to the excellent insulating properties of their dwellings but also to the fact that most of them can subsist on a variety of food. The larder has as its main item large supplies of nectar obtained regularly through spring and summer from honeydew produced by aphids and other "ant cows," which the *Camponotus* workers visit on surrounding plants. The ants also gather considerable quantities of insect flesh. They work both as scavengers, collecting dead insect bodies in the neighborhood of their nest, and as predators, bringing in freshly killed insect victims. The foragers are generally able to bring their live captives under control by biting them with their powerful mandibles and also by squirting especially resistant subjects with formic acid.

In diurnal species such as *C. pennsylvannicus*, which do most of their foraging in the daytime, an intermittent traffic of workers is usually to be observed making repeated excursions to nearby plants where aphids are feeding. Each time a worker mounts a plant, she begins to stroke the aphids with slowly oscillating antennae, thereby stimulating the emission of their sticky, sweetish secretion. After lapping up enough of the nectar to fill her crop, thereby stretching out the walls of the gaster, or abdomen, very noticeably, the worker hurries off to the nest with her heavy afterpart waggling in a manner that the observer is likely to find quite amusing. At the home site, the load is regurgitated to other workers, with a frenzy of rapid strokes of antennae as the food transfer begins, then with slow regular antennal movements as the food transfer gets under way. Emptied of her load, the aphid visitor rushes off with crop contracted and abdomen small to obtain a refill at the source of supply. The trips continue in this way for many hours, and one worker may make dozens or scores of food-gathering trips in a single day. It is interesting to note that the nectar gatherer may make most or all of her visits on a single day to the same part of the same aphid colony on a particular plant. At the same time, other foragers are specialized in capturing and lugging either dead insect hulks or freshly killed prey.

The destructiveness of carpenter ants to wood is not always easily appraised, and there are divided opinions on the question, even among specialists. It is argued on the one hand that while these ants and their work frequently may become a considerable nuisance, especially around dwellings, the actual extent of the damage they do may not be nearly so great as imagined. In most cases, it is contended, the carpenter ants make their nests in wood that is already softened by decay or penetrated by the burrows of wood-boring beetles. The *Camponotus* technique of wood-riddling may actually no more than hasten the inevitable decay of presoftened wood. The degeneration of doomed trees, logs, and stumps is of course an ordinary and a biologically essential factor in the life processes of any forest, and *Camponotus* colonies incidentally make their contribution to these processes.

There are others, with many forestry specialists and entomologists among them, who insist that *Camponotus* colonies are destructive. It is pointed out that in less settled areas the more common *C. pennsylvannicus* generally nests in standing timber and not only in partially rotted trees but also in sound ones. This species also has been found tunneling in the sound dry wood of telephone poles, cabin posts, and the rafters of buildings, which may have been invaded in the first place through cracks as well as through damaged or decayed places. This species, therefore, is put down as a frequent offender against man's interest in timber and in the wood that he uses. It appears also that relatives, such as members of the American *C. herculeanus*, which live in the coniferous forests of the northern states and Canada, frequently enter standing trees and hasten their destruction. The various *Camponotus* species are not equally blameworthy from this standpoint; for example, *C. ferrugineus* is found almost always in predecayed wood, such as that of logs beneath which the colonies have excavated their nests in the soil.

With the advent of European man and his wooden structures in America, *Camponotus* has had the opportunity to invade human habitations in much the same way as wood is entered in the forest. *C. pennsylvannicus*, in particular, is frequently found in houses near woodlands. Where cracks, crevices, and faulty joints exist in beams and other exposed wood parts, the entrance of these ants is facilitated, and nests may be established if the interior wood is soft enough to be worked. Colonies may also establish themselves in piled lumber, sometimes moving over from fireplace logs heaped nearby.

It is doubtful that *Camponotus* often causes serious damage to really sound wood. The unpopularity of these ants in many quarters seems rather to result more from their nuisance value than from any actually identified destruction.

The Clock of the Bees

MAXIMILIAN RENNER

[1959]

Nowadays, if we resolve to do something at a certain time, we seldom rely on our time sense. One glance at a clock or watch suffices to tell us how many hours of the current day have already become part of the past. Or, if we know the compass and something about astronomy, we can orient ourselves in time without a watch by looking at the sun by day or the moon by night. Assume we know that the sun stands in the east at 6 a.m., in the south at noon, and in the west at 6 p.m. Then, when we see the sun in the southeast, we know the time must be about 9 a.m., or about 5 p.m. if the sun's position is west-southwest.

If we want to wake up during the night at a predetermined hour, without the help of an alarm clock, it is more difficult. Many people cannot do this with any reliability. But the number of those who can do so with precision is not so small as one might assume. Before going to bed, these people simply resolve to wake at a certain hour. Seldom does their "internal clock" deceive them by more than a quarter of an hour. Today, few persons depend upon this mysterious ability, since alarm clocks are common. But until late in the past century many farmers, hunters, and fishermen depended upon such internal clocks.

It has been known for a long time that not all men are equally endowed with this ability to wake up at a predetermined time. It has also been known that a certain concentration of mind is required if the determination to waken is to be successful. The various methods devel-

91

oped by different peoples indicate the extent to which mankind has been occupied with this problem. Take a few examples from Germany. In the Spreewald, a man would grasp his big toe after going to bed, concentrate on the predetermined hour, and repeat to himself: "I want to wake up at [such and such an hour]." In the Rhineland and Westphalia, he who wanted to awake at four o'clock stamped four times under the bedstead. The farmer in central Germany knocked the number of the hour against the wall of his bedroom; the Bavarian farmer rapped it out against his bedpost.

Naturalists know that animals divide their days, too. In their habits they are, of course, bound to the changes of night and day. During daylight, the "day animals," such as songbirds, are active, while during the hours of darkness the "night animals," such as owls and many rodents, go about their business. When the one group is active, the other rests. Yet, it is a mistake to attribute this rhythmic behavior exclusively to the rhythm of day and night; that is, the presence or absence of light. Such animals will also maintain their characteristic rhythm under continuous artificial light or in continuous darkness.

How is this possible? Does the animal orient itself in time through external influences that are perceivable even in illuminated or darkened rooms? Or does the animal possess something like man's internal clock? In what follows, we will not attempt a broad discussion of this intriguing problem, for this would demand a recitation of all that we know about diurnal rhythms and orientation in time of many different animals. Instead, we shall limit our examination to the behavior in the honeybee that is especially related to our problem. The bee's ability to orient itself in time has been thoroughly investigated because it was the observation of its behavior that first gave rise to an exact examination of this whole problem.

Some fifty years ago, the Swiss physician and scientist August Forel observed that the bees that frequented his porch every morning, to nibble from the sweets on his breakfast table, would appear at the usual time looking for the coveted food, even when there was none. Forel concluded that the alluring effect of the smell of the sweets (or any other stimulus emanating from them) could *not* have been the cause for the timely visit of the bees. Some simple experiments confirmed his conjecture. "The bees remembered," Forel concluded, "the hours at which they had usually found sweets. . . . They have a memory for time."

A few years later, another scientist, von Buttel-Reepen, called this remarkable ability "time sense." He observed that the fragrant, richly colored buckwheat fields were only frequented by bees until about 10 o'clock in the morning—the same hours during which the buckwheat flowers secrete nectar. Even though smell and color were the same in the afternoon, no bees were then to be seen. Yet, at an early hour the next day, hundreds of thousands of these industrious insects turned up again to collect the buckwheat nectar for as long as the sources flowed.

Evidently, the bees had quickly learned that the buck-wheat flowers secrete nectar only at certain hours. Therefore, they did not start out on what would have been vain flights during the nectarless hours. Only the assumption that the bees possessed a time sense could, in Buttel-Reepen's opinion, explain this highly practical behavior.

Today we know that the conclusions of both scientists were correct, although their evidence was not compelling. The work of the zoologist Karl von Frisch has familiarized us with the "language" of the bees. He has shown that worker bees, having found a rich source of nectar, can by means of their dances induce many of their hive-fellows to join them in a collective flight to the source.

If only a few scouts, which could well escape the eye of even the most careful observer, had reconnoitered Buttel-Reepen's buckwheat fields from time to time during the nectarless hours, for example, they could have alerted their hive-mates quickly as soon as the nectar flowed again. Forel's experimental arrangement, to be sure, excluded such a possibility. He could overlook his porch: if even a few bees had come there except at breakfast time, they would have been noticed. There is, however, an explanation other than time sense for their punctuality. It is possible that Forel's bees connected the position of the sun—or some other phenomenon of the daytime hours—with the experience of a rich food source, and thus oriented themselves in time. In other words, they would have flown to Forel's porch when the sun's position was the same as at breakfast time the preceding day. Such behavior would not demonstrate a true time sense. Rather, it would prove the bees' ability to connect—for the purpose of their orientation in time—certain experiences with events recurring periodically each day. We could speak of a true time sense only if their orientation in time would function after all such possible factors of daily rhythm had been excluded.

Whether bees have such an *internal* time sense (that is, an "internal clock"), or whether they find out about time by *events recurring periodically each day* (that is, by an "external clock"), has occupied a number of research workers since 1929. In that year, Ingeborg Beling, a student of von Frisch's, subjected the ability of bees to orient themselves in time to an exact analysis.

For a proper understanding of what follows, it is necessary to acquaint the reader with the method worked out by Miss Beling, a method that has been adopted by all later researchers. Twenty to thirty nectar-collecting bees, numbered individually by dots of color, are fed sugar water at an artificial feeding place for several days—each day from about 10 a.m. to noon. For the rest of each day, the bowl containing sugar water is empty. Bees looking for food before 10 a.m. or after noon return unsuccessful to their hive. After six or eight such "training" days, the feeding station, while otherwise unchanged, is left empty all day long. On this "test" day, an observer, sitting next to the station, notes both the time of visit and the identity of each bee that comes to the bowl.

It is surprising to see how exactly the bees have learned the training hours—not only the start of the feeding period but also, and even more exactly, its end. Almost precisely at the appointed time, they appear at the feeding station to search persistently and intensively for the coveted sugar water. On a test day, the observer might judge by their behavior that the bees cannot "believe" that the table has not been laid for them as usual. Over and over again, they come flying, run round searchingly, stretch out their proboscises into the bowl to reassure themselves that there is really nothing sweet in it. The most industrious ones among them extend their searches after a while to the wider environment and lick all glittering objects—such as the watch and the pencil case of the observer—and some especially audacious ones will even poke their proboscises into the wrinkles of the note-taking observer's bent hand. When the usual time of feeding comes to an end, the bees' visits become rarer: hardly half an hour later, the feeding station is deserted and quiet.

At the beginning of the training period, the bees are less punctual. Frequently they arrive a little beforehand —a behavior that has yet to be cleared up. In its effect, however, this behavior appears to be expedient, for "early bird" collectors can start to work quickly and in full strength as soon as the source of food begins to flow.

The next step in these studies was to eliminate the effect of those environmental phenomena that recur periodically during the day—for example, the position of the sun or temperature variations—that might function as time indicators. To accomplish this, a bee colony was placed for its training period in a specially devised room. This experimental room was kept at a constant temperature, and its illumination was constant both day and night.

A man would very soon lose any orientation in time under such circumstances; the bees, however, appeared punctually at the feeding place. They were not reading the time from the position of the sun or the brightness of the day. As subsequent studies established, neither the electrical conductivity of the air nor cosmic radiation (which both show a daily rhythm) served them as an external clock. In the gallery of a salt mine, some six hundred feet below the surface of the earth, where neither of these factors is effective, training was successful. Thus, it appears that the clock of the bees works independently of periodically recurring influences of the day.

There is, however, one problem. Can we be sure that *all* external factors which might function as time indicators have been eliminated in these "bee room" tests? Before attempting an answer to this question, we should acquaint the reader with the results of some other experiments.

One possibility that soon comes to mind—namely, that the clock of the bees is nothing but a hunger rhythm —has, of course, been taken into consideration, even though this appeared to be improbable from the outset. Worker bees do not take nectar—or sugar water—as direct nourishment. Rather, they fill their honey bag, an extension of the esophagus. After their return to the hive, the honey bag's contents is regurgitated and turned over to other worker bees, which store it in the cells and process it until it has ripened into honey after about two weeks.

Therefore, the training period is not a feeding period for the collector bee, in the sense of a "meal," although we frequently and incorrectly call it just that. It is true, at the same time, that the collector bees will also take nourishment; for he who works must take nourishment, too. But—and this was proven by exact investigations— the collectors also nourish themselves when they are *not* collecting—that is, whenever they are hungry. Nonetheless, the hunger-cue possibility was investigated with scientific exactitude: it was found that the time sense of the bees is definitely not governed by a hunger rhythm.

How then do the bees remember time? Do they keep in mind the *time of day* at the beginning and at the end of the training period? Or do they, instead, register the *interval* between two successive training periods? The result of experiments made to arrive at an answer to this question was surprising: the time memory of the bees is inseparably bound to an interval of 24 hours.

All attempts to train bees to a periodicity distinctly different from this—for example, to induce them to come to the feeding table every 19 or every 27 hours— were not successful. While the results of other experiments at first seem to contradict this finding, closer observation makes it clear that these seeming contradictions actually confirm the 24-hour periodicity. Training the bees to come two or more times in one day—no matter when these times are—is possible without any difficulty, if only the intervals between successive periods are not less than 2 hours each. In contradistinction to the unperiodical 19-hour or 27-hour training, the training hours in these latter cases recur at the same time each day. It is, therefore, a matter of two or more training periods in the 24-hour rhythm fitted into one another (the physicist would refer to "shifted phases").

But our initial question—whether bees recollect times of day by means of an external clock or an internal one —has still not been answered. The fact that bees are bound to a diurnal rhythm, while seeming to justify the assumption of an external time indicator, does not prove it. An *internal* 24-hour clock, situated perhaps in the metabolic system, could achieve the same effect. In that case, metabolic changes would also alter the time sense: that is, increased metabolism would result in the bee's clock being fast, decreased metabolism in its being slow. Experiments have proved that bees are late at the feeding table by several hours when they are put in a refrigerator after the last training period and kept there for 5 hours at a temperature of 4–5 degrees C. After a short time, they are completely stiff and numb: their metabolism is substantially decreased. Back in a warm temperature, they thaw in a few minutes and return without any visible damage to the hive. However, parallel attempts to induce the bees to come to the feeding table ahead of schedule—by giving them drugs to accelerate their metabolism—have had no success. Yet, the experiments with cold proved the dependence of the bees' time orientation upon organic factors.

To believe that this finding is conclusive proof of the existence of an internal clock, however, is to forget that the cold could have done no more than paralyze the bees' ability to perceive an external time indicator. Indeed, until recently, the possibility could not be excluded that some external factors not yet taken into account—such as the gravitational force of the sun and the moon, recurring periodically each day, or even some factor completely unknown to us—play a role in the bees' time orientation. The problem seemed insoluble. How could factors that were unknown be positively eliminated?

Still, there was a solution. It was pointed out by von Frisch as early as 1937. His considerations were the following: all environmental phenomena that show a daily rhythm derive their periodicity, directly or indirectly, from the rotation of the earth. These phenomena, including the elevation of the sun, occur at places of different longitude on the earth at different times, corresponding to the local time zones of each area.

This being known, the following experiment would provide a definite answer to the question concerning the nature of the time sense in bees: they would be trained in one local time zone for a period and then tested in another local time zone. If environmental phenomena are decisive, they would come to the test dish either *before* or *after* the 24-hour period—that is, 24 hours minus or plus the difference in time between the two local zones. If, on the other hand, their time sense does not depend upon external factors but is governed by an internal clock, which maintains its 24-hour rhythm, they would come to feed as usual—exactly 24 hours after their last training. The following description of such a relocation experiment, conducted in the summer of 1955, illustrates these theoretical considerations.

In this age of air travel, it is possible to transport a bee colony a great distance in a short time. Because of their favorable air connection, Paris and New York were selected as the two local areas: the bees could be trained in a bee room on one side of the Atlantic and tested on the other. The difference in time between New York and Paris is large enough to make for an indisputable result. Two identical—and portable—experimental rooms were built in Munich, and one was sent to Paris and the other to New York. Forty bees were trained in the Paris bee room under conditions of constant illumination for the period 8:15 to 10:15 p.m., French Summer Time. After a last training, the hive was packed into a box and flown to New York on June 13/14. Not quite 20 hours later, the hive was set up in an identical New York bee room.

The observer sat expectantly next to the feeding table. When would the bees come to the bowl? Twenty-four hours after their last training (which would be between 3:15 and 5:15 p.m., Eastern Daylight Time), or at the local New York time corresponding environmentally to the time of training in Paris—between 8:15 and 10:15 p.m., EDT: that is 24 + 5 = 29 hours after their last training? Would they come at all, or had the long air journey from one continent to the other disturbed them so much that their memory for time and locations had suffered?

The bees did not take long to answer these questions, and they answered in the clearest possible way. At 3:15 p.m., EDT, the first bees came out of the hive and started flying about the room, as if their location had never changed. And the ensuing visits to the feeding place were so numerous and thorough that it was difficult for the observer to note down each visitor correctly.

The result of this experiment, as well as the reverse one (training in New York and testing in Paris), has clearly answered the question as to the nature of the bees' orientation in time: the trained collector bees maintained their 24-hour rhythm, independently of external influences that periodically recur during the day. Bees have an *internal* clock, governed by their organism.

It may be asked what purpose the time sense of the bees fulfills? Even if some plants, such as buckwheat, secrete nectar only in the morning, there are certainly others that secrete nectar during the noon hour or in the afternoon. True: bees could certainly collect nectar without their time sense. But with it, their daily activities become easier and more rational and, as we know, everything in the bee colony is organized rationally.

The collector bees, which have been exploiting one source of nectar for hours, do not at once desert it when it becomes temporarily exhausted. They make good use of the rest period and retire to a quiet corner of the hive. Far away from the busy intercourse in the area of the front comb alleys, they take a rest from their strenuous work. Only when the hour approaches at which "their" flowers secrete nectar, do they resume their collecting. It would be a waste of honey and energy if they had to fly out for reconnaissance every twenty minutes or so to ensure their arrival at the very time the source would flow again.

Even so, the bees' time sense might still be dispensed with, were it not that the sense is absolutely necessary for the bees' orientation in space—for which they use the sun as a compass. The solar compass, as we saw in our initial examples, can function *only* if the time of day is taken into consideration. And, finally, when the collector bee returns to the hive from a nectar reconnaissance, the direction and the distance of the source is communicated to other workers by means of a dance. For the correct execution and comprehension of this dance, a time sense that works exactly is also an absolute requirement.

The Square-Mouthed Rhinoceros

THEODORE ROOSEVELT

[1911]

On our trip in Africa for the Smithsonian, in addition to the series of specimens of big game for the Smithsonian itself, we also prepared a few skins of the largest and rarest animals for other collections: a head of the white rhinoceros for Mr. Hornaday's noteworthy collection, a bull elephant for the University of California, two cow elephants and a bull and cow of the white rhino for the American Museum of Natural History. I was especially anxious to get this pair of white rhinos, because the American Museum is in my own city, because my father was one of its founders, and because my admiration is great for the work of the men who have raised this institution to its present high position. The skins of the two cow elephants were prepared by Carl Akeley, with whom I had gone after them; the other specimens were preserved by Edmund Heller and R. J. Cunninghame as a labor of love.

The white rhinoceros is, next to the elephant, the largest of existing mammals. There are three groups of existing rhinoceros: the two-horned species of Africa, the one-horned species of the Indian region, and the little Sumatran rhinoceros—the three separate stems of ancestry going back at least to early Pliocene and probably to Miocene times. At one time rhinos of many different kinds and covering the widest variety of form and habit abounded in America, and in Europe species lasted to the days of Paleolithic man.

There are two wholly distinct kinds in Africa, differing from one another as much as the moose does from the wapiti. They are commonly called the black and the white, but as in fact they are both of a dark slate hue, it is better to call the former the hook-lipped and the latter the square-mouthed. They intergrade in size, but the square-mouthed averages bigger and longer-horned. The hook-lipped or common black kind is still plentiful in many places from Abyssinia to the Zambezi; it is a browser and feeds chiefly on twigs and leaves. The white or square-mouthed kind is now found only in a game preserve in South Africa and on a narrow stretch of territory along the west bank of the Upper Nile. It is purely a grazer.

In its range the square-mouthed rhino offers an extraordinary example of discontinuous distribution. It was originally known from South Africa, south of the Zambezi, and was believed to exist nowhere north of that river. Then, when it had been practically exterminated in South Africa, it was rediscovered far to the north beyond the equator. In the immense extent of intervening territory it has never been found.

We spent over a month in the Lado, the present habitat of this huge sluggish ungulate. We collected a good series of specimens, nine in all—bulls and cows and one calf. Of course, we killed none save those absolutely needed for scientific purposes. All told, we saw thirty or forty individuals and Kermit got some fine photographs, the first ever taken of living members of the species. Their eyesight was so dull and their brains so lethargic that time and again we got within a score or so of feet and watched individuals as long as we cared to.

They drank at night, either at the Nile or at some pool, and then moved back, grazing as they went, into the barren desolation of the dry country. About nine o'clock or thereabouts they lay down, usually under the scanty shade of some half-leafless thorn tree. In mid-afternoon they rose and grazed industriously until sundown. But as with all game, they sometimes varied their times of resting, eating, and drinking. Ordinarily we found the bulls singly and the cow along with her calf, but occasionally three or four would go together. Cow herons frequently accompanied them, as they do elephants and buffaloes, perching unconcernedly on their heads and bodies.

They were not difficult to get, as our trackers followed their trail with little difficulty, and they seemed less excitable and bad-tempered than their hook-lipped cousins, although on occasion they charge with determination, so that a certain amount of care must be exercised in dealing with them.

Bitten by a Fer-de-lance

❖❖❖❖❖❖

ARCHIE CARR

[1969]

Not long ago I was bitten by a fer-de-lance. When I failed to succumb, my friends, knowing my vices, assured me that if I ever stopped talking about the experience, I would surely start writing about it, but I said they were wrong. The fright was too personal to write about, I said; and besides, after talking so incessantly about the misadventure, setting it down in print would seem superfluous. But as days passed and raw emotion faded, certain aspects of the happening stuck in my mind because they seemed to shed light upon the natural history of man and *Bothrops*. On this pretext I decided that if I failed to drop dead on the nineteenth day, as Shefton Martinez, the major-domo at the Green Turtle Station, said was likely, I would write my impressions of the curious little nightmare.

I was out looking for reptiles when the *terciopelo* bit me. The terciopelo is *Bothrops atrox;* terciopelo, the local Costa Rican name for the species, is Spanish for "velvet," and is applied to the snake because of the soft, naplike look of the dorsal dark patches in the color pattern. In Honduras the same snake is known as *barba amarrilla*—"yellow chin." The more widespread vernacular name fer-de-lance spread out of the French West Indian island of Martinique, where a similar species lives. *Bothrops* is a genus of the pit vipers, related to the rattlesnakes, copperhead, and cottonmouth moccasin of the United States. The single species *B. atrox* bites more people each year than all the poisonous snakes of the United States put together. This is because its usual habitat is cutover country, in which scattered small farms alternate with second growth in various stages of succession. Terciopelos avoid the depths of homogeneous forest except along streams and sloughs, and clearly lean to country in which the crops and clearings of man have extended the habitat of the rodents and ground birds on which the snakes feed. There is a lot of such country in Central America, and the terciopelo bites an alarming number of the people who work in it.

It was in that kind of place that the terciopelo and I came together—the Caribbean coast of Costa Rica—on the narrow strip of land between the Tortuguero River and the sea. I was out looking for snakes at the time. Five days before, we had cut a trail from the little airstrip on the beach back through dense *caña de cristo* brake to the river, which runs parallel with the shore some three hundred yards away. When the snake bit me I was reconnoitering that trail as a possible reptile-hunting route. The tropical biology class of the Organization for Tropical Studies was coming down in a few days, and I was trying to map out some field trips for them. That circumstance increased the bitterness of the mishap. Being bitten when you are out looking for snakes only adds humiliation to the other misery.

Being so newly cut, the trail was not very promising, herpetologically. It takes longer than four days for a new strip of lighted ground to mellow and draw in the little trailside associations of insects, mice, reptiles, and birds that gravitate to clearings in the wet tropics. But the *guamil,* dense second-growth stands of canelike grasses and herbaceous vegetation, around the station is so impenetrable that there just being a trail to walk on at all tempts one to walk. So I was out there that afternoon moving slowly along the narrow *pisada,* trying hard not to overlook any lizard basking on a stem or any slinking chain of snake in the confusion of dark and light at my feet. Two butterflies dodged past me down the open aisle, and a crab hawk whistled from a dead tree beside the trail. But there were no reptiles to see, not even a half-grown basilisk or baby green iguana or even

one of the silk-sided *Ameivas,* the teiid lizards that ran
so abundantly about the station grounds 200 yards
away. I reached the riverbank pretty disgusted, and
stood there a while looking out across the river for a
tarpon rolling or for somebody paddling by in a log
canoe. But there was nothing on the river either, and
nothing across in Obed's clearing, where tapirs sometimes stand beneath an *almendro* tree. Toucans were
creaking in the woods over there, but there was nothing
alive to see at all. I turned and started walking back to
the beach, and I had gone about halfway back along the
trail when the snake bit me.

The blow hit low on the back of my right calf, just
as my foot was lifting for a step. It was hard enough to
hurt, and to knock the foot forward a little. My first
thought was that there couldn't be anything that could
hit like that in a place with no woody stems to get bent
down, spring back, and slap you hard, as they sometimes do. I tried hard to believe that a snapping-back
stem had done it, but the idea wouldn't stick. What
came clawing its way into my mind instead was that it
had to have been a snake. In that place—down among
newly cut, soft green stems of three-year-old seaside
guamil—the expected, prevalent, and really quite common snake was the terciopelo, and I knew this well.
Nevertheless, I grabbed at the one straw of hope I could
find in my mind and said, "Boa. It could have been a
big, old, bad-tempered boa." But that thought wouldn't
stick either, and three paces down the trail from where I
had been struck I stopped and slowly turned, and walked
back two of the longest steps I ever took, and looked
down into the confusion of withering leaves and shadows
and spots of light; and clearly, inescapably, I saw the
terciopelo there. It was a female. She was just about six
feet long and big in the middle with a recent meal. She
was uncoiling and sliding slowly away through the
thickly set green stems. I grabbed wildly about for
something to hit her with, but everything was soft, and
either flexible or brittle. I quickly saw that to find a
stick I would have to run clear back to the river or out

to the beach, and in the same rush of thought it came to me how you never run when a snake bites you, but sit quietly, or better, lie down till help comes. So I only watched numbly as the big snake slid out of sight. Then I raised my foot, pulled the pants leg up above the hurt place—four inches above the top of my tennis shoe—and saw a big drop of blood coming out of one perforation, and over a little way, a short slash connected with a row of tiny blood drops. It was no classic viper wound, and I grasped at that thought too, but guiltily, knowing I was only looking for comfort; and the next thing I knew, I was running. After decades of living around snakes, of thinking forward to the time I might be bitten, and of urging others to be calm and never run in case of snakebite, I found myself running in panic down the trail toward the beach and home.

It took ten paces or more for me to come to my senses and stop running, and then force myself to walk slowly out to the beach and down toward the station, yelling and whistling as I walked, and stopping a couple of times to look dismally at the punctures on the back of my leg and squeeze out all blood that would come. I stopped once to knot my handkerchief about my leg and twist it as a tourniquet. I couldn't even recall for sure whether tourniquets were still in vogue as first-aid treatment of snakebite, but I put one on anyway; and then thought of slicing the wounds open, but believed I remembered some reaction against this practice too, as a field measure, at least. Anyway, my hunting knife was blunt-pointed and dull and would have had to be hammered in to bring the hoped-for release of supposedly poisoned blood. So I only walked on, intermittently whistling as loud as I could and yelling.

I was sure my wife would hear me, and she did; but being a slow runner she called Marlin Simon and Mark Spaulding, who were tagging some turtles that lay on the beach up north of the station. I could see them start running in the hot, deep sand and on the wind heard Marlin yelling to ask what the trouble was. I yelled back, "Terciopelo," but in the wind the word got no farther than where Marjorie was standing in the station yard. But she heard it plainly, and I could see her go inside to get things ready to do whatever could be done for a snake-bitten husband on that lonesome coast. As I reached the station yard Shefton came running out and said, "What was it, Doctor?" and again I said, "Terciopelo." He looked as if I had hit him, because he once had vomited blood for eighteen hours after a terciopelo bite, and says he has never since been the man he was. Marlin and Mark came running up and heard what my problem was. Marlin said, "OK, hold on to us and take it easy." They hobbled me over to the house and up the stairs, and Margie guided them to my bed.

It was 3:30 in the afternoon by then. There was no way out to the hospital except by airplane, and the obvious move was to try to call one in. But there was no radio in the place. Marlin, who is an outboard racing man, and Alvin Brian, our neighbor from the village, who knows boats and river travel as well as anybody on the coast, put two big outboard motors on a little aluminum boat not rated for even one motor that size and went streaking down the lagoon to Parismina, twenty-four miles away. There was a radio at Parismina. There was another at Barra del Colorado, sixteen miles up the beach the other way. To be safe, our carpenter took Shefton's horse and made off for The Bar.

After looking at the marks of the bite and asking me if it hurt and hearing that it didn't, Margie got out the antivenin and the snakebite kit and began to read instructions. Under the pressure of the moment neither of us could remember anything about the subject with any confidence, and the antivenin directions were printed too small to read without a magnifying glass, and finding one had taken quite a while. By the time Margie had dug out a rough grasp of the procedures, another half an hour had gone by, and since almost anything you do really ought to be done during the first half hour, we were getting pretty discouraged.

But then I suddenly realized that except for the first feel of the snake's strike, like a blunt-edge blow across the calf with numbness afterward, I had felt no pain at all. A slight initial swelling just above the bite had spread no farther up after the first five minutes, and now almost an hour had passed since I was bitten. A little wave of optimism went over me—no genuine relief, but enough of an uncertainty to let in the edge of an unlikely hope and to make me want to hold off incising myself. As for injecting antivenin, we were not about to do that until we could work out from Wyeth's microscopic prose exactly how you test a person for allergic reaction to horse serum.

Before previous injections I had been found tolerant of horse serum; but they say you can change on short notice, and besides, I had recently been scared by the stuff when it killed a boy I knew. He had been bitten while chopping brush on his little farm up the beach a way, and had come to us for help. He came in dragging a terciopelo, and showed us where it had struck him, halfway up the front of the shin. Like my own set of punctures his had not been diagrammatically diagnostic, being in his case slashes instead of holes. And since he had no symptoms an hour after the snake had bitten him, we just gave him some coffee and suggested that he lie down a while before we did anything else. But he insisted that he needed the antivenin. I told him that for some people horse serum could be worse than snakebite, but he had the local faith in *inyecciones* and argued with growing anxiety. I looked at his leg again and saw no swelling, and him with no pain, no nausea, and no trouble breathing. I still couldn't bring myself to give him the injection, and told him so.

"*Bueno, pues,*" he said in Spanish, "will you give *me* the serum?" and I said that was exactly what I advised against. "No," he said, "I mean, will you give me the antivenin to take to an *inyeccionista?*" The nearest injectionist would be up at The Bar, almost to Nicaragua. I knew that traveling that far by dugout, up the log-choked reaches of *Caño Palmas* lagoon, was the last thing the boy should do, but after we had argued a while longer I told him that if he would lie down and rest until afternoon and if then he still insisted on taking the serum to The Bar and would promise to find an *inyeccionista* who knew how to give the immune-reaction test, he could have the stuff. But I said I still advised him not to take it unless some kind of symptoms appeared.

About three o'clock he got up, still with no pain or swelling, and said, like a man who had kept his side of a bargain, "*Bueno*?" So I gave him three packs of anti-venin, and his friend took him away. If I had known he would ride the canoe only up to the pass and then go on the fourteen miles to Simon Lagoon on foot, I would have stopped him, but that is the way he made the trip. When he got to The Bar they gave him the shots, kept him in bed a few hours, and let him go; and eight days later he died in convulsions.

So as curiously uneventful as my own bite was remaining, and as hard as the test directions were to read, Margie and I decided to hold off all treatment except the tourniquet and the less heroic or more inescapable ministrations of local well-wishers, until I could produce a sensible symptom.

The only classic snakebite symptom I could come up with, however, was fright; and as time passed even that began to wane a little. Or rather I should say, divergent possibilities materialized: either my symptoms were, for some reason, being postponed or I had not got any poison with the bite. As the minutes passed the latter lost some of its senseless sound, although in the predicament we were in you can't afford to indulge in overoptimism. When it got to be five-thirty and still no airplane had come to take me away, Mark and my son David poured diesel oil in all the cans they could find and outlined the landing strip with them, against the unlikely arrival of some wild pilot who would have no light to take off by.

As hope for getting me out waned, the bush medicine began to be made. From the time I got into bed Shefton had begun bringing coffee, made to the consistency of melted roofing compound, and standing by to be sure I drank it before I began vomiting blood. Margie loyally helped me drink it, but as soon as a pot was emptied Shefton brought more. On one return he handed me a foot-long, tar-black rope of locally grown tobacco, which he had kept under his bed for three years against just such an emergency as this, and anxiously insisted that I eat it. I gnawed off as small a piece as possible and unhappily started chewing it. Shefton watched a while and went away, urging Margie to be sure I ate it all. Word of the accident had quickly reached the village two miles away, and the first thought of Sibella Martinez, my oldest Tortuguero friend, was that her daughter Junie, who was washing clothes at the station, was pregnant, and so a dire threat to my existence. Any man, Sibella says, bitten by a terciopelo and seen by a pregnant woman will die within eight hours—or perhaps it is nine. So she almost killed herself running up the beach in the deep, hot sand to warn Junie to keep looking the other way. Don Chico Montalban came trotting up from his dugout on the river and asked Margie if I had killed the snake. She told him I had not, and he said that was bad. Not killing the snake was the worst possible omen, he said. So long as the snake was at large a cure was just about impossible. He nevertheless worked both himself and my wife up to the point of tears trying to make her get me to drink two fingers of kerosene.

At six-fifteen the boat came back from Parismina, having traveled fifty miles in three hours on a wild lagoon that never knew such speed. In it, with Marlin and Alvin, there came a pleasant young woman named Marta, who was the *curandera,* the curer, of Parismina. She was neither a doctor nor a *sukia,* a professional practitioner of bush medicine, only a woman with sense and a knack for doing the best that can be done in medical emergencies in isolated places. She was the wife of a solid Parismina citizen, and she spent much of her time fishing for tarpon and snook, treating illness only because, as I said, she had a good head and steady hand and sometimes knew better what to do than her fellow villagers did. When the boat docked she came straight up to where they showed her I was lying on the bed.

When Alvin had introduced her she looked at me and without formalities started asking about my symptoms: swelling, breathing trouble, nausea—all the right things to ask about in a case of *Bothrops* bite. She looked closely at the wound, which by now was an unpleasant blue-green patch two inches across at the site of the punctures, but nothing more. She poked about briefly, thought for a moment, and then said, "It might be he didn't inject you." I eagerly told her that that was what I was beginning to think—that counting the boy who died of the antivenin, this was the fourth sure, solid terciopelo bite we had seen at the station, and none had produced snakebite symptoms. She said she had seen the same thing many times, but added that she had also seen a man die two hours after being bitten. "Anyway, be careful for a few hours more," she said. "Sometimes the trouble comes later." She showed us the Butantan serum she had brought, and looked at our antivenin packs; we decided to give her some of ours to add to her collection. "The injections work," she said. "If you put in enough and put it in soon, they serve; but also they are dangerous." And that, too, we agreed with.

After telling us a few snakebite stories, she saw I was pretty sleepy in spite of the coffee. She picked up the little bag with her medicine in it and started to go to her room. When she reached the door she stopped and looked back and said in Spanish, "Señor, it is important to kill a snake that bites you," and I asked her why. "Because sometimes there is no serum for a long time," she said. "They say that then you should split open the head of the snake and take out the brain and mash it up on the bite. Tie it there with a bandage. It helps, when there is no antivenin. *Dicen* [they say]," she said.

The airplane came at daylight. It came tearing in out of the mist, buzzed the house, banked, and landed on the grass and sand of the seaside strip. Margie and I got in it, and an hour later we were in San Juan de Dios Hospital, and Dr. Pacheco was saying, "I can tell you without any doubt that you were not injected with poison." I asked him if he ever before heard of anybody being struck hard and squarely by a big *Bothrops* and coming away with no poison, and he said yes. We thanked him and he congratulated me, and we left and spent the rest of the day lying around the hotel to get over the coffee, the tobacco juice, and the scare. The next morning, early, we flew back to the station.

For some days Miss Junie was hampered in her work trying to keep from seeing me. Nobody seemed to know how long it took for that hazard to die down. It made it hard on both of us having to slide around the walls to keep her from seeing me. She also made my wife hide the pants I was wearing at the time I was bitten. It was suicide to wear them again, she said. Shefton said he was glad I was alive, but he cautioned me that there was no real cause for relief until the nineteenth day, on which bitten people are prone to drop dead. Before that, though, he said—after about a week—the discolored area where the snake had hit would loosen up, right down to the bone, and fall out to the ground. But I was feeling so good by then that his forebodings didn't bother me very much, and anyway, Bertie Downs, our only neighbor for half a mile down the lagoon, said nothing at all would happen to me. His reasoning was like this: "The snee-ek that hit you hob a boll in the mid-del, a *conejo* or nex quality of onny-mal. Before the terciopelo eat any smoll onny-mal she croll to the sea and wash the mouth to clean, to put out the py-sen. So any time the boll in the belly, the terciopelo can not do no dom-age at all." Hearing that, Shefton shook his head and out of the corner of his mouth mumbled, so Bertie couldn't hear, "This ridiculous, Doctor. This only Greytown superstition."

Bertie's notion was superstition, all right, but it seemed to me pretty noteworthy. It showed that folk belief is not just wild imagining but is more often the result of an honest effort to put two and two together. In this case, the myth probably arises from the combination of two observations that the coastal people have made. One is that the bite of a snake that has just fed is less likely to be severe than that of a hungry snake. This may be partly because poison is used up in feeding, partly because more poison is secreted by a hungry snake, and partly because the virulence of the poison of an unfed snake may be higher. Whatever the real reason, the mouth-washing belief rests on age-long, and valid, observation of the correlation between a mild bite and a "ball in the belly" of the snake. With no books or herpetologists around, it is little wonder that the real cause of the correlation is overlooked and a more picturesque explanation adopted. The belief is reinforced by the other observation, which is that terciopelos do anomalously turn up on the beach, where they are no doubt returning to land after having been rafted out of river mouths on floating debris.

It was really the *curandera's* telling so matter-of-factly about the snake-brain treatment that set me to wondering how sensible people like the Tortuguereños ever came by the seeming nonsense of their snakebite remedies. Two factors make it turn out that way, I think. One is the desperation of having no other recourse than your own experience and imagination, and those of your forebears and neighbors. The other is the apparently high frequency of false bites that terciopelos deliver. In fact, an important basis for all bush cures for snakebite —a factor that keeps intelligent people believing in them—may be the frequency of cases in which no venom or small quantities of venom are injected when the bite glances or hits a bone or otherwise misfires, and patients get well in spite of the treatment. The disaster of a full terciopelo bite in country without medical help would lead anyone to grasp at straws, to accept a neighbor's treatment without demanding to know how it works, simply because it is all there is. And if the incidence of aborted bites is high enough, the cure would be bound to take hold as part of the folk medicine of the country. If generations keep getting 40 percent recovery from snake brains, kerosene, and chewing tobacco, they have to be unnaturally skeptical not to stick to these as treatment. Modern medicine has few specifics that cure at such a rate.

Those ideas appear to apply better to the bites of *Bothrops atrox* than to those of, say, the rattlesnakes. I never heard of anybody's being bitten by a diamondback, hard and squarely on an unprotected surface, and showing no symptoms of poisoning. So the next question is, why does the fer-de-lance, one of the most dangerous poisonous snakes on earth, deliver false bites? The answer is unknown.

But why might it not be that the terciopelo, a big viper that eats little rodents and kills them by injecting venom, has evolved the useful trait of bluffing oversized, inedible intruders by striking with fangs folded, instead of by stabbing them with its elegantly long, thin teeth? When Harold Hirth was down at Tortuguero he measured a lot of terciopelo fangs and found that they are longer, per foot of snake, than those of any American viper except perhaps the bushmaster. A six-foot *atrox* has fangs just about an inch long. They are also exceedingly slender, and surprisingly easy to snap off. So the bluffing-bite theory might go on to suggest that the twenty-odd kinds of rattlesnakes don't abort their strikes because they can avoid unnecessary fang damage and waste of poison by bluffing in another way: by rattling. That is, having a rattle to sound allows a rattlesnake to advertise its presence and identity to big, inedible, hard-footed animals, and so to avoid both the hazard of being stepped on and the useless loss of teeth and venom. The cottonmouth does the same thing by opening wide his cotton-white mouth, you could go on to say. Why the copperhead has not faced up to this problem I can't suggest—maybe it has. Anyway, very few people are hurt by copperheads. Also, the theory leaves nothing said about the host of other fang-folding vipers of the American tropics and of the Old World. But that is no reason not to try to explain the false bites of the viper at hand, nor to see in its fantastically elongate, delicate, brittle teeth an asset too dear to squander on the shinbone of a tapir. Man, of course, is too recently arrived in *Bothrops* country to have been involved in the evolution of the tendency, but now that he is there, he no doubt falls in with the other creatures that seem, to the snake, too big to swallow and too heavy to be stepped on by. For a terciopelo to strike, out of fear or anger, at the legs of peccaries, tapirs, or deer—or johnny-come-lately American man—might not have enough survival advantage to outweigh the inconvenience of broken-off fangs, even though these are quickly replaced by spare ones. Going no further afield than the terciopelo and the rattlesnakes, one might sum this up by suggesting that the latter protects its fangs and husbands its venom by rattling, and when the warning fails, strikes always to inject poison. The fer-de-lance, on the other hand, having no rattle, strikes to stab a big intruder only when it feels clearly hard-pressed and delivers fangless strikes when the need is just to scare somebody badly. Anyway, that is what I have been stirred to think, and I hope it is not just moonshine from excess adrenalin let loose by the recollection of my *Bothrops* bite.

A Stone Age Naturalist

❖❖❖❖❖❖

E. THOMAS GILLIARD

[1957]

A few dark worlds still remain hidden among the remote inland areas of New Guinea, and the scientific treasures they hold are among the most enticing in the South Pacific.

New Guinea is the hub of a constellation of some five hundred islands, and the fount from which they have derived most of their plant and animal life. From its hot mangrove swamps to its perpetual snow peaks, it includes all the earth's climatic zones from tropical to arctic. Unknown birds, mammals, plants, insects, and other creatures await investigation deep in its mountain recesses, where men still live a Neolithic life.

Looking back over my visits to this naturalist's paradise, one experience in particular seems especially interesting, because it ties the past to the present and, indeed, to the future. It has to do with one of the most unusual ornithological assignments I ever undertook and with a strange personage who played an important part in it—a Stone Age bird expert.

My chance of penetrating the biologically unexplored heart of New Guinea—the region of the Victor Emanuel and Hindenburg Mountains—came when Mr. Fred Shaw-Mayer, a veteran collector for Lord Rothschild and the British Museum, told me of a secret wartime airfield built high in the very headwaters of the mighty Sepik River. In a valley between these two mountain ranges, at a place called Telefolmin, paratroopers had been dropped and an emergency strip prepared. Shaw-Mayer said Telefolmin had recently been reoccupied by

117

two patrol officers of the Australian Division of Native Affairs.

I immediately began to organize an expedition to attempt to collect the animal life—chiefly, the birds— of this remote region. This undertaking was backed by the American Museum of Natural History, the National Geographic Society, the C. R. Vose Exploration Fund of the Explorers Club, and the Frank M. Chapman Memorial Fund. My wife, Margaret, a veteran of previous expeditions to the Philippines and New Guinea, set out with me in October, 1953.

But on our arrival in New Guinea, we found our path temporarily blocked. On November 8, we learned that one of the two patrol officers in the Telefolmin area, Geoffrey Harris—who had been keeping bird lists in expectation of our arrival—had been killed in an ambush. A day later, another bulletin told us that the second patrol officer, Gerald Szarka, and two native policemen, had also been killed.

The Australian authorities quite naturally held up their approval of our visit to the area. It was more than four months later, in March of 1954, that we made a stormy voyage along the north coast of New Guinea and landed at Wewak to make a final plea to the District Commissioner for permission to enter the region. We were delighted to find that the District Commissioner could think of nothing better than to have a naturalist and his wife go to Telefolmin. It would help convince the natives, he felt, that normalcy was soon to replace the martial law that had been enforced since the murders. Of course, we would have to follow some special rules. Foremost: I was expected to take five armed men with me and, in addition, accept a police escort that would accompany us day and night. Obviously, a most unusual collecting trip!

The next day, Margaret and I, with our team of Sepik natives, boarded a Norseman monoplane and were soon laboring across the ridges of the Prince Alexander Mountains. Here the aborigines had cut huge "windows" 30 to 50 feet wide in the mountain forest, causing the sharpest ridges to resemble upended saws. Across the openings they had stretched intricate nets to catch the flying fox, the world's largest flying mammal. Soon, the braided Sepik River came into view below, and we flew southwest toward a distant line of peaks projecting jagged edges through a sea of cotton cloud.

After two hours in the air we came close to a tremendous Matterhorn of a peak and turned east around a heavily forested bluff on the Mittag Range, marking the westernmost end of the Victor Emanuel Cordillera. There, at 6,000 feet with walls of mountain on either side, lay the Telefolmin clearing. We hit the grass strip and stepped out to find three native-style houses, a stockade, and a dozen little sheds, with the Australian flag waving from a pole just under the mist.

We set up base camp in an abandoned mission house about a mile from the patrol post. But explore and collect we could not, because Frank Jones, the Assistant District Officer, would not let us out of his sight. Beyond the Telefolmin perimeter were uncontrolled natives still smarting from their defeat at the hands of 100 police and a team of white officers—natives who had nearly succeeded in throwing the white men out of their mountain fastness. The police guard stuck to us like glue, and we were forbidden even to go to the latrine without a loaded weapon.

As the days at Telefolmin wore into weeks, the local natives became acquainted with our collecting and began to come into our camp. We offered matches and salt for specimens brought in, and children began calling early in the morning for small transparent envelopes in which to bring us butterflies.

Using sign language and a "turnie talk" (interpreter), we paid generously for specimens and gradually amassed quite an assortment from an ever-widening range. More important, the older men began to come.

Often they repeated the name "Femsep." Clearly, this Femsep had an exceptional reputation as a local naturalist. If I showed a picture of a rare bird, my pidgin-speaker was apt to say, *"Femsep e savy dispela* [Femsep knows this one]."

When the natives realized that we had nothing to do with the Government or the Mission, we felt ourselves "accepted." Gradually, our interest in the animals important to them formed a bond such as the men at the patrol post had probably never enjoyed. At last, Mr. Jones granted us permission to call on the famous Femsep—a permission necessary to obtain because this local naturalist was implicated as one of the murderers —perhaps the leader—who had ambushed the two patrol officers in 1953. Taken mortally sick after his arrest and imprisonment at Wewak, he had been returned to his native valley by the Australian authorities so that he might die in his home district.

We found Femsep in one of the little villages we had flown over. Sitting in the round entrance to his dwelling, he was a tiny man, emaciated by dysentery and fever. His eyes were yellow and dull, his strength at low ebb. He was totally naked, and the holes in his nose lacked the slender decorative cassowary quills other men wore. His hair was shorn in a prison cut—the strands that had once intertwined in a great horn of carefully wrapped cane shafts were gone.

Mournfully, a harem of women helped him forward, and we squatted on the ground between the houses. Femsep accepted my tobacco but quickly handed it to a full-breasted girl. One by one, I turned the colored pictures of birds: the Superb Bird of Paradise, with its great cape extended, the Queen Carola Bird of Paradise, with its six-flagged hatpins and violet chest shield, and the rest.

At sight of each, the old man's hollow voice uttered the name. High and low on the mountains, near and far, he knew them all and where they lived. He seemed to know more about New Guinea birds than is contained in the books and reports of a century of exploration. His knowledge extended from the tropical forests of the Fly River to the headwaters of the Strickland. It even reached over the Mittags into the tropical lowlands of

the Sepik. Most important of all, his knowledge in
cluded the stunted mountain moss forest that scraped
the sky all about us—home of a birdlife little known to
white men.

Then, pictures to one side, he and I talked of paradise birds of the highest mountain forest, the so-called
Astrapias—represented by amazingly different species
on all of the isolated ranges thus far explored. One that
he named the *Dan* lived in the "place cold," and with
a shudder he wrapped his frail arms around his shoulders and shivered. Others there included the rare *Inem*,
the fabulous King of Saxony Bird of Paradise. I could
not identify some he mentioned, including one that he
named over and over—the *Kondimkait*.

Like veteran naturalists, Femsep and I were soon
lost in the atmosphere of scientific ornithology. Our
"turnie talk" was left far behind, for we invented our
own language—a hodgepodge of grunts, hand signals,
and broken pidgin. It was not long before I knew I was
not only safe but welcome in his realm. Ornithology had
bridged the gap between a Neolithic naturalist and his
modern counterpart, even as it crosses racial and political boundaries in our more troubled and bloodier
modern societies.

Although his hollow abdomen clung to his back-
bone, Femsep was nevertheless still a monarch in the
Victor Emanuels. Despite the ominous charges against
him, one understood why, when he was near death in
jail on the coast, government officers, doctors, and pilots
had rushed this man of prestige and power back to his
mountain retreat to die among his own.

I could easily imagine Femsep young and lithe, with
legs like a mountain goat. His childhood would have
accustomed him to the semi-nomadic life of his family,
never staying long at any one of the huts his father
built of split timbers here and there in valleys far apart
in the forest.

His youthful nights would have been spent behind the
little barred opening of a fortified hut, warmed by a

smoky fire, the boy curled up among the big sows and the women.

At dusk, he would have watched his father join the other village men to pass the night in the large "house of mystery," about which many strange tales were whispered. A place of eerie voices and sounds, the "house of mystery" was heavily protected against attack, with arrow portholes in the walls and surrounded by a barrier fence beyond which children never strayed and women could not pass.

During his family's many journeys to mountain gardens and on nights spent in the forest, Femsep would have noted his father's equipment—bow and arrows, fire-starter, and two little string bags, one worn under the chin, and the other behind like a tiny knapsack. In these were his father's treasures: tobacco and a few bird plumes, a string of dog teeth, some cassowary quills, and a crown made of red feathers from the flanks of a large parrot. When entering a village not visited for some time, he would have seen his father put on his greatest trophy, a headdress of King of Saxony Bird of Paradise plumes.

Femsep's mother would have traveled naked except for two whiskbroom-sized fans at the waist, one in front and one behind. She would have carried a large string bag, its top forming a tumpline over her forehead, while its lower parts bounced against her buttocks. Following on the rough trails, Femsep the boy would have emulated his parents, rarely whimpering even in the face of bitter weather.

Anything edible found along the trail was quickly captured and eaten raw—tree frogs, lizards, insects, grubs. Often a lizard would be stunned and carried half-alive in a net bag to provide a needed snack. The tender hearts of palms and tall grasses were eaten, as was a kind of watercress found beside the few streams. Occasionally, a *kapul* or rat would be spied, and everyone would take after it hastily like a pack of hounds. The confused animal would dive into shelter under forest debris and be easily caught.

The most daring expeditions involved long trips across the "deathlines"—territorial boundaries between tribes that almost no stranger may pass without risking his life—into no man's land to search the highest forests for the oily nut of the wild pandanus. These palms grew in a fairyland of moss- and orchid-festooned forest, usually buried in gray mist. Their kernel-bearing fruits resembled giant pineapples, growing one to a palm.

On one such journey, I learned, Femsep's family had visited a peak in the Hindenberg Mountains, called Ilkaveep, where the boy helped to build a low shelter from wild banana and split palm leaves. There the little tribe shivered in a mass of naked humanity each night. For many days, they searched for pandanus nuts, eating them raw or after burning the huge composite "fruits" to release the kernels.

Again and again on this Ilkaveep sojourn, Femsep's family saw signs of other wandering tribes. One afternoon they met a group of strangers. At first, there was a very careful interchange of talk. Finally, the strangers gathered around the Telefolmin fires, drying their wet bodies and exchanging news. The newcomers were Fegelmen people, from the Isam River—one of the headwaters of the Fly.

Later, when everyone had been lulled into a state of good fellowship, the Fegelmen warriors suddenly slashed the throats of ten of Femsep's group. The more agile Telefolmin women and children escaped, racing down the precipitous trail in terror, Femsep among them.

The Fegelmen group hacked off the heads and extremities of their victims and carried the trophies back to the Isam River amidst great laughter. A joyous feast was held, and soon thereafter ten new skulls decorated the walls of the Fegelmen "house of mystery."

Such was the environment in which Femsep grew to manhood. Sometimes long periods would pass without killings, but always there loomed the death-line at the edge of Telefolmin territory, and always there was a score to be settled—a payback, a life taken—for tribal memory was long. Femsep's fame spread. He became a sage, and he alone among the tribes—the Ifitamin, the Minyamin, the Feramin, and all except the Fegelmen— could cross the death-lines and smoke with neighboring tribal leaders.

From Femsep's viewpoint, World War II was a time that brought white men with guns and tools into his quiet valley to appropriate the driest part of the flat land for their own purposes. The missionaries who followed the soldiers were, to Femsep, other unimaginable strangers who mocked his ancestral beliefs. His own faith held firm, but the conviction grew among the Telefolmin youth that Femsep's ancient teachings were as out of date as the stone ax he carried.

The departure of the whites after the war was a time of brief joy for Femsep and the other old people of Telefolmin. It proved a brief respite. By 1949, Femsep had to face another invasion from the sky. That year, a noisy little plane came with two white men in uniform and some foreign blacks with rifles. These new whites were friendly, but their presence meant inevitable change: soon, each healthy man found he must work four days a month for the "Government."

During those five years that passed before I met him, what had gone through Femsep's mind as he clung to ancient ways? Had he been a leader in the steps to regain his sovereign land? No one knows for sure. But one day the airstrip had been furrowed when the bothersome little plane came in to land. And someone among the Telefolmin had decided that the two patrol officers should be ambushed, even as the Fegelmen had ambushed Femsep's father.

The blow came one day when the two officers were on separate patrols, far from the post. Both were approached by seemingly friendly natives. There was laughing and then bartering of pigs and food. Even the native policemen confidently left their rifles standing in the camp. Suddenly arrows flew and stone axes flailed.

Norman Draper, a Baptist missionary—the only other white man in the 70,000-square-mile wilderness—happened to be at the patrol post when an escaping native policeman returned to give the alarm. He rallied the police and radioed Wewak. Within a few hours, planes brought reinforcements from the coast. Twenty suspects, including Femsep, were rounded up and sent to Wewak for trial.

I have related how Femsep, taken sick, had been sent home to die. The other nineteen who stayed behind in Wewak for trial were sentenced to death. The Australian authorities later decided that such wild people could not be held accountable by white men's law and sent the nineteen back to their home district to serve out sentences of ten years at hard labor.

My meeting with Femsep made possible the series of explorations that my wife and I thereafter undertook into the magnificent moss forests and mountains around Telefolmin. It was Femsep who supplied the carriers and directed them to guide us over hidden trails. There, among the pandanus, we were at last able to study the birds he knew so well—the Astrapias—the Magnificent Bird of Paradise, the King of Saxony, and 124 others. Femsep's huntsmen brought down many of our scientific specimens with arrows. All, that is, but the *Kondimkait*, a bird so rare that Femsep had seen only a few in his lifetime. I am sure that some day it will be found where Femsep said it lives.

After we came back down from the forests, Femsep was strong enough to visit us. Day after day he would shuffle into our camp to examine the bird skins and to tell me what he knew. He pantomimed with his body the dances of the birds of paradise. He formed the nests with his hands; he imitated their calls. On the ground he scratched the shapes of their plumes in full display. He even drew good maps and understood the scale and orientation of mine. When forming a map, he often stopped to gaze into the distance and to point, describing range after range surrounding the Telefolmin region.

Thus an important part of my ornithological map of

New Guinea has been filled by the words that flowed from Femsep's lips—eagerly spoken, razor-keen words —transmitting a lore which is almost certainly doomed. Criminal or history-crossed patriot, Femsep of Telefolmin is a naturalist with whom I am proud to have worked.

PART TWO

On Fossils,
Famous and Obscure

Today, most people so readily accept the general idea of evolution that they do not understand the excitement and controversy that surrounded paleontologists and their fossils only a few decades ago. (Of course, there are still a number of vociferous and regionally powerful Special Creationists who challenge Darwin's theory, but since they usually cancel their subscriptions to *Natural History,* they are unlikely to read this book.) At first glance, paleontologists are like enthusiastic children digging in the earth for pieces of a giant puzzle. Their efforts can be charming, such as George Gaylord Simpson's collecting in a cave under a St. Louis brewery, or technologically impressive, as when Edwin H. Colbert organizes a bulldozer and teams of workers in a New Mexican desert to cut out large clay chunks filled with dinosaur bones for their safe transportation.

But when the early paleontologists returned to their laboratories and analyzed their discoveries, when they related the bones they found to geologic strata and put life on earth into a time frame of hundreds of millions of years, their findings stirred intense public reaction. Their

127

conclusions about the evolution of life were not compatible with a literal interpretation of the biblical myth of creation or with Archbishop James Ussher's date of 4004 B.C. for that event. Implicit in their studies was an acceptance of the processes of evolution, yet as late as 1925 the high school teacher John Thomas Scopes was tried and convicted for teaching the theory in defiance of Tennessee law.

For more than a half-century after the publication in 1859 of *On the Origin of Species* with its implication that man descended from an ape, the search for fossils of the "missing link" was fruitless. A few men—in China, Java, and Africa—dedicated their lives to finding fossil proof of early man. Pierre Teilhard de Chardin, Franz Weidenreich, and G. H. R. von Koenigswald were major characters in the drama of the search for early man, and their articles read like battlefield reports, especially when the Japanese invaded the prime collecting areas and the scientists had to hide their precious fossils. Today numerous discoverers have shown that there is no simple "missing link," but rather a series of "missing chains" that are slowly being pieced together.

In comparison with early man, Pleistocene fauna and the first Indians occupied America only yesterday in geologic time—some 10,000 years ago. But many parts of that story are missing, too. Colbert in 1940 raised one of the most perplexing questions of the period: why did the mammoth and many other large animals suddenly become extinct? Twenty-seven years later Paul S. Martin, in a study that reflects decades of investigation and progress by numerous scientists, answered Colbert's question.

Bones in the Brewery

GEORGE GAYLORD SIMPSON

[1946]

Three currents of history meet at the corner of 13th and Cherokee Streets in St. Louis, Missouri. South of Cherokee, where 13th does not run through, there is now an immense shoe factory. On the northeast corner of the intersection, there is a large but apparently rather plain brick house. The northwest corner is a lot with only one small structure, which looks like a one-car garage. Each of these buildings is more than it seems to be, because each has a historical significance. The shoe factory was formerly a brewery: it recalls a current of history that started in the Rhineland more than a century ago. The house turns its plain side to the street but when viewed from the east, within its own spacious grounds, it is seen to be a stately mansion with a graceful, pillared portico; its history traces back through the De Menils and the Chouteaus to the pioneer days of the Mississippi. The apparent garage is really the entrance to a cave that rambles beneath the surrounding buildings: its history is the most ancient of all, and in it are buried animals that lived before man ever saw the site of St. Louis.

Our introduction to this convergence of history at 13th and Cherokee Streets began with a letter. Lee Hess, a pharmaceutical manufacturer in St. Louis, wrote to say that he had found some bones in the cellar of a brewery. Would the Museum be interested? Many such letters come to a curator's desk. Nine times out of ten, they do not lead to anything of value, but we always follow them up as far as possible because the tenth letter may be a clue to an important scientific discovery.

129

We wrote to Mr. Hess asking him to send some of the bones so that we could determine their possible importance.

The bones sent to us had been considerably broken by the workmen who found them, but when we pieced them together in the laboratory we found that they included a skull of an extinct peccary, *Platygonus compressus* by name. Now, *Platygonus* is not a particularly rare fossil. Its remains had already been found in many places throughout the United States. For instance, twenty-two skulls (twelve of them nearly complete) had been collected for the United States National Museum in a cave near Cumberland, Maryland; five partial skeletons had been found in a peat bog near Belding, Michigan, and nine nearly complete skeletons had been discovered at Goodland, Kansas, in the clay pit of a brickyard, and sent to the University of Kansas. One of the Kansas skeletons, obtained from the university by the American Museum of Natural History, was restored and mounted in a lifelike pose and has been exhibited there for years.

In spite of these and other previous discoveries, we became quite excited about the bones from St. Louis. *Platygonus* had never turned up in a beer cellar before, and extinct animals are rarely found in the heart of a great city. How they came to be there was a mystery worth solving, and we resolved to go to St. Louis and try to clear up the mystery with a little geological detective work. I wrote to Mr. Hess asking whether more bones remained in place and whether we could come out and investigate the find. His reply assured us that many bones remained to be excavated and cordially invited us to study the occurrence. In a few days George O. Whitaker, of our fossil vertebrate laboratory, and I were off for what turned out to be an unexpectedly fascinating rendezvous with history, ancient and recent.

Mr. Hess met us in St. Louis and drove us immediately to the De Menil mansion, the historic home at 3352 South 13th Street. This house, unoccupied but restored by Mr. Hess with sufficient modernization for comfort, was our camp throughout our stay: a camp such as a bone-digger has seldom enjoyed in his wildest dreams of luxury. Before we were through, it was also our bone laundry, shellackery, and packery. Here we dropped at once into an atmosphere of old St. Louis of the pioneer days before the Civil War. The house was originally built in the 1840s by Henri Chatillon, a western guide and hunter of that period. In 1854 it was purchased by Dr. Nicholas N. De Menil, and in 1863 he enlarged it by adding several spacious rooms and the magnificent portico on the east side, overlooking his large garden and the slope of Arsenal Hill down to the Mississippi.

Nicholas De Menil, who had come to America on a visit (which proved to be life-long) in 1833, was a physician who established the first successful chain of drugstores in St. Louis and became one of the aristocrats of that growing center. He married Emily Sophia Chouteau, linking his family with the real pioneers of the region, for she was the great-granddaughter of Marie Therese Chouteau, the first white woman to settle in St. Louis and still revered as the mother of that city.

Alexander De Menil, son of Nicholas, lived in the house throughout his long life. By the time he died, Arsenal Hill was no longer a swanky residential district but had been overgrown with smoky factories and surrounded by slums. His heirs chose not to live there, and the property finally passed out of the family when they sold it to Mr. Hess, almost a century after the family acquired it. Like his father, Alexander was a physician, but he was also interested in literature and became a poet of local renown. Among his voluminous productions is a rather quaint but forceful defense of his great-great-grandmother, the famous Madame Chouteau. (She left her husband in New Orleans because of his cruelty to her and formed an irregular union with Laclede, who became the founder of St. Louis; her solution of a marital problem when divorce was impossible was approved by her contemporaries but became a worry to some of her descendants.)

We often thought of these vanished occupants as we roamed through the house or rested on its spacious balconies and watched spring come to the garden. If, however, the ghosts of the Chouteaus and the De Menils roamed through the house at night, we never knew it, for we slept soundly after our hours of bone-digging. Ghosts still more exotic might conceivably have troubled our slumbers. The fascinating hodgepodge accumulated by Mr. Hess with a view to future exhibition included a reconstruction of a Damascus palace with its furnishings. After display at the St. Louis world's fair in 1904, these oriental trappings had been crated and stored until recently when our host acquired them and piled them into the De Menil house. Thus it happened that our library included an Arabic Bible, along with Hedin's *My Life as an Explorer,* the Catholic Directory, Boccaccio's *Decameron,* and *How to Develop a Winning Personality.* Pending the availability of more space and the sorting of all these treasures, our quarters were furnished in a medley of styles in charming confusion. Tubular metal modernistic chairs jostled a mid-nineteenth century chaise longue, over which was thrown a vivid Mexican serape and beside which was an old Turkish tabouret of ebony inlaid with mother-of-pearl. The introduction of our prehistoric peccaries struck no jarring note but seemed only to complete this remarkable mixture.

It was, after all, the prehistoric peccaries that had called us here and that claimed most of our attention, but even these brought us into contact with history as well as with prehistory. Unrest in the Rhineland well over a century ago was one of the influences that led to our journey to St. Louis and to the exhuming of these ancient remains. It was in the 1820s that one Gottfried Duden came to the Mississippi Valley to spy out the land for his German neighbors. Here in St. Louis he found several caves in the limestone underlying the city and he reported that the site was propitious for breweries. Before the coming of artificial refrigeration, successful brewing on a large scale required natural repositories where the temperature was constant and low throughout the year. These caves, which retain a temperature near 55 degrees regardless of the weather outside, were ideal for the purpose. Rhineland brewers migrated to St. Louis and converted the caves into storerooms for their lager. It was one of these immigrants, Adam Lemp, who cleared out the cave at 13th and Cherokee and built his brewery above it.

Toward the end of the nineteenth century, air-conditioned storehouses made the caves unnecessary, and they were abandoned by the brewers. One or two were converted into underground beer parlors and places of amusement: Uhrig's Cave was such an establishment in the gay nineties and is nostalgically remembered by St. Louisians. But the cool, dark dampness of the caves, so suitable for beer before it is drunk, seemed to depress the customers after they drank the beer. Uhrig's Cave became an open air theater above the actual cave. The cave itself enjoyed only one more brief flair of fame when a large distillery was discovered in it during prohibition. The other caves were closed, their entrances walled up or blocked with debris, and eventually they became vague memories. The Lemp Brewery went out of business during prohibition, its buildings were sold to the International Shoe Company, and its cave, the Cherokee Cave, was forgotten until Lee Hess conceived the idea of reopening it as a site of historical and geological interest.

When we arrived, we took only a quick glance at the noble De Menil mansion ("our pup tent," George called it), and then hurried down into the cave. A circular, brick-lined shaft about 35 feet deep had been reopened and a spiral iron staircase installed. At the foot it opened into a long series of storage rooms, once full of lager beer but now dismally empty. The rooms were formed simply by clearing out a natural cave, a former underground river channel within the solid limestone, and by dividing it by masonry walls. The first room at the bottom of the shaft still bears traces of its use for private theatricals and parties by a gay blade of the Lemp family who took it over when the beer was moved out. Across one end he constructed artificial scenery made of wire screen and plaster. The scenery represents a fair imitation of the wall of a cave; this hiding of a real cave wall behind an artificial cave wall is one of the touches that made us feel at times as if we had stepped into Alice's Wonderland. There are still remains of the crude but serviceable floodlights used to illumine this scene.

The cave extends in an easterly direction for some 200 feet beyond this "theater." There it is joined by another channel, coming from under the former bewery to the south, also cleared and converted into storage rooms. At the intersection is a concrete-lined pool, presumably used as a reservoir in the old brewing days and reputedly used as a swimming pool in the later (but now also old) days of theatricals and parties, although we thought that a party would have to be very stimulating, indeed, to tempt us to plunge into those Stygian waters!

This was the end of the cave so far as the brewery was concerned. It terminated here with a masonry wall. To see where it went beyond, Mr. Hess had the wall broken down with a hydraulic jack and was disconcerted to find that although the cave did, indeed, continue, it was almost completely filled by a deposit of stiff, wet clay. This made it impassable for anything much larger than a rat. He had workmen dig a narrow passage in the clay, following the ancient channel of the cave. Within 20 feet from the wall it turned to the left, northward, and had, at the time of our visit, been followed in that direction for some 200 feet farther, with no sign of ending, or of coming out to the surface, or of joining another, adjacent old brewery cave. The point where the cave turns is almost under the porch of the De Menil house, where we used to relax at lunch or in the evening, 40 or 50 feet straight above our diggings.

A more talented and imaginative writer might contrast these superposed scenes in a sort of allegory. In the upper world it is spring. The air is warm and balmy, and the sun is shining. The grass is green and sprinkled with violets. Bushes and trees are in bloom, and innumerable birds are setting about their seasonal loves and labors. The caretaker's pretty baby girl toddles about, learning to walk. The world of life is developing its future in a scene just old enough to be leisurely and pleasantly mellowed.

In the lower world there are no seasons. The motionless air is always cool but never cold. The humidity is always near 100 percent and nothing is ever quite dry. The white limestone ceiling is dewy as if perspiring quietly, and water drips slowly from the tips of the scattered stalactites. The water is limpid but it carries in solution minute quantities of lime, the slow, imperceptible precipitation of which through the ages has formed the stalactites, stalagmites, and cave onyx, all forms of what has appropriately been called dripstone. Yellow lights illumine a scene that has never known the sun and make temporary islands of light in a sea of absolute darkness that has been lightless for hundreds of thousands of years. Smeared from head to foot with yellow mud, workmen slide along the narrow passage, digging out the sticky clay, penetrating still farther into the mysterious entrails of the earth where man has never been before. In spite of this rash intrusion, the strange scene seems as ancient and timeless as a tomb. And it is a tomb, a place of mass burial, sealed away as a monument of the dead past, before the first Indian ever hunted a deer along the top of the hill inside which it lies.

That filling of clay is an exasperating and expensive nuisance to the men who want to reopen the old cave channel, but it is a delight to the bone-digger. It was in this clay that the workmen found the bones that brought us to St. Louis, and we began finding more bones as soon as we dug into it for ourselves. In the week that we were there, we found too many bones to count, but we guess that we excavated between 2,000 and 3,000 of them, some almost too small to see, while others were large, complete skulls.

As we dug bones, we began our detective work. What the bones are is perhaps the least part of the mystery, and their identification had to be done back in New York, anyway, where we could study and compare the bones at our leisure. Here the problem was how the bones came to be here, in the core of Arsenal Hill under the De Menil house. Some clues are still missing, but we did soon find enough for a tentative solution of the mystery.

As Clue No. 1, there is the cave itself. By that I mean the long, branched, channel-like cavity in the limestone, regardless of the fact that it is or has been nearly filled up with clay. It averages 20 to 25 feet wide, with solid limestone walls and ceiling. We do not know how long it is, where it comes from, or where it goes to: important missing clues. We do not even know how deep it is or what the floor is like, because as deep as anyone has yet dug (12 to 15 feet in places), the bottom of the clay has not been reached.

Clue No. 2 is the clay, or, rather, this is a series of clues, because the clay proves on investigation to be complex and to include several distinctive superposed layers. The lowest layer visible, as far as it has been excavated, is massive, yellowish gray, and somewhat gritty. We found no traces of bone in this. At its top in some places but not in all is a layer of dripstone (cave or "Mexican" onyx) from which rise stalagmites, buried by the overlying layers of clay. The next higher clay layer, sometimes absent but in other places 2 feet or more thick, is very smooth and fine, without grit, and is deposited in thin, horizontal layers. There are no bones here, either, except occasionally right at the top where they probably sank in from above when the clay was less compact. The top of this is sharply distinguished from the overlying bed but it has no layers of dripstone so far as we saw. Next higher is a bed of clay quite variable in thickness but averaging 18 to 20 inches, also fine and plastic, but without layers and containing many scattered chunks of limestone and of dripstone. Almost all the bones are in this bed of clay, which we called "the peccary layer." Above it there is occasionally, but not usually, a thin layer of dripstone. At the very top is a bed, usually less than a foot thick, of relatively loose, granular, earthy clay. In places it fills holes extending down into the lower layers. A few very small bones were found in this bed. In some places where there is a small unfilled space above this top layer there are small stalagmites on it, and where these occur they are usually set on small plaques of dripstone.

Our major clues are the bones themselves, not only because of what they are but also because of how they occur. As I have said, almost all the bones are in the "peccary layer." You cannot dig long in any part of that particular stratum without finding bones, but they do usually tend to be more common toward the bottom of the layer. Even when several are found together, they are just piled up at random. No two bones of the same animal are found together. Most of the long bones are buried in a more or less horizontal position, but some are oriented without regard for the natural bedding of the deposit and they may even be vertical. Small, solid individual bones are usually whole, but the longer and more fragile bones are usually broken. We did not find a single complete rib. A few of the bones have tooth marks and had been gnawed before being buried here. Bones of the extinct peccary are by far the most common, but there are also a few bones and teeth of other extinct animals and of some living species in this layer; I will give the list later.

The rare bones in the highest layer tend to occur in a few pockets, scattered but sometimes with the remains of one individual near each other. Except for one or two bones apparently washed out of the peccary layer, there are no extinct animals in this bed and most of the bones belong to small, burrowing rodents.

Those are the main clues. This is my proposed solution, so far as it has yet been carried:

The very first thing that left traces here happened so long ago that it is only indirectly involved in our problem of the bones. This was the deposition of the limestone, which occurred in a sea that covered this site about 300 million years ago. Much later, perhaps only a million years or so ago (the event has not been very exactly dated, and it took a long time), the cave was formed. The sea had withdrawn long since and the region had been uplifted gently. Water began to percolate along the cracks and seams of the limestone and as it went, it slowly but steadily dissolved the rock. Eventually it formed a large underground channel which was, and is, the cave. At this stage the cave was free of any extensive deposits of clay, and it probably had a subterranean stream or river at the bottom. This probably reached the surface some distance away and eventually flowed into the Mississippi.

Somehow the exit from the cave became clogged and the clay and silt brought in by streams from the surface, instead of being washed on through the cave and out again, began to pile up in the cave. These sediments eventually filled the cave up to within a few feet of its ceiling. Then for a long time there was no particular activity except the slow dripping of lime-filled water within the cave, developing dripstone deposits here and there on the top of the silt which now formed the floor of the cave. This floor was not even but contained shallow depressions. The next recorded event, which probably occurred during a particular rainy period of the Ice Age, was the filling of these depressions with water, forming within the cave a lake, or a series of small lakes. Tiny, insoluble clay particles were slowly washed into this standing water and they accumulated at the bottom, forming the bed of horizontally banded clay that we found below the peccary layer.

Now came what is for us the great event: the deposition of the bones in the cave. The evidence shows clearly that these animals did not live or die in the cave and it strongly suggests that this was not the first place in which they were buried. The animals probably fell into a sinkhole or fissure somewhere near the cave, perhaps a hole that had been an entrance to the cave but had been sealed off from it by the older accumulation of clay or by a fall of rock. The exact spot has not been found and search for it would not be very hopeful now that the whole region has been built up as part of a great city. The bones of many animals, hundreds certainly and perhaps thousands, piled up in this sinkhole or fissure and were buried there in mud and clay that washed in over their bones. Then the accumulation—clay, bones, and all—was somehow washed into the cave. There are several ways in which this could have occurred. Perhaps the most likely is that the sinkhole or fissure filled up with water above the clay and bones, that this water found an outlet into the cave, and that it suddenly flushed the whole deposit into the cave and spread it out over the older clay deposits of the cave. The nature of the peccary layer in the cave suggests that it came there rapidly, perhaps in an hour or two—one dramatically rapid event in a sequence where most changes can only be measured in terms of thousands or hundreds of thousands of years.

After this sudden change, things quieted down again. A little more clay was washed in from time to time. Rodents occasionally wandered into the cave, rooted around a bit in the top clay, and died there. These later events did not matter much so far as our interests go, until the final event of the reopening of the cave by man. It is surprising that the discovery of prehistoric animals here was delayed until 1946. When the brewery cleared part of the cave, many tons of clay were removed and in this there must have been thousands of bones. So far as is known, no one paid any attention to them. Presumably they were carted off with the clay, dumped somewhere, and buried again: their third burial.

The bones that have now been recovered and saved for scientific study include all anatomical parts of numerous individuals of the extinct peccary, *Platygonus compressus.* Both sexes and all ages are represented, from tiny jaws of peccaries newborn, or perhaps actually not yet born when they died, to skulls of big, tough boars. North America was peccary headquarters for millions of years. Numerous extinct kinds have been discovered, and there are two kinds still living in South and Central America, one of which, the collared peccary *(Tayassu angulatus)*, ranges as far north as southern Texas, New Mexico, and Arizona. Peccaries are sometimes called "wild pigs" and they do look much like pigs, but the real relationship is not very close. They do

not belong to the pig family (Suidae) but to a distinct
family of their own (Tayassuidae). True pigs have
never been native to the Western Hemisphere.

The living peccaries are rather small animals, seldom
over 20 inches high at the shoulder. They usually run in
bands and are inoffensive vegetarians, although their
sharp, curved tusks give them a somewhat fierce appearance. Some travelers have told horrendous tales of being
attacked by large bands of peccaries, but more reliable
observers report that they will not attack except as a
last resort when they are molested. The normal use of
the tusks is to pull up and cut roots for food. Our
extinct peccaries from Cherokee Cave had the same
habit, because several of the tusks that we found have
grooves worn in the sides from rubbing against gritty
roots. In fact, these ancient peccaries must have looked
and acted very much like their surviving cousins, except
that they were about twice as large.

We had hoped to find remains of other animals that
lived at the same time as the peccaries, and in this we
were successful, but only one of our additional discoveries was particularly striking. Apparently the trap
in which these animals were originally buried, the
sinkhole or fissure from which their remains were
flushed into the cave, was specially adapted for catching
peccaries. Few other animals fell into it, but we did find
scanty remains of a black bear, a raccoon, and a porcupine, all much like those still living in the region when
white men arrived there. The unexpected discovery was
an extinct armadillo, related to the recent Texas armadillo but larger. This is an important new record, because St. Louis is much farther north than any other
known occurrence of an armadillo, living or extinct.
Recent armadillos range no farther northward than
Texas, and the only comparable previous finds of
extinct armadillos were in Florida.

Both the armadillo and the peccary, also a warmth-
loving animal, suggest that when these animals lived
there the climate of the region was milder than at
present. They may have lived just before or just after

the last glacial stage of the Ice Age, for these were times of relative warmth. Aside from this inference, it is impossible to give a very close answer to the question as to how old the bones are. The difficulty is increased by the fact that the bones were not originally buried where they are now found. They may have lain for a long time in their original tomb before being washed into the cave. They are pretty surely more than 20,000 years old, and it is not likely that they are more than 500,000 years old—the interval gives a good deal of leeway. In any case, they are very ancient in terms of human history but are quite young as fossils go.

Hermetically sealed in continuously damp clay since shortly after the animals died, the bones have been unusually well preserved. The marrow and other soft animal matter have decayed and disappeared but the hard bone substance has not changed at all. The bones were roughly jolted when they were flushed into the cave and many of them were broken then, but even the fragments are strong and fresh and some of the unbroken bones look almost as if they were the remains of last night's pork roast. This beautiful preservation made the bone-digger's job much simpler and quicker than it usually is. It was not necessary for us to apply preservatives to the bones immediately on exposure or to encase them in reinforced plaster before moving them— procedures usually necessary with fossil bones. After carefully exposing them on one side, they could immediately be pried out of the clay without damage. The problem of cleaning them was also unusually simple. No slow grinding, scraping, and chiseling to remove the rock in which most fossil bones are buried. We simply soaked them in a wash basin for an hour or two and then scrubbed off the clay with a stiff brush.

With the help of Mr. Hess and the gang of workmen he provided, we developed a mass-production system in our bone-digging. The bones were piled up in boxes as we dug them out, and the full boxes were then taken up to the De Menil house, where we had what we called our bone laundry. Here, in the old kitchen, they were set to soak, and when the clay had softened sufficiently, they were thoroughly scrubbed. The clean, wet bones were then spread out to dry on tables in the dining room. Like fresh bones, they do tend to crack when dry; the fact that they had not been dry for thousands of years is a reason for their exceptional preservation. So the next step in the production line was to paint them thoroughly with thin white shellac and then to dry them again. The shellac soaks in sufficiently to seal all the incipient cracks and forms a transparent protective coating that will preserve them practically forever. Then they were ready for the last step and were moved on along the line into the parlor, where they were carefully wrapped and packed in boxes and barrels for shipment to New York. Between the cave and the mansion, our bone mine, laundry, shellackery, and packery hummed all day and sometimes far into the night. In only one week we had what would ordinarily be a good bag for a whole collecting season. Not only that, but nine-tenths of the bones were all ready for study or exhibition when we shipped them, requiring none of the usually tedious additional preparation in the New York laboratory.

So the mystery of the bones in the brewery was solved and a goodly sample of the bones moved on to the Museum by way of the De Menil house. De Menils and Chouteaus; peccary knuckles and beer; caves and palaces—these were some of the ingredients in a unique adventure in bone-digging. It was a curious mixture, so strange that at times we were hardly sure whether we were awake or dreaming. But as I write these last lines a peccary skull looks at me blankly, reassuring me that the fascinating medley of history and prehistory was real.

Little Dinosaurs of Ghost Ranch

❖❖❖❖❖❖

EDWIN H. COLBERT

[1947]

Ghost Ranch lay dreaming in the brilliant sunlight of a morning in mid-June—a patch of soft, verdant color quite unexpected in the New Mexican desert. At the edge of the fields the low houses nestled among large trees, all but hidden from sight.

To us, the cool shade of this green oasis was a luxury not to be enjoyed during the day, for we were after fossils, and fossils would be found in the flaming red and yellow and orange cliffs. All morning we had climbed up and down and back and forth, searching along the foot of the cliffs and up the talus slopes for fragments of fossil bones. It was hot and tiring work and for the most part unrewarding. We had found only a few scraps of fossils, none of them very promising.

So as lunchtime drew near we made our way back to the jeep with our thoughts centered more on food and a refreshing rest in the shade than on fossils.

As Thomas Ierardi, a member of our expedition, and I approached the jeep, we saw the third member of our group, George Whitaker, sitting in the car waiting for us. He had been up one of the canyons exploring all morning, while we had been up another, so there was information to be exchanged. We certainly didn't have much to offer. Our main consolation for several hours of tramping and climbing was a certain amount of geology and a powerful lot of colorful scenery.

But Whitaker had some interesting fossils to show us. As we drew near, he hauled them out of his pocket and held them in the palm of his hand. To a casual observer, they didn't look like much—a few small fragments, none of them larger than a walnut. Yet they were strange, not at all like the fossils we had been finding in these rocks. There were some pieces of small vertebrae and a few sections of limb bones. One of the pieces, no bigger than the end of your finger, was to determine our entire season's work and lead to a program that would require several years to complete. This piece could only be the articular end of a compressed claw belonging to one of the earliest and smallest dinosaurs.

As I looked at it, I felt the excitement that comes to one who glimpses treasures in the earth. For years we had hoped to find traces of these primitive little dinosaurs, and the features shown by these fossils could not be mistaken. The bones were small and delicate, and they were hollow. And the little piece of claw, by reason of its size and compressed shape, could have belonged to no other animal.

The Triassic period in earth history, to which these animals belong, is of particular interest to students of organic evolution. It began some 200 million years ago and lasted about 35 million years. It was the opening phase of the Age of Dinosaurs, when various lines of large reptiles were becoming established as the dominant land animals. It was a period of changes in the landscape and climate of the earth. Intense geological forces were in action, and life forms were becoming adapted to the new environmental conditions. Certain lines of evolution that were holdovers from earlier periods were in the last stages of their decline. And many comparatively new evolutionary lines that had had their beginnings in the preceding Permian period were becoming well established and were setting the general direction that evolution was to take during the later portions of the great Age of Dinosaurs.

For these reasons, we had decided some years earlier to conduct a strong program of fieldwork in rocks of Triassic age in order to build up our collections and knowledge of the animals of this period. Ghost Ranch was a good place to look for these fossils.

Fossils had been found here before. Indeed, there is some reason to think that Ghost Ranch may have been named because of an early encounter with fossils in the great cliffs nearby. A half-century ago a Spanish shepherd had a terrifying experience while riding in a large rincon, a sort of natural amphitheater formed by the huge cliffs just east of the present ranch houses. It was a hot day in the middle of summer, and perhaps he was a bit drowsy. At any rate, his lethargy was suddenly shaken by the sight of a huge rattlesnake coiled on the side of the cliff, its head weaving to and fro, its scaly body pulsating in the brilliant sunlight. This was no ordinary snake; it was the king of all snakes, thirty feet in length and as big around as a barrel!

That was enough for the horseman. He immediately whirled his mount and rode out of the place at a good gallop, and when he reached the nearest little town, he had a great tale to tell. Thus the legend of a giant serpent, a sort of "ghost," grew and took on color as the years passed.

More recently paleontologists came, especially from the University of California and the University of Chicago. One day, Mr. Arthur Newton Pack, the present owner of Ghost Ranch, rode out to watch one of the parties excavating a prehistoric skeleton. It was a big phytosaur, an animal of considerable size, that had been preserved in a coiled position, with the head pulled around toward the tail. As Mr. Pack and his companion approached the excavation, they could see the skeleton in the rock; and as it was a hot day, the heat waves distorted things so that the skeleton seemed to shimmer and move in the bright sunlight. The thought immediately came to Mr. Pack's mind that perhaps this was the original serpent seen by the old Spaniard.

As with many picturesque names, there are other tales to explain the origin of "Ghost Ranch," but we liked this one because we could easily imagine that we were living among the ghosts of animals that had died many millions of years before, when the landscape was quite different from our present campsite.

Whether or not their spirits hung over the place, we did know that fossils were to be found here. For instance, phytosaurs, large crocodilian-like reptiles that were common during Triassic times, had inhabited this region. And *Typothorax,* a queer, elongated reptile covered with a fantastic array of armor plates, had been found at this place. But most important to us now were the "pocket-size" ancestors of the great dinosaurs, and it was with high hope of finding them that we returned to the spot where Whitaker had found his fragments.

It was a long sloping cliff, largely covered with loose rocks—a most unpromising place to look for fossils. High up on the cliff we found the level from which the specimens had come, a layer of bones in the Triassic clays making up the Chinle formation. At first, the bones were not very apparent, but as we brushed away the loose, weathered dirt, the fossils began to appear. The more we brushed, the more of them we saw. It was evident that this was more than a sporadic occurrence of isolated fossil bones.

Until now, Triassic dinosaurs from this part of North America had been known from only the most fragmentary kinds of fossils—scraps of vertebrae, pieces of limb bones and hip bones, isolated portions of skulls. Nor was the material from other parts of North America much more abundant. Here we were finding almost complete backbones and legs. After a day or so of exciting prospecting, we knew it would be necessary to begin operations on a big scale. We would have to settle down here for a long stay, for lots of digging and a great deal of heavy work. Ghost Ranch was the ideal place to have made such a discovery.

We began to excavate a big hole in the cliff to expose a considerable expanse of the bone layer. Most of the hard clay above the bones was removed with heavy picks and shovels, but in the last few inches above the bone layer it was necessary to work carefully with light equipment. Small awls and fine brushes were used whenever there was danger of damaging any of the fossils, for these were delicate and brittle and unless treated properly as soon as they were exposed would go to pieces. So we shellacked the bones as they were uncovered, and a chart was made showing their position in the rock. The shellacked and hardened fossils were then covered with thin Japanese rice paper that was shellacked to the fossils to give added strength and protection.

When the entire bone layer within the limits of the quarry was exposed, we were stirred with mixed emotions—joy at such a rich deposit and dismay at the prospect of trying to get the material out of the quarry and to the Museum. The bone layer was almost a solid mass of dinosaurs!

These were not isolated and disconnected bones as is so frequently the case in a fossil deposit; they were completely articulated skeletons piled one on top of another. The skeletons were frequently intertwined in a most confusing way, making it difficult to distinguish clearly each individual animal. In the surface we exposed, we counted eighteen skulls, which gives some idea of the abundance of the remains throughout the extent of the quarry.

The task of removing the bones from the rock can be properly done only in a museum laboratory, so the problem was to cut channels through the bone layer and thus separate it into blocks of a size convenient to handle. And here we were faced with a decision reminiscent of Solomon's. Wherever we placed our line, we would cut right through the creatures to get them. Yet there was no alternative.

We began the job, and it proved to be the most difficult of the whole operation. As we cut down into the deposit, we found there were not merely skeletons on the top but more of them underneath, layer after layer. We would start a channel at a likely looking place, only to find a valuable skull or pelvis underneath. This would then have to be extracted or by-passed. All the fossils were carefully removed from the channels as we progressed, and careful records were made so that these parts could be restored to their proper positions when the fossils were finally prepared in the laboratory.

The cutting took a long time, and after it was completed, we were ready for the final stages of excavation. The large blocks were encased in strong bandages of burlap, dipped in plaster of Paris, and strengthened with heavy sticks and boards plastered to the block. When this had hardened, each block was undercut and turned over with the aid of an improvised derrick equipped with chain and rope hoists. We had kept the blocks as large as possible, and they were all very heavy.

How, now, were we to get these heavy chunks of rock out of the quarry, down the cliff, and to the ranch? This would have been a major undertaking if we had not had the aid of a bulldozer. The operator of the bulldozer pushed his way from the road right up to the quarry. There the blocks were loaded one at a time onto a heavy sled and hitched to the giant, panting machine. It was then child's play for the bulldozer to haul the sled with its heavy block down to the road and thence to the ranch. Once there, it was merely a case of loading them onto a truck and shipping them to the Museum, where the remains of the animals would be painstakingly removed from the rock for study.

These finds give us, for the first time, a fairly well-rounded picture of the earliest and most primitive dinosaurs known from North America. Moreover, since these animals are among the earliest and most primitive dinosaurs known throughout the world, their importance in advancing our knowledge of the ancestry and the early history of these prehistoric reptiles can hardly be exaggerated.

This early dinosaur from New Mexico was named *Coelophysis* by the great American paleontologist Edward Drinker Cope in 1889. Cope described the animal from various fragments that had been collected in the same part of the state where we found our quarry. Various additional fragments had been discovered from time to time, especially by parties from the University of California. Still it can be said that until now our knowledge of *Coelophysis* and, in general, of all primitive dinosaurs from North America has been based upon very fragmentary fossils.

Most people think of all dinosaurs as veritable giants, as long as Pullman cars and almost as heavy. *Coelophysis* was only about 6 feet in total length and so lightly constructed that he probably did not weigh more than 40 or 50 pounds. As a matter of fact, there were many small dinosaurs throughout the history of these interesting reptiles, and the truly primitive types at the beginning of the Age of Dinosaurs were quite small. Evolution among the dinosaurs was, in part, a process of development from small ancestors to giants.

Thus *Coelophysis,* one of the earliest and now certain to be the best known of the primitive dinosaurs, was a slightly built animal with hollow bones like those of birds. (In fact, *Coelophysis* means "hollow structure.") Many of the bones, particularly those of the skull, were exceedingly thin, so that as fossils they are very fragile.

Coelophysis walked in a semi-erect position on its hind legs, which were comparatively strong. Its feet were three-toed and armed with strong, sharp claws. As a matter of fact, the hind legs and feet of this reptile strongly remind one of the legs and feet of a long-legged ground bird. The hips were strongly constructed because they had to act as a fulcrum for the support of the entire body. The tail was very long and slender, and it served to counterbalance the weight of the body. The fore limbs were very small, with tiny, three-fingered hands armed with sharp claws, which served as grasping organs to aid the animal in catching and holding its prey. The neck was moderately long, serving as a noble support for the head. The eyes were large, and the mouth was armed with numerous sharp, recurved teeth. We cannot know what the skin was like, but it was probably leathery, perhaps somewhat scaly, like the skin of a small alligator or crocodile.

This is the picture of a very active and predaceous animal, a carnivorous reptile that hunted other small reptiles and amphibians and probably even fed on insects to some extent. Though strikingly small in comparison with its gigantic relatives of a later day, it was one of the aggressive predators of its time.

From ancestors such as *Coelophysis* all of the later dinosaurs evolved. Some of them continued to prey upon other creatures, and of these meat-eaters a few retained the small size of the early ancestors. But most of them became giants. By far the greater number of Jurassic and Cretaceous dinosaurs, which lived between 60 million and 155 million years ago, were plant-eaters and as such became adapted to a widely varied environment. It is among these later plant-eating dinosaurs that we find the great diversity in form and structure so characteristic of the dinosaurs as most people know them. Yet when we trace back the separate lines of these highly advanced dinosaurs, we find them converging toward ancestral forms of which *Coelophysis* is a typical example. Therefore, the discovery of complete and beautifully preserved skeletons of *Coelophysis* enables us to reverse the evolutionary process, as it were, and to journey back through time to become intimately acquainted with the first dinosaurs.

What was the land like when *Coelophysis* was alive? Obviously quite different from today. This region was a low, flat, tropical land—not the land of high, colorful cliffs and mountains and desert that we now know as northern New Mexico. It was a land of jungles and swamps, of sluggish streams flowing barely above sea level through a great monotonous expanse of green growth above which rose occasional volcanoes.

Everywhere reptiles dominated the scene. They lived on the uplands and down in the swamps; they inhabited the riverbank and the river itself. The crocodile-like phytosaurs were the largest and most predaceous of the reptiles, and it behooved *Coelophysis* to stay out of reach of their powerful, heavily toothed jaws. *Typothorax,* the strange-looking, heavily armored reptile mentioned earlier, was protected against the rapacious phytosaurs by its strong body-covering. On the uplands, a large plant-eating reptile, *Placerias,* walked on strong legs, with two long tusks protruding from its skull.

The reptiles dominated the land, but the amphibians, which had been supreme ages before when the reptiles were beginning the course of their complex evolution, were still maintaining some show of competition. There was a giant amphibian, *Buettneria*, an animal some 8 feet in length, that inhabited the streams and water-courses of the land in which *Coelophysis* lived. There were many fresh-water fishes, too—lungfish and ganoid fish with heavy, shiny scales.

But there were no birds. The first bird was still many millions of years in the future. And there were probably no warm-blooded mammals, even though some of the reptiles were at this time becoming so very like the first mammals that it is difficult for us to know whether they should be classified as reptiles or as mammals.

It was in many ways a strange world to our eyes. And there are many questions that we cannot yet answer fully. Why, for instance, were the bones at Ghost Ranch concentrated in such abundance? Why is this deposit made up so completely of dinosaur skeletons; why were not other reptiles of the time included? True, a few scattered phytosaur bones were encountered during the quarrying of the dinosaurs, but, practically speaking, we found dinosaurs almost exclusively. Just as remarkable is the complete preservation of the skeletons. Usually we expect to find a hodgepodge of random bones. What accounts for this?

It is evident that something must have killed great numbers of *Coelophysis*. Perhaps it was a volcanic eruption, for there was much volcanic activity in those days. Perhaps it was something else; we can only guess. What we can say with relative certainty is that the *Coelophysis* carcasses were deposited en masse, perhaps in some sort of an eddy or backwater. The sediments in which these dinosaurs were found appear clearly to have been laid down on a stream bottom. There was probably some process of selection whereby the dinosaur carcasses were concentrated in one spot. Since these were very light animals, their bodies may have drifted farther than did the bodies of other reptiles that may have died or been killed at the time. And whereas the bodies of other animals might have been rolled over and over and thus broken up, the little dinosaurs may have floated on to survive the vicissitudes of stream travel and thus come to rest where the power of the current was no longer sufficient to carry them farther. They were then covered by silt and thus protected against rapid decay, so that the slow process of fossilization could set in. The soft parts quickly disappeared, but the hard parts—the bones—were protected and replaced, molecule by molecule, by rock material deposited by the ground waters. So the form and structure of the bones were preserved, even though the substance was changed.

Ages passed. The land, which had been a low jungle for so many millions of years, was eventually uplifted by the mountain-making forces that built the Rockies. And as it rose thousands of feet into the air, the forces of erosion acted upon the landscape with new vigor. Streams and rivers, wind and frost, cut into the many thousands of feet of sediments deposited during the Age of Dinosaurs to form canyons and cliffs. By these slow geological processes the New Mexico of today came into being, a high desert country of brilliant cliffs and forested mountains. The former jungle stream, in which the little dinosaurs met their fate, became part of a sloping cliff. And as erosion continued, bone fragments near the surface were washed down, to be seen on one bright day in June by the sharp eyes of a fossil collector.

Ghost Ranch was tranquil in the bright autumnal sunlight when we left. The summer had run its course. The alfalfa from the irrigated fields had been stored in the barns, and all was being put in readiness for the desert winter. High on the cliffs above the ranch a drama had been unfolded—a drama of life as it had been almost 200 million years ago, a drama of the tropics of long ago, when strange animals inhabited the earth, when the

Age of Reptiles was still young, and when the dinosaurs were still fragile creatures, not in the least aware that at some date in the distant future their descendants would be giants on the earth.

Our Most Apelike Relative

❖❖❖❖❖❖❖

PIERRE TEILHARD DE CHARDIN

[1937]

Because he is anatomically the lowest known man and because more abundant remains of him have been found than of any other primitive human type, the Peking Man, who lived some hundred thousand years ago in the vicinity of the modern city of Peking, is the most important discovery of its kind ever made.

The remains are being found in what was a large cave at the time of its occupancy but which was gradually filled in by falling material from the walls and ceiling. Fragments representing approximately thirty individuals, including five fairly well preserved skulls, have been unearthed in ten years of excavating. The work has been carried on under the joint efforts of the Geological Survey of China and the Rockefeller Foundation.

Situated some 30 miles south of Peking, this treasure-field was accidentally hit upon by stone-quarriers and was first excavated by Dr. J. G. Anderson in 1921, for fossil animal remains. When, however, as a result of this early research, two human teeth were recovered by Dr. Zdansky, in association with numerous early Pleistocene animals, a thorough excavation of the site was planned by Dr. Davidson Black, Professor of Anatomy at the Rockefeller Medical College of Peking, and the work started in 1927. Fifty to 100 technicians and workmen have been continually busy, quarrying, blasting, sifting, and labeling, during each eight-month season since the work began ten years ago.

Among the very primitive characteristics of the Peking Man are the absence of chin, the shape of the teeth,

154

and the size of the orbital ridges. The brain case is elongated, very low, and a transverse section of the skull is arched as in the apes, instead of being oval as in the Neanderthaloid or in modern man. By such characteristics *Sinanthropus* represents apparently the lowest anatomical stage so far discovered in human ancestry. And yet he is unquestionably a man, as proved by the shape of his lower jaw, the capacity of his brain case (ranging between 900 and 1200 cubic centimeters as compared with the modern average of about 1450), and his ability to make tools and fire, as attested by abundant charcoal and ashes.

The remains of Peking Man are found at any level through a depth of 50 meters yet do not show any appreciable anatomical change. His stone implements, however, vary slightly but distinctly from the base to the top of the deposit. Curiously enough, the bulk of the human remains are teeth, jaws, and skulls, practically no traces of skeletons having been found, except a collarbone, a first neck vertebra, and a fragmentary leg bone.

The reason for such an artificial selection of skulls lacks satisfactory explanation.

That Peking Man brought many animals to the cave for food is shown by the enormous number of prehistoric bones, some of which were artificially broken. Most of the forms are extinct: two rhinoceroses, a big camel, a water buffalo, a twisted-horned antelope, and a curious fallow deer with extremely flattened antlers and thickened skull and jaw. A huge extinct hyena was probably a temporary dweller in the cave, likewise two types of bear and, rarely, the saber-toothed tiger. Other forms found are still living in China: the sika deer, the roebuck, the big-horned sheep. The age of this fauna, in agreement with several stratigraphic and physiographic evidences, points to early Pleistocene time, a matter of some hundred thousand years ago.

The discovery in November, 1936, of three of the human skulls in two days strongly suggests that the excavation has now reached the most promising levels.

Three more years of work will be necessary before exhausting the central part; and thanks to the kind and powerful support of the Rockefeller Foundation, the Geological Survey of China has decided to carry on to its end the thorough investigation. We have every reason for hoping that this will reveal much new knowledge concerning Peking Man's place in the history of man.

Man or Ape?

FRANZ WEIDENREICH

[1940]

In August, 1891, Dr. Eugène Dubois, then a Dutch health-officer, found near Trinil in central Java, in the left bank of the Solo River, "among a great number of remains of other vertebrates, the bones and teeth of a great man-like mammal." With these words one of the most important discoveries of human history was announced. "I have named it *Pithecanthropus erectus*, considering it as a link connecting apes and man," the discoverer continues, assigning thereby this newly found type to a place within the supposed line of human evolution.

As to the time in which *Pithecanthropus* lived, Dubois concluded that it belonged to the latest epoch of the Tertiary period. This would put the age at perhaps one million years. According to the latest geological interpretation, however, Dubois took too long a span, for *Pithecanthropus* is now believed to have lived in the Middle Pleistocene period, which might be 300,000 or 400,000 years ago, and there are those who say that even this may be too old.

The bones Dubois refers to consisted of a skullcap and a thighbone, both of them remarkable for their special appearance. The skullcap, quite different from the modern type, is small, low, and extremely flat, and provided with heavy, protruding eyebrows. The thighbone, long and strong, and resembling in all parts that of recent man, shows a strange abnormality consisting of a large and irregular bony outgrowth on the inside of the upper half. Such a pathological structure occasionally

157

occurs in exactly the same place in recent man as a consequence of a peculiar form of chronic inflammation of the muscles called ossifying myositis.

The obvious disharmony between the apelike skullcap and the humanlike thighbone at once aroused serious doubt that the two really belonged to the same individual, as Dubois assumed, or even to the same type. Yet the liveliest discussion concentrated on the identification of the skullcap. Nothing demonstrates more the great contrast of opinions in this regard than the judgment of the English anatomist Cunningham, and that of the German anthropologist Rudolf Virchow, delivered in the same year, 1895. According to Cunningham "the fossil cranium described by Dubois is unquestionably to be regarded as human. It is the lowest human cranium which has yet been described. It represents many Neanderthaloid characters but stands very nearly as much below the Neanderthal skull as the latter does below the ordinary European skull." Rudolf Virchow, however, stated that the skullcap did not belong to a man but showed, on the contrary, the greatest resemblance to the skull of *Hylobates*, the gibbon. He took the position, therefore, that in accordance with all the rules of classification, this individual, *Pithecanthropus erectus*, was an animal—in short, an ape.

In a later and more detailed paper (1924) Dubois himself defined his final standpoint as follows: "The form of the skull is on the whole not human, nor does it represent a transition between any of the man-like apes and the human type." Dubois believes that both Man and *Pithecanthropus* descend from a common primitive simian ancestor which resembled the gibbon more closely than the actual great apes as represented by gorilla, chimpanzee, and orang. In one of his latest publications Dubois actually called *Pithecanthropus* a giant gibbon but added the reservation that this designation should indicate only the special line of evolution, and insisted beyond that on his first interpretation of *Pithecanthropus* as an advanced ape intermediate between man and gibbon.

Most students, however, came to the conclusion that the type of the skullcap, disregarding the question of its exact position in the line of evolution, looks more like man than ape. Professor J. H. McGregor of Columbia University, for instance, was so convinced of the correctness of this conception that he ventured, twenty years ago, to restore not only the entire skull but also the head, giving to both the general traits of man.

But the problem itself remained unchanged as long as the skullcap of Trinil continued to be the only known representative of such an early type. In 1929, however, a very similar but more complete skull was discovered, not in Java but rather far away in northern China, and representing a type which lived contemporaneously with *Pithecanthropus.* As Davidson Black, who gave the first description of this find, saw at first glance, the general character of this skull was exactly the same as that of the Trinil skull, in spite of the differences in some details. Since Peking Man or *Sinanthropus pekinensis,* as this newcomer to human ancestry was named, proved undoubtedly human, there was no escape from the conclusion that *Pithecanthropus,* too, should be construed as man and not as ape. The human nature of the Peking Man, moreover, has been confirmed by a series of subsequent finds of skeletal remains from the same site. Altogether about forty individuals, including males and females, adult and juveniles, have been unearthed up to the present.

In the meantime Java Man himself has played an essential role in unraveling the riddle which still veiled his actual character. Here we owe the unexpectedly abundant increase of our knowledge to the farsightedness, the perseverance and energy of Dr. R. von Koenigswald in Bandong in Java. Thanks to the subsidy of the Carnegie Institution of Washington, he was able to set up a very effective organization to search systematically all the localities which had yielded fossil material of the same nature as that which once came to light in Trinil. An area west of Trinil proved particularly productive. This region, formerly a vast dome, has collapsed in its central portion, thereby exposing typical Trinil formations around the inner slopes of the whole circumference.

From this so-called Sangiran district there came in 1936 the fragment of a lower jaw with four teeth still in place, and, from another site, a brain case with some of the basal parts preserved. According to the size and the robustness of bone and teeth, the jaw must have been that of a male individual. As regards the brain case, it resembled Dubois's original skullcap as one egg does another, differing only a little from the latter in size and shape. It is distinctly smaller but relatively broader and not quite so flat. Since this second skull was more complete than Dubois's Skull I, retaining in particular the temporal bones along with the ear region on both sides, Doctor von Koenigswald has been able to demonstrate beyond all possible objections that Java Man is not an ape but a man.

Still further evidence came to light in 1938 with the discovery of a skull fragment from the same Sangiran district. This piece apparently belonged to a juvenile skull but nevertheless possessed some of the characteristics of Skulls I and II. At the same time it substantiated the close relationship of *Pithecanthropus* to Peking Man, since the top of the skull exhibits the same strong longitudinal crest.

The latest and most important find of *Pithecanthropus* was made in January, 1939. The circumstances of this discovery are so exciting and moreover suggest so strongly the possibility of further success in exploring this area that I think it justifiable to tell its story.

Doctor von Koenigswald had decided to go to Peking to study with me the *Pithecanthropus* material at the Cenozoic Research Laboratory, the best equipped place nearest to him. Some days before he left Java, one of the collectors sent him a jaw which, in spite of being covered with a thick coat of matrix, was recognized immediately by von Koenigswald as an upper jaw of a great ape or Java Man. Since the breakage was fresh, he instructed the collector to return at once to the site where the jaw was found and look for the pertaining skull. The collector did this, recovered the skull, and sent it to Peking.

After preparation it turned out that the skull consisted of the posterior three-quarters of the brain case, including the base, while the entire frontal region and the face were missing except for the upper jaw first found. The skull shows a wide cleft which passes through both cap and base in an oblique direction from in front and right to behind and left. The direction of the cleft, the straight lines of breakage and the smoothness of the margins of the split bones raise the suspicion that the crack may have been brought about by either a stone accidentally shaped like an ax or even possibly by an implement.

In addition the entire skull was crushed. Probably after the splitting had occurred, the skull was submitted to some kind of strong pressure working in transverse as well as longitudinal direction, with the result that the bones of the skull, having already lost their continuity by the cleavage, were dislocated and partly telescoped. That this even took place immediately after death can be inferred from the fact that all the dislocated fragments sticking together have been consolidated in their new position by fossilization. The upper jaw has suffered to a certain extent the same destiny, proving that the jaw actually belonged to the skull and had been separated from it subsequently. In spite of the crushing to which the skull has been subjected, both the general character and the individual details can be clearly discerned. The original size and shape, however, were difficult to ascertain in the present state.

I made the attempt, therefore, not only to restore the dislocated bones but also to reconstruct the entire skull by completing the missing parts of the frontal region, face, and lower jaw. The restoration was made on the basis of casts and executed at the Paleontological Laboratory of the American Museum of Natural History. For the configuration of the frontal region, *Pithecanthropus* Skulls I and II served as models and for the superior part of the face the corresponding *Sinanthropus* material. The lower jaw was restored on the basis of the *Pithecanthropus* fragment found in 1937 and completed by adapting it to the form and size of the upper jaw, supplementing for the missing parts data taken from *Sinanthropus* jaws.

As the restoration reveals, *Pithecanthropus* Skull IV represents undoubtedly a male individual. It is considerably larger than the other two skulls, and all the details of the muscular relief are correspondingly much more pronounced than they are in the latter. The most striking peculiarities of the brain case are its lowness, the flatness of the forehead, the heavy and protruding eyebrows, and the huge longitudinal crest extending over the top of the skull. In addition, the skull is very broad in proportion to its length and possesses a peculiar rounded back.

The upper jaw is not only enormous as a whole but also extraordinarily wide, exceeding in this regard all human and simian jaws known hitherto. In accordance therewith, it projects farther beyond the face than in any other case of fossil man. One of the most conspicuous particularities, however, concerns the teeth. They are as a whole large and robust, corresponding to the size of the jaw. Yet, the canines are relatively small, and though they surpass in height the neighboring teeth to a greater extent than has ever been observed in man with the exception of *Sinanthropus,* they do not show the characteristics of simian canines either in size or in form. Even more surprising is the fact that they are separated from the incisors by a wide gap, which is specific for all the apes but has never been found in any human skull. The enormous size and robustness peculiar to the original fragment of the lower jaw and the reconstructed jaw repeat the massiveness of the upper jaw. No chin is present, and the molars are large, increasing in size from the first to the third, unlike the usual sequence in man. The canine socket of the lower jaw is small, giving, therefore, good reason to believe that the lower canine was as small as the upper one. Moreover, no gap between the canine and the first premolar existed.

When *Pithecanthropus* Skull IV is compared with Dubois's Skull I and von Koenigswald's Skull II, it is immediately evident that the former represents a male and the latter females. But in spite of the greater size of Skull IV, it cannot have had greater brain capacity than Skull I, considering the amazing thickness of the bones. It is to be noted that in size the *Pithecanthropus* brain stands about midway between the largest ape and the average modern man. I computed the capacity of Skull IV to be not much more than 900 cubic centimeters, corresponding nearly to that of Skull I, while Skull II with a volume of 830 is clearly smaller. The maximum capacity ever observed in the great apes (gorilla) amounts to little more than 600, while the average in recent man totals about 1250 for female individuals.

Apart from the conformity in the capacity of the brain case, the three *Pithecanthropus* skulls have some specific features in common, for instance: the lowness and flatness of the brain case, the remarkable restriction of the anterior temporal region, the breadth and roundness of the back. The pronounced crest on the top in Skull IV has to be regarded as a sex character because of its slight and restricted development in Skulls I and II.

There is no doubt that *Pithecanthropus* Skull IV represents the most primitive type of fossil man ever found. This primitiveness, however, is not so pronounced in the Skulls I and II. On the other hand, Java Man is closely related to Peking Man. In some details the former is more primitive, in others the latter. But when both are compared with the remaining specimens of fossil man found throughout the world, they stand out as a special group distinctly lower in the evolutionary scale than all others which have come to our knowledge. The differences between the two types themselves are obviously equivalent to the regional differentiations such as are expressed in the various races of today. Within the special phase of evolution to which Java Man

and Peking Man have to be assigned, the former represents a crude type, the latter a refined one, just as among
modern man the Australian native and the Chinese
express primitive and advanced types of the same stage.

Dubois gave his *Pithecanthropus* the surname *"erectus"* because he deducted from the appearance of the
thighbone, attributed by him to this type, that *Pithecanthropus* already had adopted an upright posture. Dubois
tried later to confirm this view on the basis of five
more thighbones of the same character discovered subsequently among old Trinil material stored at the Museum in Leiden. Unfortunately, no more limb bones
were found in connection with the new skulls. The
conclusion, therefore, that *Pithecanthropus* possessed
erect posture still remains in doubt. But as regards
Sinanthropus, fragments of seven thighbones and one
armbone are now available, which prove that Peking
Man was certainly an erect type. This view is supported
by the nature of his cultural relics, which demonstrate
that he was an effective hunter and already knew the use
of fire. The limb bones of *Sinanthropus* reveal, therefore,
the very remarkable fact that the body already had
reached an advanced stage of evolution, while the skull,
including the teeth, lagged behind. The close relationship
between Peking Man and Java Man suggests that they
cannot have differed essentially with regard to their posture; in this connection one peculiarity of the *Pithecanthropus* Skull IV is of greatest importance. The
situation of the joint which holds together skull and
spine, as well as the configuration of the surrounding
parts of the base of the skull, resembles much more the
condition in recent man than is the case in *Sinanthropus.*
This seems to indicate that if *Sinanthropus* had already
acquired an upright position—a fact which scarcely can
be doubted—*Pithecanthropus* certainly did so. Do the
debated thighbones after all belong to *Pithecanthropus?*
The future may decide.

The answer to the question in the title of this article
is that Java Man *was* a man. That means that he was
not a giant gibbon or a creature similar to this. Neverthe-

less, Java Man was not at all identical with recent man. His skull and his teeth exhibit a number of characteristic traits strange to man of today but familiar to us when we remember the gorilla or chimpanzee. This is exactly what we have in mind when we consider man as a branch of a simian stock or what Dubois meant when he designated *Pithecanthropus* as "a link connecting apes and man." McGregor gave to his reconstruction of the Java Man, based only on the fragmentary skullcap of Trinil, the aspect of an intermediate form decisively closer to recent man than to any of the existing apes.

There is often some skepticism among laymen when the scientist, with fragmentary relics, deduces the shape of missing parts. But trust in the fundamental soundness of the methods is given when further discoveries bear out early deductions. Such a case is Doctor Mc-Gregor's reconstruction. How right he was is shown by subsequently discovered material on which the restoration of Skull IV is based.

The true nature of the relationship between man and the great apes is best illustrated by assuming that there once existed a common ape-like stem which early became divided into two main branches, one evolving in the direction of man, the other in that of the great apes. Both developed their own peculiarities: the human branch above all displayed the tendency of the brain and correspondingly the brain case to expand at the expense of the chewing apparatus but retained, on the other hand, certain primitive features which were lost during the process of differentiations in the simian branch.

When and where the division of the main stem took place, no one can tell. But so far as *Pithecanthropus* and *Sinanthropus* are concerned, their common ancestor must be buried somewhere in South Asia. Java is a very young island which emerged from the sea in late Tertiary, so it must have been peopled by an early man who came from India. That is, therefore, the place where we have to furrow if we are anxious to unveil the secret concealing man's earliest history. For the moment the most urgent task is to continue the work in Java which has now come to a standstill because of the exhaustion of available funds. There should be established a foundation taking care of all research work on early man in all parts of the world, dealing not only with his physical appearance but also with his cultural life and his entire environment.

In comparison with the vast work that remains undone, the study of man's beginning is yet in its early stages. The romance of these discoveries commands the interest of every thinking person, and science has proved how productive the search can be. The new knowledge which everyone will eagerly await, will be limited now only by the facilities for research.

Search for Early Man

❖❖❖❖❖❖

G. H. R. VON KOENIGSWALD

[1947]

In the last 150 years we have learned much about the history of our planet and the development of its plant and animal life. The oldest rocks of the earth show that at first there was no life. Then appeared lowly animals without backbones, the invertebrates. Next the fishes and amphibians came on the scene; then the reptiles, including the mighty dinosaurs, and last of all, the mammals. Some groups of animals disappeared, while others flourished. Some developed very slowly, others rapidly; but they all kept changing in an eternal process we call evolution.

Only after a vast number of observations and discoveries had revealed something of the history of animal life did people begin to realize that the human race, too, had had an ancient history.

Generally speaking, the preserved remains of prehistoric animals are by no means rare. You can find ancient shells by the million; the bones of dinosaurs and other reptiles are more precious. But when it comes to the remains of our own ancestors, we have to confess that they are among the greatest rarities. With the exception of Neanderthal Man, who is just one step away from us and who lived toward the end of the Ice Age only 100,000 years ago, we have had until recently only a few fragmentary bits.

Neanderthal Man was forced by the cold climate of the last glacial period to live in caves, and this has made it relatively easy to discover his dwelling places, workshops, and burials. But when it comes to the people who lived in the warm interglacial periods or in tropical regions where there were no marked climatic changes, we need a lot of patience, endurance, luck, and hard work. It is significant that none of the more important finds in this class have been made by accident. Schoetensack waited twenty years for the Heidelberg jaw, Berckhemer nearly as long for the Steinheim skull. When a human tooth and some other fossils came to light in a Peking drugstore in 1900, Davidson Black had to search the region around Peking most carefully in order to find Choukoutien, the site of Peking Man. And all of our finds from Java, which form the subject of this article, are the result of a long and systematic search.

The discovery of early man in Java begins with an *idée fixe*. Eugene Dubois had just finished his studies in the Netherlands in 1883 when he went to Indonesia possessed with the idea that he could discover there the oldest remains of man. He was a young man and was very much impressed by Darwin's and Haeckel's ideas on evolution. Lydekker had discovered in the Siwalik fauna of India the upper jaw of an anthropoid ape, which he thought might be an ancient chimpanzee. As the same fauna was known also in Java, Dubois concluded that Java and Sumatra, whose tropical climate had not been influenced by the Ice Age, must be especially favorable places in which to search for the origins of man. He went to the Indies as a medical doctor in the service of the Royal Dutch Army and published his ideas in Batavia. He was lucky enough to arouse the interest of the authorities and, with the full support of the government, was transferred to the Mining Bureau in Batavia to do paleontological research.

He went first to the vicinity of Padang in Sumatra and began, in "European fashion," to excavate in caves. This turned out to be very disappointing. It is commonly believed that caves in the tropics are inhabited by bats, snakes, ghosts, scorpions, evil spirits, and lizards, and it would seem that this belief is as old as mankind, for caves have nearly always been avoided by man. The only interesting finds Dubois made there were some teeth of the orangutan, which is now extinct in Sumatra. This large ape is actually regarded as a kind of man by the Malayans, from whom we get the word "orangutan," meaning "forest man."

Upon receiving a human skull that had been found in Wadjak, near the southern coast of central Java, Dubois was inspired to go to that locality. There he found the remains of a second specimen. Wadjak Man is an extinct primitive type of modern man, perhaps related to the Australian aborigines. Whether he should be regarded as "fossil" is uncertain, for the age of the associated fauna that Dubois collected has never been determined. But from what we know from other localities in Java, these finds cannot be very old and probably should be regarded as only "prehistoric."

From Wadjak, Dubois moved north into the interior of central Java. Large fossil bones, belonging mostly to extinct elephants, had long been known to the natives, who believed they belonged to giants, *raksasas,* the guardians who watch every temple in Bali and ancient Java. Near Madiun, Dubois collected the first fossilized bones of larger mammals, including elephants, hippopotamuses, and hyenas, and he also found a very small fragment of a human jaw. He concluded that these remains must be from the Pleistocene Age, the geological period popularly known as the Ice Age.

Then, moving west, Dubois discovered a very rich site not far from Ngawi, near Trinil, on the banks of the Solo River. This site could only be worked at low water level during the dry season. It was here that Dubois, in October, 1891, made his famous discovery—the top of a very low skull with a bony ridge above the eyes. He believed that it belonged to a fossil chimpanzee, the same chimpanzee that Lydekker had described from the Siwalik in India. But in August of the next year he found, only about fifty feet from this find, a complete human thighbone. It was so human in the characteristics developed for man's erect posture that it could almost have belonged to a modern man. Dubois combined his two finds and in 1894 surprised the world with his famous publication, "*Pithecanthropus erectus*, a Human-like Transitional Form from Java."

The world was shocked. *Pithecus* means "ape"; *anthropus*, "man"—the "Erect-walking Ape-Man" from Java! Not without purpose had he chosen this name, which had been coined by Haeckel in 1868 for a hypothetical being which should link man with his anthropoid ancestors. Was Dubois's *Pithecanthropus* the "missing link"? No other fossils have ever been discussed by the public with so much vehemence. Man or ape? You can scarcely open a standard book on anthropology, zoology, paleontology, evolution, or prehistory without finding a picture of this celebrated fossil.

The reason for the many different and contradictory opinions is clear; the find (the skull) is too incomplete. The most important part, the region behind the eyes on both sides, is missing, and interpretation of the fragment is indeed difficult.

Dubois tried to find more material that might solve the question, but without success. Nor did the German Selenka Expedition, which worked in Trinil in 1907–1908, find anything belonging to *Pithecanthropus*. However, they published a description of the animal remains from this geological horizon, which filled a great gap in our knowledge. It proved that this fauna, which Dubois had tried to make Pliocene (from 1 million to 7 million years old), could not be older than Pleistocene (a million years old at the most).

In 1929, news came from China that Davidson Black had succeeded in finding the skull of Peking Man. And Peking Man was really a man, not only from the anatomical point of view, but because he already knew the use of stone implements and fire. In describing the skull, Black found that it resembled the skull of *Pithecanthropus* in so many features as to indicate a close relationship between the two. So by analogy it became clear that our Java Ape-Man was a human being, in spite of his primitiveness.

Curiously enough, now that everyone else was convinced, Dubois changed his opinion completely. Basing his new ideas only on very theoretical speculations, he now regarded his *Pithecanthropus* as a gigantic gibbon, denying every relationship with Peking Man.

It seemed that the only way to convince Dubois would be to find a more complete *Pithecanthropus* skull in Java. An opportunity came when the Geological Survey of the Netherlands East Indies was established and began the systematic geological mapping of that region. In 1930 I went to Java to join the Survey as a paleontologist. Our headquarters were at Bandung, a beautiful town in the mountains of western Java. From the first moment, I hoped for a chance to solve the puzzle of *Pithecanthropus.*

We gradually collected enough specimens to learn that the animal life of Java had not been as uniform as Dubois had led us to believe, and that with the help of certain guide-fossils, it was possible to classify rock formations that were otherwise quite similar. A correlation with the formations in India could be worked out, and we could prove that Trinil was not quite as old as Dubois had suggested. At least three horizons of Pleistocene Age were represented. We showed that Trinil was of middle Pleistocene Age, which means that *Pithecanthropus* lived about 300,000 years ago.

It was shortly after my arrival in Java in September, 1931, that my colleague, the late C. Ter Haar, discovered a high-level river terrace on the Solo River north of Ngawi, at Ngandong. He brought back quite a collection of fossil bones, and this encouraged the Survey to start excavations immediately. Among the first specimens sent to Bandung were, to our great surprise, fragments of two human skulls with low, receding foreheads. They were more primitive than modern man but more advanced than *Pithecanthropus,* and they represented a type which might be classified as neanderthaloid. From the geological point of view also, this so-called Solo Man was younger than Trinil Man.

During the excavations in Ngandong, which lasted until December, 1933, we found more than 25,000 bones, mostly belonging to elephants, rhinoceroses, hippopotamus, deer, and cattle. One of the most striking animals was a water buffalo whose horns spread more than two yards from tip to tip. Among this enormous collection were fragments of eleven human skulls and two shinbones. No other parts of man were discovered. As all the skulls had been broken and damaged in a very peculiar way, it is probable that they had been used by the ancient people as "skull bowls."

My first personal encounter with Early Man came on a hot day in June, 1937. A report had come that our workers in Ngandong had found what might be a human skull. They had left the find untouched and were waiting for assistance. So we went out—slim, always good-humored Ter Haar and I. We went by train to Ngwai and then set out on foot for the Solo River, followed by a whole caravan of coolies carrying our baggage on bamboo poles on their bare shoulders. It was about six miles to the site. We passed through the dense teakwood forest of the Kendeng Hills, and then, quite suddenly, we were standing on the bank of the Solo River. Our excavation was almost within the small hamlet of Ngandong, which consisted of only a few bamboo huts. Sixty feet or so above the river, spared from erosion, was a very limited remnant of a gravel deposit, only about one to three yards thick. From this came all our bones.

Our collectors had covered the precious find with sand for protection. We carefully began to remove the earth. Then, suddenly, there came to light the object we had expected but were thrilled to see—the upper part of a human skull! It lay upside down in the gravel, partly covered by a cemented crust of sand. I was so excited that I overexposed all of my pictures! It was skull No. VI, the finest specimen in the whole series of Solo skulls.

For *Pithecanthropus* himself we had to wait longer. In 1936 my colleague Duyfjes, a very able young geologist who died in a prison camp during World War II, had one of our native collectors working near Modjokerto, west of Surabaja. Here this man discovered a small ac- cumulation of fossil bones. Digging only about a yard deep, he found a curious human skull, very small and with very thin bones. It was the fossilized skull of a baby. A direct comparison with Dubois's find was impossible, but the skull came from a deeper level, known to be older than the layer where his was found. We called the baby *"Homo" modjokertensis* and suggested that it might belong to *Pithecanthropus*. We had, for the first time, proved the existence of human beings in the Lower Pleistocene of Java. But we could not convince Dubois, either by this find or by a fine fragment of a lower jaw (*Pithecanthropus* B), which closely resembled the lower jaw of Peking Man. This latter had been found by my collectors in 1936, but it only came to my attention in 1937 after my return from America.

This first trip to America had a special significance for me. When the Depression came, the budget of the Geological Survey was greatly reduced, leaving many of us out of a job. From 1935 to 1937, I could only continue my scientific work by means of grants. I had just been married, and we were having a very hard time. But I had Sangiran on my mind—the most promising site I had ever seen in Java. It had large natural outcroppings of black clay containing a rich Lower Pleistocene fauna (saber-toothed tigers and primitive cattle!) covered by tuffs and conglomerates yielding Trinil fossils. Every wet season, erosion brought thousands of bones, teeth, and jaws to the surface. Here, more than anywhere else, might we find a second *Pithecanthropus!* So, with very little money but assisted by good friends, we set out to collect material. We found the remains of many mammals not previously known to have lived in Java, but in the first years no *Pithecanthropus* came to light, with the exception of one broken and doubtful tooth.

From the outset of my work in Java, I had also begun to make a collection of the teeth of extinct mammals from China. These teeth are sold also outside of China—even in New York—by the Chinese drugstores as "dragon teeth," and they are considered a special and very powerful medicine. By visiting one drugstore after another in Java, it was fairly easy to collect teeth of rhinoceroses, *Hipparion* (a three-toed horse), a large giraffe, and other mammals of the Tertiary area. They are heavily mineralized, and often damaged on purpose to show the small calcite crystals in the pulp cavities.

Even fossil collecting in the Orient seemed to have been affected by the Depression, for from about 1932 on, second-rate dragon teeth became more and more abundant in the drugstores of Java. They were not as completely fossilized and apparently were more recent than the earlier finds. No horses or giraffes were noted, but there was a different aggregation of animals, including bears, tapirs, giant pandas, and pigs. And in this material, which came from caves in Kwangi and Kwantung in southern China, we discovered a fossil orangutan.

With the exception of a doubtful canine tooth from India, no fossil orang had ever been recognized. We were now able to prove, by our "drugstore fauna," that there had been more than one invasion of mammals into Java from Asia. An older Tertiary one had brought animals from India. A later one, from southern China, had brought the orangutan, gibbon, tapir, and bear to the present Malayan region.

The whole problem was so important for us that in 1935 I managed twice to go to Hong Kong and Canton for material. There, in the wholesale drugstores, lay enormous numbers of dragon teeth. Visiting these shops with my Chinese prescription and carefully looking over their stocks, I collected thousands of teeth, including about 1,500 that could belong to fossil orangutans. The prices were high, and the druggists charged by weight. They could never understand why I preferred to have so many small teeth in place of one large, and probably more powerful, elephant tooth. Sometimes the prices were ridiculous, and I had to depart empty-handed. Once, in Hong Kong, I saw a complete skull of a large saber-toothed tiger, surely a new species, but the price was "only" $5,000. I left the shop and cried.

Among these isolated teeth from China there were three large molars (I discovered a fourth one in 1939) that belong to the largest higher primate ever found, much larger than any gorilla. I described them as a new species, *Gigantopithecus blacki,* meaning "the gigantic ape of Black," named after Davidson Black, the discoverer of Peking Man. From the beginning, some of the characteristics of these teeth, known only in human teeth, puzzled me. It was not until many years later that new finds in Java helped us to interpret them.

But let us turn back to Java. Our search for human ancestors was very seriously limited by lack of funds. Then I received an invitation to attend the Symposium on Early Man at the Academy of Natural Sciences of Philadelphia in 1937. We went there, taking with us casts, slides, and samples. And then came help. The late Dr. John C. Merriam, president of the Carnegie Institute of Washington, became interested, and I left the United States with a Carnegie grant as research associate. I returned to Java via China, paying a visit to Peking to collect more dragon teeth.

Now we could reorganize our search for *Pithecanthropus.* I had two Indonesian chief collectors, and under them there were hundreds of natives to aid in the search. Every fragment of a fossil that they found was bought. We paid premiums for important finds and stimulated interest by means of festivals with *gamelang* and *rongengs*—native orchestra and dancing girls. We paid good collectors in advance and sent sick children to hospitals. Most of the material obtained was worthless and had to be thrown away, but we had to encourage collectors. We had to buy everything because if a man found three pig teeth, he would not look for more until these were bought. So we had to spend quite a lot of money for nothing (some people certainly regarded me as a fool), but it seemed the only way to get results.

And results came! Only a few months after my return to Java, my men sent me a fragment that was unmistakably part of an ancient human skull. I went directly out to the collecting fields. There, on the banks of a small river, nearly dry at that season, lay the fragments of a skull, washed out of the sandstones and conglomerates that contained the Trinil fauna. With a whole bunch of excited natives, we crept up the hillside, collecting every bone fragment we could discover. I had promised the sum of ten cents for every fragment belonging to that human skull. But I had underestimated the "big business" ability of my collectors. The result was terrible! Behind my back they broke the larger fragments into pieces in order to increase the number of sales!

We collected about forty fragments, of which thirty belonged to the skull. They were very thick, averaging about one centimeter (0.39 inch), and could easily be fitted together. They formed a fine, nearly complete *Pithecanthropus* skullcap. Now, at last, we had him!

It would be difficult to find, without careful selection, two modern skulls that resembled each other as much in detail as did the Trinil find and this new skull, except that the latter is more complete. This time, the important side parts were preserved on both sides, and now we could prove beyond doubt that *Pithecanthropus* belonged to the human family.

I immediately informed Professor Dubois, who was living in Haarlem. His attitude was very disappointing. He published the photograph of my find, which I had sent him only for personal information, and he tried to prove by misleading measurements that the new skull—which belonged, as he had to admit, to a human being—was more or less a fake. According to him, my find belonged to a young representative of Solo Man, while his *Pithecanthropus* had to remain an ape. He made any collaboration between us impossible and refused to acknowledge that a single one of the new finds belonged to *Pithecanthropus*. During the German occupation of the Netherlands, only a few weeks before his death, he still published a very confused article, the last of a whole series on this subject.

Davidson Black had suggested a relationship between Peking Man and *Pithecanthropus*. To study this problem further, I was invited by his successor, Professor Franz Weidenreich, to bring my specimens to the Rockefeller Institute in Peking for comparison. The Geological

Survey agreed. Our studies there, in 1939, proved that Davidson Black had been right. The resemblance between these two early human types was even greater than we had formerly believed. We were also able to demonstrate that Dubois's interpretation of his own find was wrong. The thick piece of bone that he had thought to be part of the ear was actually only the remnant of a thick bony ridge. X-ray pictures of the new skull revealed sutures not visible on the surface which proved that my reconstruction was correct.

But *Pithecanthropus* II was not the only find. In 1938 came No. III, from a new site not far from the locality that yielded No. II, and certainly from the same level. It is only a small fragment, consisting of the back of a juvenile skull. And in 1939 we found *Pithecanthropus* IV, the back part and upper jaw of a crushed skull, and this specimen came from the lower level. The barren hillside where this find came to light seems dull and uninteresting. But this is a very important specimen, enabling us for the first time to make a trustworthy reconstruction of the entire skull. This skull is larger and heavier than either II or III, and has been called *Pithecanthropus robustus* by Dr. Weidenreich.

Early in 1941 one of our collectors sent us part of an enormous human jaw, which had likewise been found in the lower horizon. For years I had kept some large isolated teeth, which I felt could not belong to an orang-utan, but human teeth of this size seemed against all theory. Now, however, we had a jaw that surpassed a gorilla's in size yet showed unmistakable human characteristics. I carried the fragment in my pocket for days to get accustomed to the idea! We had discovered a giant, which we named *Meganthropus palaeojavanicus* (*Megas,* "great," *anthropus,* "man"). It was only one step farther to recognize the enormous teeth from China as human.

The political clouds had gathered, and the dark time of the war had come. In the first month of 1942, a request came from my American friends to evacuate our most important finds to the U.S.A. But it was already too late. After the surrender of Singapore, we had to give up Java, and I, being in the military service, became a prisoner of war in the hands of the Japanese. We were forced to work in our office during the first month of the occupation, and we were able, with much difficulty, to conceal at least part of the material. We put some jaws among other, unimportant specimens and substituted casts for some of the originals in the safe. The Japanese later became suspicious but never discovered the truth. The upper jaw of *Pithecanthropus* IV was hidden by my wife; the rest of the skull and the big jaw were protected by my Swiss colleague, Dr. W. Mohler, and the tooth collection, with *Gigantopithecus,* went to Rolf Blomberg, a Swedish friend of ours, who packed them in milk bottles for better protection. The Japanese, feeling sure they would win the war and keep Java, treated our museum and its collections fairly well. Only one of the Solo skulls was sent to Tokyo as a birthday present for the Emperor, but even this was eventually recovered.

When the atomic bombs had done their work and Japan surrendered, I came back to life again. I was deeply moved to find my little family alive, saved by destiny through the terrors of the Japanese occupation. My happiness was complete when I learned that all my precious specimens had been saved. Large parts of my collections, many of my books, and all of my clothes had been stolen, but Early Man had survived the disaster.

Because of the damage caused by the Japanese, however, it was impossible to continue my scientific work in Java. It was very fortunate, therefore, that, through the generous efforts of my American friends, especially Professor Weidenreich, I was able to come to America to continue my research. The Rockefeller Foundation, which already had helped us in Java, gave me a grant to work out my finds in this country, in collaboration with Professor Weidenreich, at the American Museum of Natural History in New York. The Viking Fund provided us with traveling expenses. The Netherlands

Government kindly gave me permission to take all the available material from Java to America. And so we came to this country, bringing with us for study and comparison a whole branch of our family tree.

We left Java with all of its troubles in time to arrive in the United States during a shipping strike. And here, Early Man had his last difficulties—passing through the picket line in Philadelphia.

These new finds, the oldest remains of man yet discovered, are surely about 500,000 years old. They show us a new aspect of human evolution, for they indicate that man's ancestors were giants and that we reached our present physical proportions through a decrease in the size of our jaws and teeth—a conclusion wholly unsuspected until now.

Mammoths and Men

❖❖❖❖❖❖❖

EDWIN H. COLBERT

[1940]

Among the animals that appeared at the beginning of
the Great Ice Age, a million years ago, were two groups
of mammals each of which was destined to occupy a
different but a dominant position on the lands of the
earth. These two groups of preeminent, ruling animals
were elephants and men.

Until the beginning of the Ice Age, or Pleistocene
period, there were no true elephants or men in the
world—only their forerunners. These were the ancestral
elephant-like proboscideans, animals of large size, with
elongated trunks or proboscises, enlarged tusks, and
straight, post-like legs; and ancestral man-like apes, or
anthropoids. It was with the advent of the Pleistocene
period about 1 million years ago, an age marked by the
successive advances and retreats of great continental
sheets of ice from the north polar regions, an age which
inaugurated a period of increasingly rigorous climatic
cycles, that true elephants finally evolved from their
more primitive proboscidean ancestors and true men
developed from their apelike progenitors.

Having made their separate entrances onto the Pleistocene stage, elephants and men advanced along their
distinct but comparable lines of development, the former
to attain the maximum of body power among the later
land animals of geologic history, the latter to evolve the
maximum of brain power. Consequently these two
groups of animals were enabled by their heritage to
dominate their environment, the one by sheer force of
bulk and strength, the other by the less spectacular but
more effective use of intelligence.

From almost the beginning of the Pleistocene period to modern days, men and elephants have been associated. Man has been, throughout his evolutionary history as a man, first an elephant hunter and more recently an elephant master, while the elephant has been to man first a casual but formidable enemy and finally a surprisingly amenable slave.

At the beginning of the Pleistocene the ancestral elephants or mammoths made their appearance in the Old World, probably in southern Asia, possibly in Africa, and from these progenitors various lines of elephantine evolution developed, resulting in the differentiation of several distinct types of specialized mammoths or elephants.

The Pleistocene mammoths made up an impressive array of elephants, particularly when it is realized that most of them were living at the same time during the Ice Age. Great herds roamed over Europe and Asia, across Africa and through the Indies, and into North America, virtually unchallenged by any of their contemporaries and certainly afraid of nothing on their horizon. Only Australia, the isolated oceanic islands, and South America were without them, and even in the latter continent, as in North America, there persisted various kinds of mastodonts (the relatively primitive proboscideans from which the mammoths sprang).

Yet at this same time some other mammals, rather unimpressive on the whole, were developing side by side with the elephants. These were the early men, appearing at the beginning of the Ice Age and evolving through the duration of that period.

Just prior to the beginning of the Pleistocene period, the immediate apelike ancestors of the first men were living in North India. This is known from the evidence of fossils discovered there during the past twenty years. And from recent discoveries it is evident that intermediate "man-apes" or "ape-men," bridging the gap between the Oriental ancestors and the first men, were living in South Africa in the Pleistocene. It was from beginnings such as these that the true men of the Pleistocene evolved in the Old World.

Some of the first true men appeared almost simultaneously in China and in the East Indies. These were the men known as *Sinanthropus* and *Pithecanthropus,* living respectively in North China near Peking and in Java, but representing essentially a single human type. These people had characteristically low foreheads and skulls, heavy eyebrow ridges, and probably extremely wide noses; the jaw projected beyond the upper part of the face, and the chin was rather receding.

From such primitive men there evolved the more highly developed Neanderthal Man, *Paranthropus,* of Eurasia and Africa, an early hunter using fire and well-made tools, but still preserving many of the ancestral characteristics of the Java and Chinese men.

Finally there appeared the modern men belonging to the genus *Homo,* an early member of which was the Cro-Magnon Man of Europe, a highly developed human, using bone and stone tools, and noted for his unusual artistic ability. Succeeding Cro-Magnon Man came the recent men as we know them, following different lines of development and showing various characteristics by which we distinguish races. All of these later men were advanced over their more primitive pithecanthropoid and neanderthaloid predecessors in that they had high foreheads and highly domed skulls, a highly bridged nose, and a pronounced chin. The posture was completely upright.

As compared with the contemporaneous mammoths, the Pleistocene men were probably scattered and certainly not very important; yet as they developed with the passing of time, they were destined to become increasingly disturbing to the animals around them—even to the mammoths, then the giants of the earth. For these early men were evolving a new thing under the sun, a giant intellect, which eventually was to overpower all of the beasts with which men had to contend.

With the gradual increase of the primate brain to a point where it became human, there developed a struggle for dominance between man and the animals around him, and not the least important of man's adversaries in this struggle were the elephants or mammoths. As has been pointed out, it was a contest between a giant physique and a giant intellect. Yet there were other factors involved, to make the struggle between man and the elephants of particular interest in retrospect. It was not only a struggle involving a maximum of body size against a maximum of brain development, but also one of intellect against intellect. The elephants are and always have been remarkably intelligent mammals, and even though their intelligence was no match for the cunning and the reasoning powers of primitive man, still it was sufficiently advanced to make the struggle between these two adversaries all the more intense.

Not only that, but there was a struggle in manipulation. Man had his two hands, which were not necessary for locomotion and therefore could be used for skillfully manipulating objects to his own uses. On the other side of the picture, the elephant had his trunk, an organ of almost unbelievable mobility, strength, and tactile delicacy, with which he could manipulate objects, likewise without regard for the necessities of locomotion. Yet the higher intelligence won, because it could fashion tools as an aid to the handling of objects, while the lesser intellect could use its power of manipulation only for direct contact with things—the tearing down of trees and bushes or the pulling up of roots.

Again, man, having fashioned tools or weapons with his hands, could use them to increase his effective strength. As compared with this, the elephants, particularly some of the extinct mammoths, had strong, efficient tusks that served not only as weapons but also as tools for digging and prying. Here again the higher intellect won out—tools in hands directed by a logically reasoning brain were more effective than powerful tusks, directed even in the most intelligent fashion by a brain of lesser abilities.

Man has been a gregarious animal throughout his history. Elephants, too, are and have been gregarious.

But because of his superior intelligence, man has been able to use his gregariousness to much better advantage than the mammoths and their kin; for he, even in his most primitive stages, had devised methods of cooperation and a division of labor far beyond anything attained by other mammals.

Two other traits may be cited whereby these contending animals have paralleled each other. Both man and the elephants are slow breeders, and both are long-lived.

To the early men of Eurasia and Africa, the ubiquitous and powerful mammoths must have been formidable adversaries in a difficult and constant struggle for existence. Not that the mammoths were particularly inclined to bother their early human contemporaries, because to such great beasts, mere man, lacking powerful weapons of offense and defense, must have been on the whole hardly worthy of much attention. And the mammoths, like the modern elephants, were undoubtedly peaceful and tractable animals when let alone. Yet we know the helplessness of modern African natives, lacking modern weapons, against a herd of elephants that decides to "take over" their village and to raid their gardens. There is just nothing much to be done by these men against a group of wandering elephants, and such must have been the situation for Stone Age men. The mammoths went where they pleased, and the men adapted their activities accordingly.

Naturally, the large carnivores, the lions and panthers and bears, were a more active and constant threat to the well-being of Stone Age man than were the peaceable mammoths. One had only to stay away from the mammoths to be safe from them. But it must have been bitter medicine at times to the primitive hunter, to see these uncouth beasts wallow in the best fishing streams, or tear apart some selected trees of wild fruit. Every dead mammoth was one less mammoth, and a dead mammoth, moreover, would provide food for an entire village.

Consequently, at a fairly early stage in his social

evolution, man became an elephant hunter. The first elephant hunts undoubtedly were accidental, as when a mammoth was by chance discovered mired in a bog or disabled in some other way, so that it could be finished off by the use of spears and stones. But with the increase of his intellect, man sooner or later began to devise traps or pitfalls whereby the mammoths could be put out of action at a time and place advantageous to the primitive hunter.

The mammoths spread throughout the extent of their range at the beginnings of the Ice Age, but man, during the greater part of his evolutionary history, was confined to the Old World. Consequently it was in Europe, Asia, and Africa that man "grew up" with the mammoths, and wherever we find the remains of primitive man in the Old World, we usually find those of some of the mammoths.

The earliest humans of Eurasia were associated with the ancestral mammoth, *Elephas planifrons,* but as man evolved during the Pleistocene he became well acquainted with all of the various mammoths of the Old World. Of these, it was the woolly mammoth, *Elephas primigenius,* of which we have the greatest amount of evidence as to association with man, because the woolly mammoth was unusually abundant during the later phases of the Pleistocene, when man had progressed to such a stage that he was something of an artist. Therefore we know quite a lot as to the appearance of the woolly mammoth in life, from numerous drawings and carvings made by cavemen artists. And there are indications—one case in particular in Moravia—of ancient elephant hunts, where Paleolithic man had pursued, trapped, and killed numbers of woolly mammoths.

Here Dr. Carl Absolon of the University of Prague discovered, some fifteen years ago, a large accumulation of mammoth bones, with numerous indications that these were the remains of animals trapped and killed by primitive men. The conclusions of this authority as to the method of hunting are expressed in the following words.

"There cannot be the least doubt that the hunters did

not attack these powerful animals face to face, but caught them by cunning, enticing or driving them into large pitfalls. . . . Mammoths trapped and caught were killed by large stones, trimmed to serve such a purpose. I have found one such stone, trimmed like a big pear, or bomb, one meter long, and weighing over 120 pounds. These stones might have been suspended in strong leather straps and thus let down on the animals by the united efforts of several men, in the same way that navvies drive piles into riverbeds by means of rams."

Some of our most accurate knowledge of the woolly mammoth comes from direct evidence. During many centuries the tusks of woolly mammoths have been excavated in Siberian Russia in enormous numbers and the ivory exported for commercial use. Occasionally frozen carcasses of woolly mammoths have been found in various stages of preservation. All of which means, of course, that the woolly mammoth has been extinct for no very great period of time, either from the standpoint of geology or from that of human prehistory.

Of the various woolly mammoth cadavers thus discovered, perhaps the most completely preserved and best known is the Beresovka mammoth, found in Siberia in 1900 and excavated by an expedition from the Russian Academy of Sciences. This animal was partially buried in a pit, the result of its having fallen into a natural trap or having become mired in soft ground. The front legs were still raised as they had been at the time of the animal's death—indicative of the vain struggles made by this mammoth in an effort to free itself. The flesh was remarkably fresh—so much so that it was eagerly devoured by the explorers' sledge dogs, although it was not sufficiently palatable to be eaten by humans, despite many popular legends and newspaper accounts of banquets at which "mammoth steaks" were served to ghoulish scientists. The trunk of this mammoth was well preserved, as were many of the internal organs and some of the blood, while a greater part of the skin was intact. The coat consisted of a dense, woolly underfur and a coarse hairy outer covering of a reddish-brown color.

And it is evident, from a study of this animal, that the woolly mammoths grazed upon tundra grasses and the leaves of willows and coniferous trees in the northern arctic forests.

Man did not cross the Arctic bridge from Siberia to Alaska until a geological yesterday. Perhaps it was as much as 20,000 or 30,000 years ago that certain Mongoloid peoples first pushed to the northeast and entered a new world—a date seeming remote to us but representing actually a very late stage in the prehistory of humans, a stage when polished stone implements were in use, and when the bow and arrow probably had been invented and the dog domesticated.

The first human migrants to the New World found a fauna that would seem strange to us in many respects. Among the most numerous of the animals roaming the plains and forests of North America at that time were the three American mammoths, which had arrived on this continent many hundreds of thousands of years before their human followers. These, the Columbian mammoth in middle North America, the imperial mammoth to the south, and the woolly mammoth to the north (together with the American mastodon, a distant proboscidean cousin which had an origin and history quite separate from that of the mammoths), must have dominated the landscape in all sections of man's newfound home. That the first men in America knew the mammoth is becoming increasingly evident from discoveries of recent years. In the north, man was associated with the woolly mammoth and the mastodon, farther to the south with the Columbian mammoth and the giant imperial mammoth. Here, as in the Old World, man was an elephant hunter. At least it would seem so, to judge from the numerous spearheads found in association with mammoth remains, especially in some of the southwestern states.

This was the picture near the end of Pleistocene times—elephants and men living side by side, contending with each other, and together dominating the scene throughout the length and breadth of the Old World and in the northern half of the New World. Then, at the end of the Ice Age, when the last of the great continental glaciers was retreating to its present arctic limits, there was a relatively sudden and widespread extinction of mammoths throughout the world. The woolly mammoth disappeared from northern Europe, Asia, and North America, as did the more southerly types in these continents. In the western hemisphere the mastodons, too, became extinct. Only two types of proboscideans survived the transition from Pleistocene into recent times, the Indian elephant of the Orient and the African elephant of the Ethiopian region.

What was the reason for the wiping out of the mammoths? Why should these huge and seemingly successful animals suddenly disappear from a scene which they had so long dominated? Was man concerned with their extinction? It hardly seems probable, for even though at this late date he was a clever and an efficient hunter, he was still rather scattered—certainly not a numerous member of the faunas to which he belonged. Therefore, it is difficult to see how primitive hunters might have prevailed against the mammoths to such an extent as to cause their sudden and almost complete destruction.

The answer to this question may always remain a secret. Something caused the disappearance of most of the elephants from a great part of the earth's surface. The dominance of size and strength came to a sudden end. The dominance of intellect, which had been slowly developing through the millennia, became even more firmly fixed than before, once the giant mammoths had largely disappeared, and when the intellect became established as the most important factor in evolution, it developed at an increasingly rapid rate. Now its dominance is virtually complete throughout the world, with results that are at the same time happy and tragic.

Pleistocene Overkill

❖❖❖❖❖❖

PAUL S. MARTIN

[1967]

About 10,000 years ago, as glaciers retreated into Canada and as man moved southward at the end of the last Ice Age, North America suddenly and strangely lost most of its large animals. Native North American mammals exceeding 100 pounds in adult body weight were reduced by roughly 70 percent. The casualty list includes mammoths, mastodon, many species of horses and camels, four genera of ground sloths, two of peccary, shrub oxen, antelope, two genera of saber-toothed cats, the dire wolf, the giant beaver, tapirs, and others totaling over 100 species. Despite this fantastic loss of large animals during the Pleistocene, the most recent geologic epoch, the fossil record shows no loss of small vertebrates, plants, aquatic organisms, or marine life.

One need not be a Pleistocene geologist to ask the obvious question: What happened? To date there is no obvious answer, certainly not one acceptable to any consensus of scientists interested in the mystery. The question of just what occurred to bring about this unprecedented extinction continues to provoke a storm of controversy.

Extinction, we know, is not an abnormal fate in the life of a species. When all the niches, or "jobs," in a biotic community are filled, extinction must occur as rapidly as the evolution of new species. The fossil record of the last 10 million years bears witness to this fact, for it is replete with extinct animals that were sacrificed to make room for new and presumably superior species.

189

But this is a normal state of affairs from a paleontologist's point of view.

However, the extinction that took place at the end of the Pleistocene did not comply with biological rules of survival. Unlike former extinctions, such as occurred in the Miocene, Pliocene, and Early Pleistocene, Late Pleistocene extinction of large mammals far exceeded replacement by new species that could easily have been accommodated by the prevailing habitat. The complete removal of North American horses, for example, represents the loss of a lineage of grass-eaters, without the loss of the grass. It left the horse niche empty for at least 8,000 years, until the Spaniards introduced Old World horses and burros. Some of these then escaped to reoccupy part of their prehistoric range. Today, tens of thousands of wild horses and burros still live along remote parts of the Colorado River and in the wild lands of the West. Certainly nothing happened at the end of the Pleistocene to destroy horse habitat. What, then, caused these animals, not to mention mammoths, camels, sloths, and others, to become extinct?

Like the horses, camels first evolved in North America many millions of years ago. They then spread into South America and crossed to the Old World by means of the Bering bridge. Crossing in the opposite direction were elephants, which soon prospered in the New World, judging by the abundance of mammoth and mastodon teeth in Pleistocene outcrops. From their evolutionary center in South America came a variety of edentates, including ground sloths and glyptodonts, the former spreading north to Alaska. But by the end of the Pleistocene, the majority of these herbivorous species had completely disappeared. Only relatively small species within these groups survived—the alpaca and llama among the camels of South America, and the relatively small edentates such as anteaters, armadillos, and tree sloths.

There was no obvious ecological substitution by other large herbivores competing for the same resources. Too many large mammals were lost, too few were replaced, and there was too little change among smaller plants and animals to accept this extinction as a normal event in the process of North American mammalian evolution.

One hypothesis commonly proposed for the abrupt and almost simultaneous extinction of large mammals is that of sudden climatic change. We know that climates did change many times in the Pleistocene—a 3-million-year period of repeated glacial advance and retreat—so perhaps the great herds were decimated in this way. A sizable group of vertebrate paleontologists believe that that is indeed what happened. They maintain that with the retreat of the glaciers the early post-glacial climate grew more continental—summers became hotter and winters colder and supposedly more severe than they had been during the time of the ice advance. The result was an upset in the breeding season, a lethal cold sterility imposed on species of large mammals adapted for reproduction at what came to be the wrong season. Perhaps also the large Ice Age mammals were confronted for the first time with excessive snow cover and blue northers, which even today can kill thousands of cattle and sheep in the High Plains. Paleozoologist John Guilday at the Carnegie Museum believes that accelerated competition occurred among the large mammals before they could readjust to the change in vegetation and climate. They proceeded to exterminate their food supply and themselves in a morbid togetherness. Then, according to Guilday, the early North American hunters who arrived over the Bering bridge delivered the coup de grâce to the few remaining large mammals after the great herds were already sadly depleted.

But we have no evidence that the large mammals were under competitive stress, then or at any other time in the Pleistocene. We know that they had witnessed, and certainly survived, the advance and retreat of earlier glacial ice sheets. And among today's large mammals most are remarkably tolerant of different types of environments. Some large desert mammals can endure months without drinking; others, such as musk ox, live the year round in the high Arctic. Reindeer and wildebeest migrate hundreds of miles to pick their pasture. Why should we believe that the great mammals of the Pleistocene were less adaptable?

Furthermore, while climatic changes had some effect upon existing fauna and its habitat, extinction apparently occurred when range conditions were actually improving for many species. From the fossil pollen record we know that mastodon and woodland musk ox of eastern North America occupied spruce forests 10,000 to 12,000 years ago, a habitat then rapidly expanding northward from its constricted position bordering the Wisconsin ice sheet. And the western plains grassland was extensive and spreading at the time of the extinction of grazing horses, mammoths, and antelopes.

Another objection to cold winter climates as an explanation for extinction arises when one looks to the American tropics. There, far more species became extinct during this period than in the temperate regions. More extinct Pleistocene genera were found in a single fauna in Bolivia than are known in the richest of the fossil faunas of the United States. However, the tropics never experienced the zero temperatures of North America. This being the case, the climatic change hypothesis cannot account for the large-scale extinction in that part of the world.

Nor can it account for the extinction that occurred on the large islands of the world, such as on Madagascar and New Zealand, which did not take place until less than a thousand years ago. In the case of the giant bird, *Aepyornis,* of Madagascar, and the giant moa from New Zealand, carbon-14 dates indicate that these birds did not perish until long after the time of major worldwide climatic upset.

Without doubt, the climatic disturbances that affected North America during the Pleistocene proved equally disturbing in New Zealand. During the last glaciation one-third of the South Island was ice-covered and the remainder of the island was much colder than today. The subsequent melting of the glaciers brought a worldwide rise in sea level and divided the country in two. During

the postglacial period intense volcanic eruptions blan-
keted the North Island, so that by 2,000 years ago large
parts of it were covered by sterile ash supporting only
dwarfed vegetation. In fact, sheep raising failed in these
areas until cobalt and other trace elements were added
to the pastures. Yet, some twenty-seven species of moas
apparently survived the natural climatic catastrophes of
the Pleistocene and disappeared only after East Polynesian invaders, the predecessors of the Maori, arrived
sometime about or before A.D. 900. Thus, any credibility
the climatic-change hypothesis may have when applied
to a single region vanishes when the global pattern is
considered. Pleistocene experts generally believe that
whatever their magnitude, major climatic changes of the
last 50,000 years occurred at approximately the same
time throughout the world—the extinctions did not.

My own hypothesis is that man, and man alone, was
responsible for the unique wave of Late Pleistocene
extinction—a case of overkill rather than "overchill" as
implied by the climatic-change theory. This view is
neither new nor widely held, but when examined on a
global basis, in which Africa, North America, Australia,
Eurasia, and the islands of the world are considered, the
pattern and timing of large-scale extinction corresponds
to only one event—the arrival of prehistoric hunters.

Some anthropologists, such as Loren Eiseley of the
University of Pennsylvania, have challenged the man-
caused extinction theory on the grounds that African
megafauna did not suffer the same fate as the large
mammals of North America. At first, this appears to
be a sound argument since that continent now contains
some forty genera of large mammals that were around
during the Pleistocene. Africa's fabulous plains fauna
has long been regarded as a picture of what the American Pleistocene was like prior to extinction, at least in
terms of size and diversity of the big mammals. During
the million years of hominid evolution in Africa, it seems
as if man and his predecessors would have had ample
time to exterminate its fauna. And if, as I believe, Late
Paleolithic hunters in the New World could have suc-

ceeded in destroying more than 100 species of large mammals in a period of only 1,000 years, then African hunters, it seems, should at least have made a dent on that continent's mammals.

It turns out that they did, for today's living megafauna in Africa represents only about 70 percent of the species that were present during the Late Pleistocene. Thus, while the proportion of African mammals that perished during the Pleistocene was less than that in North America, the loss in number of species was still considerable. In addition to the large mammals that now inhabit the African continent, an imaginary Pleistocene game park would have been stocked with such species as the antlered giraffe, a number of giant pigs, the stylohipparion horse, a great long-horned buffalo, a giant sheep, and an ostrich of larger size than is known at present. In Africa, as in America, the wave of Pleistocene extinction took only the large animals.

The African extinction has also been attributed to climatic and climate-related change. L. S. B. Leakey would explain extinction of the giant African fauna as the result of drought. If so, the drought strangely did not affect nearby Madagascar. On that island, barely 250 miles from the African shore, extinction of giant lemurs, pygmy hippopotamuses, giant birds, and tortoises did not occur until a much later date, in fact not until within the last 1,000 years.

African big game extinction appears to coincide in time with the first record of fire, or at least of charcoal, in archaeological sites. In addition, most extinct fauna is last found in many locations associated with the distinctive stone tools of Early Stone Age (Acheulean) hunters. If fire was used in hunting, man-caused extinction becomes easier to understand, because fire drives necessarily involved large amounts of waste—whole herds must be decimated in order to kill the few animals sought for food. Perhaps fire became a major weapon in the hands of the Acheulean big-game hunters, enabling them to encircle whole herds of animals.

In any event, African extinction ended during the

period of the Early Stone Age hunters. This fact raises the possibility that the cultures that succeeded the Acheulean developed more selective methods of hunting and may even have learned to harvest the surviving large mammals on a sustained yield basis. Even during the last hundred years, when modern weapons have reduced the ranges of many species, there has been no loss of whole genera of terrestrial mammals, as occurred during the time of the early hunters.

The case of Australia also supports the hypothesis of man-caused extinction. On that continent, no evidence of extinction without replacement by other species can be found until after men had inhabited the island, at least 14,000 years ago. About this time, various species of large marsupials perished, including the rhino-sized *Diprotodon* and the giant kangaroo.

About 12,000 years ago, when the Paleo-Indians swept into North America across the Bering bridge, through unglaciated Alaska, and down the melting ice corridor east of the Cordilleras, we can be confident that they were old hands at hunting woolly mammoths and other large Eurasian mammals. In contrast, the New World mammoth and other species of big game had never encountered man and were unprepared for escaping the strange two-legged creature who used fire and stone-tipped spears to hunt them in communal bands. Probably the New World fauna of the time was no more suspicious of man than are the fearless animals that now live in the Galápagos and other regions uninhabited by men. In any case, radiocarbon dates indicate that North American extinction followed very closely on the heels of the big game hunters. The Paleo-Indians easily found and hunted the gregarious species that ranged over the grasslands, deserts, or other exposed habitat. As the hunters increased in number and spread throughout the continent, large animals whose low rate of reproduction was insufficient to offset the sudden burden of supporting a "superpredator" soon perished.

Early man may not have been able to avoid killing the herd animals in excess. To capture *any* members of a bison or elephant herd, it was necessary to kill them all—for instance, by driving them over a cliff. Even when big game became scarce and small animals became more important in the human diet, the pride and prestige associated with killing an elephant may have continued. This, in fact, seems likely, judging from the prestige associated with the unnecessary killing that persists even today within our own society. By virtue of his cultural development, man became a superpredator, less susceptible to the biological checks and balances that apparently prevent such predators as arctic foxes from annihilating their prey, the arctic hare.

If the overkill hypothesis is valid, how did *any* large mammals manage to survive? There are several explanations. Some species, such as tapirs, capybaras, deer, white-lipped peccaries, anteaters, and tree sloths, took refuge in the vast forests of tropical America. In temperate regions, solitary moose and bear also found refuge in wooded areas, perhaps with a few small herds of woodland bison, at the time when soon-to-be-extinct species of giant bison were being annihilated by Folsom hunters on the plains. Mountain sheep found protection on the roughest desert ranges while mountain goats escaped only in the northern Rockies.

The musk ox, that conspicuous and easily hunted game animal of the open tundra, was wiped out in Eurasia, but in America it escaped through a piece of paleogeographic good luck. Since parts of the Canadian Arctic Archipelago and Greenland were untouched by glaciation, tundra habitat was available through the Pleistocene for this species and for barren-ground caribou. Some of these animals remained in the "safe region" north of the continental ice sheet, a zone unknown to the early hunters. They thus escaped the fate suffered by most species located along the path taken by nomadic hunters as they pushed into Alaska, down western Canada, across the northern United States, and into New England. The Keewatin and Laurentian ice sheets provided a barrier to the early hunters, whose distinctive spear points and other artifacts are unknown in the eastern Canadian Arctic. With the final melting of ice, less than 6,000 years ago, the Greenland musk oxen were at last exposed to the New World Indians and Eskimos. But the wandering superpredators—the Paleo-Indians—were no longer present. The Eskimo had the good fortune, or good sense, to harvest musk oxen on a sustained yield basis, and the species was able to spread westward through northern Canada, ultimately recovering part of its Alaskan range. If the woolly mammoth had also occupied the Greenland refuge, it too might have survived the Pleistocene.

Can the overkill hypothesis be disproved by future experiments or discoveries? To discount the hypothesis one need simply identify a major wave of extinction anywhere in the world in the Late Pleistocene prior to man's arrival. To date, such evidence has not been found. Quite the opposite, in fact, since the chronological sequence of extinction follows closely upon man's footsteps—occurring first in Africa and southern Asia, next in Australia, then through northern Eurasia and into North and South America, much later in the West Indies, and finally, during the last 1,000 years, in Madagascar and New Zealand. The pattern shows that Late Pleistocene extinction did not occur in all locations at the same time, as it would have if there had been a sudden climatic change or perhaps a cataclysmic destruction of the earth's atmosphere with lethal radiation caused by cosmic ray bombardment, another common hypothesis. Since no synchronous destruction of plants or of plant communities is known, the long-held belief that climatic change caused extinction lacks credibility.

I do not pretend that the overkill hypothesis explains how, why, or even how many early hunters were involved. It seems reasonable to assume that fire and fire drives were a major weapon; possibly plant poisons were used in the tropics. To the objection that too few spear points or other Stone Age artifacts have been found in the Americas to prove that there was a sizable prehistoric human population, one may assert, tongue in cheek, that too few fossils of Pleistocene ground sloths, mammoths, camels, and saber-toothed cats have been found to prove there was a sizable prehistoric population of them either. The obvious difficulty with the "spear point" argument is that even the best fossil localities, with or without artifacts, do not yield data that can be reliably converted into population estimates. The case for overkill is best presented as a "least improbable hypothesis," and is not based on extensive knowledge of how prehistoric hunters may have carried out their hunting. Nor is there much hope that we will ever learn more of their techniques than the little we now know. The essence of the argument is based upon the simple matter of Late Pleistocene chronology. In no part of the world does massive unbalanced faunal extinction occur without man the hunter on the scene.

To certain comfortable concepts about pristine wilderness and ancient man, the implications of this hypothesis are startling, even revolutionary. For example, that business of the noble savage, a child of nature, living in an unspoiled Garden of Eden until the "discovery" of the New World by Europeans is apparently untrue, since the destruction of fauna, if not of habitat, was far greater before Columbus than at any time since. The subtle lesson of sustained yields, of not killing the goose that lays the golden eggs, may have been learned the hard way, and forgotten, many times before the twentieth century.

A related conceptual mistake, if the hypothesis holds, may be the long-held opposition of range ecologists to the introduction of exotic large mammals in America. Part of the opposition to the introduction of alien species is based on the idea that native North American mammals are already using all the available browsing and grazing space that could or should be occupied in this country. But remembering the numerous species of the Pleistocene, it is difficult to imagine that native mountain sheep, bison antelope, deer, and elk occupy all available niches in the American ecosystem. The concept of game ranching, of keeping both cattle and native game species on the same range in order to make maximum use of pastures, is catching on in Africa. Since our own ranch industry is essentially a monoculture of either cattle or sheep, perhaps it is time to take a fresh look at the unfilled niches on the American ranges. Domestic livestock, wild game, and the range itself may well benefit from a greater diversity of fauna and a partial restoration of the complex ecosystem that was America for millions of years, until man arrived.

PART THREE

On Natives and Naïveté

Anthropologists are a special breed. While other scientists usually go into the field in well-equipped and well-peopled expeditions, anthropologists often venture alone (or occasionally with spouse) into the most remote areas of the earth. They deliberately try to be unobtrusive, to avoid upsetting the delicate workings of the primitive societies they study. A year or more later they emerge from the jungle, the mountains, the desert, with their data: notebooks filled with myths, kinship ties, food consumption; and numerous photographs, mostly poorly exposed or blurred.

The consistently poor photographs are, I have concluded, a symptom of the conditions in which anthropologists work. Few cameras can long survive the dirt, dust, and sand, the humidity and rain, the bumps and dunkings of primitive means of travel. Actually many anthropologists also have difficulty surviving, although the human machine has amazing powers of recovery. (Margaret Mead casually refers to a case of malaria as hampering her fieldwork forty-five years ago, yet now, in her seventies, she keeps a travel, speaking, writing, and meeting schedule that would exhaust most people.) Despite immunizing shots and missionary medical handbooks, internal parasites and dysentery from exotic bacteria make fieldwork a physical trial for many anthropologists.

But I think the mental trials are the hardest of all. Alone in a strange culture, uncertain with the language, questioning the purpose of their activities, of their own lives, anthropologists can undergo great and varied sufferings. Some give up, others go native. Those who return with their data learn something, but how much insight can a person gain in a year or two about a culture that took thousands of years to develop? (Those that return for a second or third stint do better; at least their photographs tend to get better.) Most of all, the anthropologist in the field seems to learn about himself, and, by extension, about all humanity.

The articles that follow reveal this process: Laura Bohannan learns a disturbing interpretation of Shakespeare; Richard Lee discovers the meaning of humility, to the bushmen and to himself; Colin Turnbull questions the deepest values of human society. One article is, for *Natural History* Magazine and possibly for anthropology, the beginning of a trend: Writer N. Scott Momaday conveys, as an Indian, the meaning of the Indian dance revival. As barriers to foreign research increase, more and more of the spokesmen for other cultures probably will be natives, and American anthropologists will turn to their own culture for insights.

Shakespeare in the Bush

❖❖❖❖❖❖

LAURA BOHANNAN

[1966]

Just before I left Oxford for the Tiv in West Africa, conversation turned to the season at Stratford. "You Americans," said a friend, "often have difficulty with Shakespeare. He was, after all, a very English poet, and one can easily misinterpret the universal by misunderstanding the particular."

I protested that human nature is pretty much the same the whole world over; at least the general plot and motivation of the greater tragedies would always be clear —everywhere—although some details of custom might have to be explained and difficulties of translation might produce other slight changes. To end an argument we could not conclude, my friend gave me a copy of *Hamlet* to study in the African bush: it would, he hoped, lift my mind above its primitive surroundings, and possibly I might, by prolonged meditation, achieve the grace of correct interpretation.

It was my second field trip to that African tribe, and I thought myself ready to live in one of its remote sections—an area difficult to cross even on foot. I eventually settled on the hillock of a very knowledgeable old man, the head of a homestead of some hundred and forty people, all of whom were either his close relatives or their wives and children. Like the other elders of the vicinity, the old man spent most of his time performing ceremonies seldom seen these days in the more accessible parts of the tribe. I was delighted. Soon there would be three months of enforced isolation and leisure, between the harvest that takes place just before the rising of the swamps and the clearing of new farms when the water goes down. Then, I thought, they would have even more time to perform ceremonies and explain them to me.

I was quite mistaken. Most of the ceremonies demanded the presence of elders from several homesteads. As the swamps rose, the old men found it too difficult to walk from one homestead to the next, and the ceremonies gradually ceased. As the swamps rose even higher, all activities but one came to an end. The women brewed beer from maize and millet. Men, women, and children sat on their hillocks and drank it.

People began to drink at dawn. By midmorning the whole homestead was singing, dancing, and drumming. When it rained, people had to sit inside their huts: there they drank and sang or they drank and told stories. In any case, by noon or before, I either had to join the party or retire to my own hut and my books. "One does not discuss serious matters when there is beer. Come, drink with us." Since I lacked their capacity for the thick native beer, I spent more and more time with *Hamlet*. Before the end of the second month, grace descended on me. I was quite sure that *Hamlet* had only one possible interpretation, and that one universally obvious.

Early every morning, in the hope of having some serious talk before the beer party, I used to call on the old man at his reception hut—a circle of posts supporting a thatched roof above a low mud wall to keep out wind and rain. One day I crawled through the low doorway and found most of the men of the homestead sitting huddled in their ragged cloths on stools, low plank beds, and reclining chairs, warming themselves against the chill of the rain around a smoky fire. In the center were three pots of beer. The party had started.

The old man greeted me cordially. "Sit down and drink." I accepted a large calabash full of beer, poured some into a small drinking gourd, and tossed it down. Then I poured some more into the same gourd for the man second in seniority to my host before I handed my calabash over to a young man for further distribution. Important people shouldn't ladle beer themselves.

"It is better like this," the old man said, looking at me approvingly and plucking at the thatch that had caught in my hair. "You should sit and drink with us more often. Your servants tell me that when you are not with us, you sit inside your hut looking at a paper."

The old man was acquainted with four kinds of "papers": tax receipts, bride price receipts, court fee receipts, and letters. The messenger who brought him letters from the chief used them mainly as a badge of office, for he always knew what was in them and told the old man. Personal letters for the few who had relatives in the government or mission stations were kept until someone went to a large market where there was a letter writer and reader. Since my arrival, letters were brought to me to be read. A few men also brought me bride price receipts, privately, with requests to change the figures to a higher sum. I found moral arguments were of no avail, since in-laws are fair game, and the technical hazards of forgery difficult to explain to an illiterate people. I did not wish them to think me silly enough to look at any such papers for days on end, and I hastily explained that my "paper" was one of the "things of long ago" of my country.

"Ah," said the old man. "Tell us."

I protested that I was not a storyteller. Storytelling is a skilled art among them; their standards are high, and the audiences critical—and vocal in their criticism. I protested in vain. This morning they wanted to hear a story while they drank. They threatened to tell me no more stories until I told them one of mine. Finally, the old man promised that no one would criticize my style "for we know you are struggling with our language." "But," put in one of the elders, "you must explain what we do not understand, as we do when we tell you our stories." Realizing that here was my chance to prove *Hamlet* universally intelligible, I agreed.

The old man handed me some more beer to help me on with my storytelling. Men filled their long wooden pipes and knocked coals from the fire to place in the pipe bowls; then, puffing contentedly,, they sat back to listen. I began in the proper style, "Not yesterday, not yesterday, but long ago, a thing occurred. One night three men were keeping watch outside the homestead of the great chief, when suddenly they saw the former chief approach them."

"Why was he no longer their chief?"

"He was dead," I explained. "That is why they were troubled and afraid when they saw him."

"Impossible," began one of the elders, handing his pipe on to his neighbor, who interrupted, "Of course it wasn't the dead chief. It was an omen sent by a witch. Go on."

Slightly shaken, I continued. "One of these three was a man who knew things"—the closest translation for scholar, but unfortunately it also meant witch. The second elder looked triumphantly at the first. "So he spoke to the dead chief saying, 'Tell us what we must do so you may rest in your grave,' but the dead chief did not answer. He vanished, and they could see him no more. Then the man who knew things—his name was Horatio—said this event was the affair of the dead chief's son, Hamlet."

There was a general shaking of heads round the circle. "Had the dead chief no living brothers? Or was this son the chief?"

"No," I replied. "That is, he had one living brother who became the chief when the elder brother died."

The old men muttered: such omens were matters for chiefs and elders, not for youngsters; no good could come of going behind a chief's back; clearly Horatio was not a man who knew things.

"Yes, he was," I insisted, shooing a chicken away from my beer. "In our country the son is next to the father. The dead chief's younger brother had become the great chief. He had also married his elder brother's widow only about a month after the funeral."

"He did well," the old man beamed and announced to the others, "I told you that if we knew more about

Europeans, we would find they really were very like us. In our country also," he added to me, "the younger brother marries the elder brother's widow and becomes the father of his children. Now, if your uncle, who married your widowed mother, is your father's full brother, then he will be a real father to you. Did Hamlet's father and uncle have one mother?"

His question barely penetrated my mind; I was too upset and thrown too far off-balance by having one of the most important elements of *Hamlet* knocked straight out of the picture. Rather uncertainly I said that I thought they had the same mother, but I wasn't sure—the story didn't say. The old man told me severely that these genealogical details made all the difference and that when I got home I must ask the elders about it. He shouted out the door to one of his younger wives to bring his goatskin bag.

Determined to save what I could of the mother motif, I took a deep breath and began again. "The son Hamlet was very sad because his mother had married again so quickly. There was no need for her to do so, and it is our custom for a widow not to go to her next husband until she has mourned for two years."

"Two years is too long," objected the wife, who had appeared with the old man's battered goatskin bag. "Who will hoe your farms for you while you have no husband?"

"Hamlet," I retorted without thinking, "was old enough to hoe his mother's farms himself. There was no need for her to remarry." No one looked convinced. I gave up. "His mother and the great chief told Hamlet not to be sad, for the great chief himself would be a father to Hamlet. Furthermore, Hamlet would be the next chief; therefore he must stay to learn the things of a chief. Hamlet agreed to remain, and all the rest went off to drink beer."

While I paused, perplexed at how to render Hamlet's disgusted soliloquy to an audience convinced that Claudius and Gertrude had behaved in the best possible manner, one of the younger men asked me who had married the other wives of the dead chief.

"He had no other wives," I told him.

"But a chief must have many wives! How else can he brew beer and prepare food for all his guests?"

I said firmly that in our country even chiefs had only one wife, that they had servants to do their work, and that they paid them from tax money.

It was better, they returned, for a chief to have many wives and sons who would help him hoe his farms and feed his people; then everyone loved the chief who gave much and took nothing—taxes were a bad thing.

I agreed with the last comment but for the rest fell back on their favorite way of fobbing off my questions: "That is the way it is done, so that is how we do it."

I decided to skip the soliloquy. Even if Claudius was here thought quite right to marry his brother's widow, there remained the poison motif, and I knew they would disapprove of fratricide. More hopefully I resumed, "That night Hamlet kept watch with the three who had seen his dead father. The dead chief again appeared, and although the others were afraid, Hamlet followed his dead father off to one side. When they were alone, Hamlet's dead father spoke."

"Omens can't talk!" The old man was emphatic.

"Hamlet's dead father wasn't an omen. Seeing him might have been an omen, but he was not." My audience looked as confused as I sounded. "It *was* Hamlet's dead father. It was a thing we call a 'ghost.' " I had to use the English word, for unlike many of the neighboring tribes, these people didn't believe in the survival after death of any individuating part of the personality.

"What is a 'ghost'? An omen?"

"No, a 'ghost' is someone who is dead but who walks around and can talk, and people can hear him and see him but not touch him."

They objected. "One can touch zombis."

"No, no! It was not a dead body the witches had animated to sacrifice and eat. No one else made Hamlet's dead father walk. He did it himself."

"Dead men can't walk," protested my audience as one man.

I was quite willing to compromise. "A 'ghost' is the dead man's shadow."

But again they objected. "Dead men cast no shadows."

"They do in my country," I snapped.

The old man quelled the babble of disbelief that arose immediately and told me with that insincere, but courteous, agreement one extends to the fancies of the young, ignorant, and superstitious, "No doubt in your country the dead can also walk without being zombis." From the depths of his bag he produced a withered fragment of kola nut, bit off one end to show it wasn't poisoned, and handed me the rest as a peace offering.

"Anyhow," I resumed, "Hamlet's dead father said that his own brother, the one who became chief, had poisoned him. He wanted Hamlet to avenge him. Hamlet believed this in his heart, for he did not like his father's brother." I took another swallow of beer. "In the country of the great chief, living in the same homestead, for it was a very large one, was an important elder who was often with the chief to advise and help him. His name was Polonius. Hamlet was courting his daughter, but her father and her brother . . . [I cast hastily about for some tribal analogy] warned her not to let Hamlet visit her when she was alone on her farm, for he would be a great chief and so could not marry her."

"Why not?" asked the wife, who had settled down on the edge of the old man's chair. He frowned at her for asking stupid questions and growled, "They lived in the same homestead."

"That was not the reason," I informed them. "Polonius was a stranger who lived in the homestead because he helped the chief, not because he was a relative."

"Then why couldn't Hamlet marry her?"

"He could have," I explained, "but Polonius didn't think he would. After all, Hamlet was a man of great importance who ought to marry a chief's daughter, for in his country a man could have only one wife. Polonius was afraid that if Hamlet made love to his daughter, then no one else would give a high price for her."

"That might be true," remarked one of the shrewder elders, "but a chief's son would give his mistress's father enough presents and patronage to more than make up the difference. Polonius sounds like a fool to me."

"Many people think he was," I agreed. "Meanwhile Polonius sent his son Laertes off to Paris to learn the things of that country, for it was the homestead of a very great chief indeed. Because he was afraid that Laertes might waste a lot of money on beer and women and gambling, or get into trouble by fighting, he sent one of his servants to Paris secretly, to spy out what Laertes was doing. One day Hamlet came upon Polonius's daughter Ophelia. He behaved so oddly he frightened her. Indeed"—I was fumbling for words to express the dubious quality of Hamlet's madness—"the chief and many others had also noticed that when Hamlet talked one could understand the words but not what they meant. Many people thought that he had become mad." My audience suddenly became much more attentive. "The great chief wanted to know what was wrong with Hamlet, so he sent for two of Hamlet's age mates [school friends would have taken a long explanation] to talk to Hamlet and find out what troubled his heart. Hamlet, seeing that they had been bribed by the chief to betray him, told them nothing. Polonius, however, insisted that Hamlet was mad because he had been forbidden to see Ophelia, whom he loved."

"Why," inquired a bewildered voice, "should anyone bewitch Hamlet on that account?"

"Bewitch him?"

"Yes, only witchcraft can make anyone mad, unless, of course, one sees the beings that lurk in the forest."

I stopped being a storyteller, took out my notebook and demanded to be told more about these two causes of madness. Even while they spoke and I jotted notes, I tried to calculate the effect of this new factor on the plot. Hamlet had not been exposed to the beings that lurk in the forests. Only his relatives in the male line could bewitch him. Barring relatives not mentioned by Shakespeare, it had to be Claudius who was attempting to harm him. And, of course, it was.

For the moment I staved off questions by saying that the great chief also refused to believe that Hamlet was mad for the love of Ophelia and nothing else. "He was sure that something much more important was troubling Hamlet's heart."

"Now Hamlet's age mates," I continued, "had brought with them a famous storyteller. Hamlet decided to have this man tell the chief and all his homestead a story about a man who had poisoned his brother because he desired his brother's wife and wished to be chief himself. Hamlet was sure the great chief could not hear the story without making a sign if he was indeed guilty, and then he would discover whether his dead father had told him the truth."

The old man interrupted, with deep cunning, "Why should a father lie to his son?" he asked.

I hedged: "Hamlet wasn't sure that it really was his dead father." It was impossible to say anything, in that language, about devil-inspired visions.

"You mean," he said, "it actually was an omen, and he knew witches sometimes send false ones. Hamlet was a fool not to go to one skilled in reading omens and divining the truth in the first place. A man-who-sees-the-truth could have told him how his father died, if he really had been poisoned, and if there was witchcraft in it; then Hamlet could have called the elders to settle the matter."

The shrewd elder ventured to disagree. "Because his father's brother was a great chief, one-who-sees-the-truth might therefore have been afraid to tell it. I think it was for that reason that a friend of Hamlet's father—a witch and an elder—sent an omen so his friend's son would know. Was the omen true?"

"Yes," I said, abandoning ghosts and the devil; a

witch-sent omen it would have to be. "It was true, for when the storyteller was telling his tale before all the homestead, the great chief rose in fear. Afraid that Hamlet knew his secret he planned to have him killed."

The stage set of the next bit presented some difficulties of translation. I began cautiously. "The great chief told Hamlet's mother to find out from her son what he knew. But because a woman's children are always first in her heart, he had the important elder Polonius hide behind a cloth that hung against the wall of Hamlet's mother's sleeping hut. Hamlet started to scold his mother for what she had done."

There was a shocked murmur from everyone. A man should never scold his mother.

"She called out in fear, and Polonius moved behind the cloth. Shouting, 'A rat!' Hamlet took his machete and slashed through the cloth." I paused for dramatic effect. "He had killed Polonius!"

The old men looked at each other in supreme disgust. "That Polonius truly was a fool and a man who knew nothing! What child would not know enough to shout, 'It's me!' " With a pang, I remembered that these people are ardent hunters, always armed with bow, arrow, and machete; at the first rustle in the grass an arrow is aimed and ready, and the hunter shouts "Game!" If no human voice answers immediately, the arrow speeds on its way. Like a good hunter, Hamlet had shouted, "A rat!"

I rushed in to save Polonius's reputation. "Polonius did speak. Hamlet heard him. But he thought it was the chief and wished to kill him to avenge his father. He had meant to kill him earlier that evening. . . ." I broke down, unable to describe to these pagans, who had no belief in individual afterlife, the difference between dying at one's prayers and dying "unhousell'd, disappointed, unaneled."

This time I had shocked my audience seriously. "For a man to raise his hand against his father's brother and the one who has become his father—that is a terrible thing. The elders ought to let such a man be bewitched."

I nibbled at my kola nut in some perplexity, then pointed out that after all the man had killed Hamlet's father.

"No," pronounced the old man, speaking less to me than to the young men sitting behind the elders. "If your father's brother has killed your father, you must appeal to your father's age mates: *they* may avenge him. No man may use violence against his senior relatives." Another thought struck him. "But if his father's brother had indeed been wicked enough to bewitch Hamlet and make him mad that would be a good story indeed, for it would be his fault that Hamlet, being mad, no longer had any sense and thus was ready to kill his father's brother."

There was a murmur of applause. *Hamlet* was again a good story to them, but it no longer seemed quite the same story to me. As I thought over the coming complications of plot and motive, I lost courage and decided to skim over dangerous ground quickly.

"The great chief," I went on, "was not sorry that Hamlet had killed Polonius. It gave him a reason to send Hamlet away, with his two treacherous age mates, with letters to a chief of a far country, saying that Hamlet should be killed. But Hamlet changed the writing on their papers, so that the chief killed his age mates instead." I encountered a reproachful glare from one of the men whom I had told that undetectable forgery was not merely immoral but beyond human skill. I looked the other way.

"Before Hamlet could return, Laertes came back for his father's funeral. The great chief told him Hamlet had killed Polonius. Laertes swore to kill Hamlet because of this, and because his sister Ophelia, hearing her father had been killed by the man she loved, went mad and drowned in the river."

"Have you already forgotten what we told you?" The old man was reproachful. "One cannot take vengeance on a madman; Hamlet killed Polonius in his madness. As for the girl, she not only went mad, she was drowned. Only witches can make people drown. Water itself can't hurt anything. It is merely something one drinks and bathes in."

I began to get cross. "If you don't like the story, I'll stop."

The old man made soothing noises and himself poured me some more beer. "You tell the story well, and we are listening. But it is clear that the elders of your country have never told you what the story really means. No, don't interrupt! We believe you when you say your marriage customs are different, or your clothes and weapons. But people are the same everywhere; therefore, there are always witches and it is we, the elders, who know how witches work. We told you it was the great chief who wished to kill Hamlet, and now your own words have proved us right. Who were Ophelia's male relatives?"

"There were only her father and her brother." Hamlet was clearly out of my hands.

"There must have been many more; this also you must ask of your elders when you get back to your country. From what you tell us, since Polonius was dead, it must have been Laertes who killed Ophelia, although I do not see the reason for it."

We had emptied one pot of beer, and the old men argued the point with slightly tipsy interest. Finally one of them demanded of me, "What did the servant of Polonius say on his return?"

With difficulty I recollected Reynaldo and his mission. "I don't think he did return before Polonius was killed."

"Listen," said the elder, "and I will tell you how it was and how your story will go, then you may tell me if I am right. Polonius knew his son would get into trouble, and so he did. He had many fines to pay for fighting, and debts from gambling. But he had only two ways of getting money quickly. One was to marry off his sister at once, but it is difficult to find a man who will marry a woman desired by the son of a chief. For if the chief's heir commits adultery with your wife, what can you do? Only a fool calls a case against a man who will someday be his judge. Therefore Laertes had to take the second way: he killed his sister by witchcraft, drowning her so he could secretly sell her body to the witches."

I raised an objection. "They found her body and buried it. Indeed Laertes jumped into the grave to see his sister once more—so, you see, the body was truly there. Hamlet, who had just come back, jumped in after him."

"What did I tell you?" The elder appealed to the others. "Laertes was up to no good with his sister's body. Hamlet prevented him, because the chief's heir, like a chief, does not wish any other man to grow rich and powerful. Laertes would be angry, because he would have killed his sister without benefit to himself. In our country he would try to kill Hamlet for that reason. Is this not what happened?"

"More or less," I admitted. "When the great chief found Hamlet was still alive, he encouraged Laertes to try to kill Hamlet and arranged a fight with machetes between them. In the fight both the young men were wounded to death. Hamlet's mother drank the poisoned beer that the chief meant for Hamlet in case he won the fight. When he saw his mother die of poison, Hamlet, dying, managed to kill his father's brother with his machete."

"You see, I was right!" exclaimed the elder.

"That was a very good story," added the old man, "and you told it with very few mistakes. There was just one more error, at the very end. The poison Hamlet's mother drank was obviously meant for the survivor of the fight, whichever it was. If Laertes had won, the great chief would have poisoned him, for no one would know that he arranged Hamlet's death. Then, too, he need not fear Laertes' witchcraft; it takes a strong heart to kill one's only sister by witchcraft.

"Sometime," concluded the old man, gathering his ragged toga about him, "you must tell us some more stories of your country. We, who are elders, will instruct you in their true meaning, so that when you return to your own land your elders will see that you have not been sitting in the bush, but among those who know things and who have taught you wisdom."

Eating Christmas in the Kalahari

❖❖❖❖❖❖

RICHARD BORSHAY LEE

[1969]

EDITOR'S NOTE: The !Kung and other Bushmen speak click languages. In this article three different clicks are used:
1. The dental click (/), as in /ai/ai, /ontah, and /guago. The click is sometimes written in English as tsk-tsk.
2. The alveopalatal click (!), as in Ben!a and !Kung.
3. The lateral click (//), as in //gom.
Clicks function as consonants; a word may have more than one, as in /n!au.

The !Kung Bushmen's knowledge of Christmas is third-hand. The London Missionary Society brought the holiday to the southern Tswana tribes in the early nineteenth century. Later, native catechists spread the idea far and wide among the Bantu-speaking pastoralists, even in the remotest corners of the Kalahari Desert. The Bushmen's idea of the Christmas story, stripped to its essentials, is "praise the birth of white man's god-chief"; what keeps their interest in the holiday high is the Tswana-Herero custom of slaughtering an ox for his Bushmen neighbors as an annual goodwill gesture. Since the 1930s, part of the Bushmen's annual round of activities has included a December congregation at the cattle posts for trading, marriage brokering, and several days of trance-dance feasting at which the local Tswana headman is host.

As a social anthropologist working with !Kung Bushmen, I found that the Christmas ox custom suited my purposes. I had come to the Kalahari to study the hunting and gathering subsistence economy of the !Kung, and to accomplish this it was essential not to provide them with food, share my own food, or interfere in any way with their food-gathering activities. While liberal handouts of tobacco and medical supplies were appreciated, they were scarcely adequate to erase the glaring disparity in wealth between the anthropologist, who maintained a two-month inventory of canned goods, and the Bushmen, who rarely had a day's supply of food on hand. My approach, while paying off in terms of data, left me open to frequent accusations of stinginess and hardheartedness. By their lights, I was a miser.

The Christmas ox was to be my way of saying thank you for the cooperation of the past year; and since it was to be our last Christmas in the field, I determined to slaughter the largest, meatiest ox that money could buy, insuring that the feast and trance dance would be a success.

Through December I kept my eyes open at the wells as the cattle were brought down for watering. Several animals were offered, but none had quite the grossness that I had in mind. Then, ten days before the holiday, a Herero friend led an ox of astonishing size and mass up to our camp. It was solid black, stood five feet high at the shoulder, had a five-foot span of horns, and must have weighed 1,200 pounds on the hoof. Food consumption calculations are my specialty, and I quickly figured that bones and viscera aside, there was enough meat—at least four pounds—for every man, woman, and child of the 150 Bushmen in the vicinity of /ai/ai who were expected at the feast.

Having found the right animal at last, I paid the Herero £20 ($56) and asked him to keep the beast with his herd until Christmas day. The next morning word spread among the people that the big solid black one was the ox chosen by /ontah (my Bushman name; it means, roughly, "whitey") for the Christmas feast. That afternoon I received the first delegation. Ben!a, an outspoken sixty-year-old mother of five, came to the point slowly.

"Where were you planning to eat Christmas?"

"Right here at /ai/ai," I replied.

"Alone or with others?"

"I expect to invite all the people to eat Christmas with me."

"Eat what?"

"I have purchased Yehave's black ox, and I am going to slaughter and cook it."

"That's what we were told at the well but refused to believe it until we heard it from yourself."

"Well, it's the black one," I replied expansively, although wondering what she was driving at.

"Oh, no!" Ben!a groaned, turning to her group. "They were right." Turning back to me she asked, "Do you expect us to eat that bag of bones?"

"Bag of bones! It's the biggest ox at /ai/ai."

"Big, yes, but old. And thin. Everybody knows there's no meat on that old ox. What did you expect us to eat off it, the horns?"

Everybody chuckled at Ben!a's one-liner as they walked away, but all I could manage was a weak grin.

That evening it was the turn of the young men. They came to sit at our evening fire. /gaugo, about my age, spoke to me man-to-man.

"/ontah, you have always been square with us," he lied. "What has happened to change your heart? That sack of guts and bones of Yehave's will hardly feed one camp, let alone all the Bushmen around /ai/ai." And he proceeded to enumerate the seven camps in the /ai/ai vicinity, family by family. "Perhaps you have forgotten that we are not few, but many. Or are you too blind to tell the difference between a proper cow and an old wreck? That ox is thin to the point of death."

"Look, you guys," I retorted, "that is a beautiful animal, and I'm sure you will eat it with pleasure at Christmas."

"Of course we will eat it; it's food. But it won't fill us up to the point where we will have enough strength to dance. We will eat and go home to bed with stomachs rumbling."

That night as we turned in, I asked my wife, Nancy: "What did you think of the black ox?"

"It looked enormous to me. Why?"

"Well, about eight different people have told me I got gypped; that the ox is nothing but bones."

"What's the angle?" Nancy asked. "Did they have a better one to sell?"

"No, they just said that it was going to be a grim Christmas because there won't be enough meat to go around. Maybe I'll get an independent judge to look at the beast in the morning."

Bright and early, Halingisi, a Tswana cattle owner, appeared at our camp. But before I could ask him to give me his opinion on Yehave's black ox, he gave me the eye signal that indicated a confidential chat. We left the camp and sat down.

"/ontah, I'm surprised at you: you've lived here for three years and still haven't learned anything about cattle."

"But what else can a person do but choose the biggest, strongest animal one can find?" I retorted.

"Look, just because an animal is big doesn't mean that it has plenty of meat on it. The black one was a beauty when it was younger, but now it is thin to the point of death."

"Well I've already bought it. What can I do at this stage?"

"Bought it already? I thought you were just considering it. Well, you'll have to kill it and serve it, I suppose. But don't expect much of a dance to follow."

My spirits dropped rapidly. I could believe that Ben!a and /gaugo just might be putting me on about the black ox, but Halingisi seemed to be an impartial critic. I went around that day feeling as though I had bought a lemon of a used car.

In the afternoon it was Tomazo's turn. Tomazo is a fine hunter, a top trance performer, and one of my most reliable informants. He approached the subject of the Christmas cow as part of my continuing Bushmen education.

"My friend, the way it is with us Bushmen," he began, "is that we love meat. And even more than that, we love fat. When we hunt we always search for the fat ones, the ones dripping with layers of white fat: fat that turns into a clear, thick oil in the cooking pot, fat that slides down your gullet, fills your stomach and gives you a roaring diarrhea," he rhapsodized.

"So, feeling as we do," he continued, "it gives us pain to be served such a scrawny thing as Yehave's black ox. It is big, yes, and no doubt its giant bones are good for soup, but fat is what we really crave and so we will eat Christmas this year with a heavy heart."

The prospect of a gloomy Christmas now had me worried, so I asked Tomazo what I could do about it.

"Look for a fat one, a young one . . . smaller, but fat. Fat enough to make us //gom [evacuate the bowels], then we will be happy."

My suspicions were aroused when Tomazo said that he happened to know of a young, fat, barren cow that the owner was willing to part with. Was Toma working on commission, I wondered? But I dispelled this unworthy thought when we approached the Herero owner of the cow in question and found that he had decided not to sell.

The scrawny wreck of a Christmas ox now became the talk of the /ai/ai water hole and was the first news told to the outlying groups as they began to come in from the bush for the feast. What finally convinced me that real trouble might be brewing was the visit from U!au, an old conservative with a reputation for fierceness. His nickname meant spear and referred to an incident thirty years ago in which he had speared a man to death. He had an intense manner; fixing me with his eyes, he said in clipped tones:

"I have only just heard about the black ox today, or else I would have come here earlier. /ontah, do you honestly think you can serve meat like that to people and avoid a fight?" He paused, letting the implications sink in. "I don't mean fight you, /ontah; you are a white man. I mean a fight between Bushmen. There are many fierce ones here, and with such a small quantity of meat to distribute, how can you give everybody a fair share? Someone is sure to accuse another of taking too much or hogging all the choice pieces. Then you will see what happens when some go hungry while others eat."

The possibility of at least a serious argument struck me as all too real. I had witnessed the tension that surrounds the distribution of meat from a kudu or gemsbok kill and had documented many arguments that sprang up from a real or imagined slight in meat distribution. The owners of a kill may spend up to two hours arranging and rearranging the piles of meat under the gaze of a circle of recipients before handing them out. And I also knew that the Christmas feast at /ai/ai would be bringing together groups that had feuded in the past.

Convinced now of the gravity of the situation, I went in earnest to search for a second cow; but all my inquiries failed to turn one up.

The Christmas feast was evidently going to be a disaster, and the incessant complaints about the meagerness of the ox had already taken the fun out of it for me. Moreover, I was getting bored with the wisecracks, and after losing my temper a few times, I resolved to serve the beast anyway. If the meat fell short, the hell with it.

In the Bushmen idiom, I announced to all who would listen: "I am a poor man and blind. If I have chosen one that is too old and too thin, we will eat it anyway and see if there is enough meat there to quiet the rumbling of our stomachs."

On hearing this speech, Ben!a offered me a rare word of comfort. "It's thin," she said philosophically, "but the bones will make a good soup."

At dawn Christmas morning, instinct told me to turn over the butchering and cooking to a friend and take off with Nancy to spend Christmas alone in the bush. But curiosity kept me from retreating. I wanted to see what such a scrawny ox looked like on butchering, and if there *was* going to be a fight, I wanted to catch every word of it. Anthropologists are incurable that way.

The great beast was driven up to our dancing ground, and a shot in the forehead dropped it in its tracks. Then, freshly cut branches were heaped around the fallen carcass to receive the meat. Ten men volunteered to help with the cutting. I asked /gaugo to make the breastbone cut. This cut, which begins the butchering process for most large game, offers easy access for removal of the viscera. But it also allows the hunter to spot-check the amount of fat on the animal. A fat game animal carries a white layer up to an inch thick on the chest, while in a thin one, the knife will quickly cut to bone. All eyes fixed on his hand as /gaugo, dwarfed by the great carcass, knelt to the breast. The first cut opened a pool of solid white in the black skin. The second and third cut widened and deepened the creamy white. Still no bone. It was pure fat; it must have been two inches thick.

"Hey /gau," I burst out, "that ox is loaded with fat. What's this about the ox being too thin to bother eating? Are you out of your mind?"

"Fat?" /gau shot back, "You call that fat? This wreck is thin, sick, dead!" And he broke out laughing. So did everyone else. They rolled on the ground, paralyzed with laughter. Everybody laughed except me; I was thinking.

I ran back to the tent and burst in just as Nancy was getting up. "Hey, the black ox. It's fat as hell! They were kidding about it being too thin to eat. It was a joke or something. A put-on. Everyone is really delighted with it!"

"Some joke," my wife replied. "It was so funny that you were ready to pack up and leave /ai/ai."

If it had indeed been a joke, it had been an extraordinarily convincing one, and tinged, I thought, with more than a touch of malice, as many jokes are. Nevertheless, that it was a joke lifted my spirits considerably, and I returned to the butchering site where the shape of the ox was rapidly disappearing under the axes and knives of the butchers. The atmosphere had become festive. Grinning broadly, their arms covered with blood well past the elbow, men packed chunks of meat into the big cast-iron cooking pots, fifty pounds to the load, and muttered and chuckled all the while about the thinness and worthlessness of the animal and /ontah's poor judgment.

We danced and ate that ox two days and two nights;
we cooked and distributed fourteen potfuls of meat and
no one went home hungry and no fights broke out.

But the "joke" stayed in my mind. I had a growing
feeling that something important had happened in my
relationship with the Bushmen and that the clue lay in
the meaning of the joke. Several days later, when most
of the people had dispersed back to the bush camps, I
raised the question with Hakekgose, a Tswana man who
had grown up among the !Kung, married a !Kung girl,
and who probably knew their culture better than any
other non-Bushman.

"With us whites," I began, "Christmas is supposed to
be the day of friendship and brotherly love. What I can't
figure out is why the Bushmen went to such lengths to
criticize and belittle the ox I had bought for the feast.
The animal was perfectly good and their jokes and wisecracks practically ruined the holiday for me."

"So it really did bother you," said Hakekgose. "Well,
that's the way they always talk. When I take my rifle and
go hunting with them, if I miss, they laugh at me for the
rest of the day. But even if I hit and bring one down,
it's no better. To them, the kill is always too small or
too old or too thin; and as we sit down on the kill site
to cook and eat the liver, they keep grumbling, even
with their mouths full of meat. They say things like, 'Oh
this is awful! What a worthless animal! Whatever made
me think that this Tswana rascal could hunt!' "

"Is this the way outsiders are treated?" I asked.

"No, it is their custom; they talk that way to each
other too. Go and ask them."

/gaugo had been one of the most enthusiastic in making me feel bad about the merit of the Christmas ox. I
sought him out first.

"Why did you tell me the black ox was worthless,
when you could see that it was loaded with fat and
meat?"

"It is our way," he said smiling. "We always like to
fool people about that. Say there is a Bushman who has
been hunting. He must not come home and announce

like a braggard, 'I have killed a big one in the bush!' He must first sit down in silence until I or someone else comes up to his fire and asks, 'What did you see today?' He replies quietly, 'Ah, I'm no good for hunting. I saw nothing at all'—pause—'just a little tiny one.' Then I smile to myself," /gaugo continued, "because I know he has killed something big.

"In the morning we make up a party of four or five people to cut up and carry the meat back to the camp. When we arrive at the kill we examine it and cry out, 'You mean to say you have dragged us all the way out here in order to make us cart home your pile of bones? Oh, if I had known it was this thin I wouldn't have come.' Another one pipes up, 'People, to think I gave up a nice day in the shade for this. At home we may be hungry but at least we have nice cool water to drink.' If the horns are big, someone says, 'Did you think that somehow you were going to boil down the horns for soup?'

"To all this you must respond in kind. 'I agree,' you say, 'this one is not worth the effort; let's just cook the liver for strength and leave the rest for the hyenas. It is not too late to hunt today and even a duiker or a steenbok would be better than this mess.'

"Then you set to work nevertheless: butcher the animal, carry the meat back to the camp, and everyone eats," /gaugo concluded.

Things were beginning to make sense. Next, I went to Tomazo. He corroborated /gaugo's story of the obligatory insults over a kill and added a few details of his own.

"But," I asked, "why insult a man after he has gone to all that trouble to track and kill an animal and when he is going to share the meat with you so that your children will have something to eat?"

"Arrogance," was his cryptic answer.

"Arrogance?"

"Yes, when a young man kills much meat he comes to think of himself as a chief or a big man, and he thinks of the rest of us as his servants or inferiors. We can't accept this. We refuse one who boasts, for someday his pride will make him kill somebody. So we always speak of his meat as worthless. This way we cool his heart and make him gentle."

"But why didn't you tell me this before?" I asked Tomazo with some heat.

"Because you never asked me," said Tomazo, echoing the refrain that has come to haunt every field ethnographer.

The pieces now fell into place. I had known for a long time that in situations of social conflict with Bushmen I held all the cards. I was the only source of tobacco in a thousand square miles, and I was not incapable of cutting an individual off for noncooperation. Though my boycott never lasted longer than a few days, it was an indication of my strength. People resented my presence at the water hole, yet simultaneously dreaded my leaving. In short I was a perfect target for the charge of arrogance and for the Bushmen tactic of enforcing humility.

I had been taught an object lesson by the Bushmen; it had come from an unexpected corner and had hurt me in a vulnerable area. For the big black ox was to be the one totally generous, unstinting act of my year at /ai/ai, and I was quite unprepared for the reaction I received.

As I read it, their message was this: There are no totally generous acts. All "acts" have an element of calculation. One black ox slaughtered at Christmas does not wipe out a year of careful manipulation of gifts given to serve your own ends. After all, to kill an animal and share the meat with people is really no more than Bushmen do for each other every day and with far less fanfare.

In the end, I had to admire how the Bushmen had played out the farce—collectively straight-faced to the end. Curiously, the episode reminded me of *The Good Soldier Schweik,* and his marvelous encounters with authority. Like Schweik, the Bushmen had retained a thoroughgoing skepticism of good intentions. Was it this independence of spirit, I wondered, that had kept them culturally viable in the face of generations of contact with more powerful societies, both black and white? The thought that the Bushmen were alive and well in the Kalahari was strangely comforting. Perhaps, armed with that independence and with their superb knowledge of their environment, they might yet survive the future.

A People Apart

❖❖❖❖❖❖❖

COLIN M. TURNBULL

[1969]

Near Pirre, Uganda

This is written from inside a small, circular mud hut, dark—despite the brilliant sunshine outside—because the door has to be closed to ward off unwelcome visitors who are not deterred even by the eight-foot stockade around the house. There are no windows, but some light and air come in through the eaves, where the thatched roof clears the wall by four or five inches. The floor slopes at a ridiculous angle, and the furniture, a bed and two tables made of saplings lashed together with vine, only seems to add to the discomfort. Outside, however, life is even less comfortable, for there is no shelter from the blazing heat, any more than there is from the freezing rain that is likely to follow in an hour or two, blown down the valley by gale-force winds. Distances between villages may not be enormous, but because of the rugged mountain terrain, with ravines a thousand feet deep to be negotiated, it may take a good eight-hour trek to cover as little as ten miles or less, as measured by a straight ruler on a flat map. And even where the land is level for a few hundred yards it is covered with sharp thorns that tear at the arms and legs and, when broken off, penetrate the stoutest soles. Yet, except in moments of temporary despair, it all seems worthwhile, for although it is like taking blood from the proverbial stone, there is much knowledge to be had from such conditions. The field worker unlucky or unwise enough to have made such a choice is bound to learn not only about the people he is studying but also about himself.

228

Perhaps even more important, when conditions are as extreme as they are here, in the very northeastern-most corner of Uganda, they make the anthropologist think very carefully about the validity of his results. Here the human environment is just as difficult to cope with as the geographical, and if it is hard for the field worker to survey accurately and conscientiously mountain farmland that frequently slopes at an angle of over 70 degrees, it is even harder for him to maintain his equilibrium while attempting to relate to a people who, while not wishing him any harm, nonetheless wish to strip him of everything he possesses, whether they can conceive of any use for it or not. Nor is it easy to feel at home with a people who regard each other in a similarly covetous light, and who consequently surround themselves with a barrage of deception and ring their homes with tight, virtually impenetrable stockades and thorn fences, dividing brothers from each other and parents from children. While it is true that the anthropologist is no more separated from such people than they are from each other, it is questionable whether he can in a brief year or two ever truly penetrate such formidable defenses and understand just how such a society can survive. Even the hardest head, professing the greatest scientific detachment, can surely not fail to judge harshly when a plump, hearty youth is seen beating a starving, tiny, demented girl for the fun of stealing from her the only food she has seen for a day or two; or when an adult audience roars with laughter as one of their number sneaks food from the bowl of a blind elder as he is eating; or when parents abandon children (or vice versa) to die, not because they could not be fed, but because it would simply take too much trouble —any amount of trouble being too much. The field worker may eventually learn to penetrate the stockades by wriggling through the low doorway on his stomach or on his side, having first announced his intention so as to avoid being attacked, but can he ever penetrate a mentality that looks on with mild amusement as food and water that could save a life are stolen from the dying?

Anthropologists all too often claim to have understood and explained primitive societies *in toto,* as though there was no more to be said on the matter. They present a clearly defined system that would work admirably, like a mechanical model; but also like a mechanical model, it would get nowhere. Perhaps we are all too much concerned with explanation, and too little concerned with understanding. A society like this one, however, defies any explanation, at least for a very long time; none of the standard social systems of which the theoreticians are so fond and so proud fit even in part; the field worker is driven, rather like the people he is studying, simply to concentrate on surviving, in the hope that understanding will come, even if system does not.

Anthropology, the study of man, is divided into several different areas in these days of specialization. It is a study of man as a biological entity, as a historical entity, and as a social entity. One of the pities of such specialization is that there is an inevitable tendency to separation, as though man were capable of being rent into discrete parts and still exist. Even within a division, such as social anthropology, there are subdivisions. There are those who seek to answer very specific theoretical problems, and who select a society for study because it illustrates those problems. Others answer a call to solve more empirical problems, such as those posed by the rapid social changes taking place in formerly undeveloped areas. Others, like myself, prefer to undertake a more general quest without any specific expectation except the broadening of our knowledge of human society. We choose a society to study because, in the first place, it is unknown and promises fresh data, and perhaps also because it is generally in line with our own interests, likes, or dislikes.

I like forests, and I am interested in hunters and gatherers, so when casting about for somewhere to go for further research I first chose the Andaman Islands, where the Onge still live (on the Little Andaman) in depleted numbers, but still relatively untouched by civilization. The study would have provided invaluable data for comparison with other hunters and gatherers in similarly forested environments; it would have been of particular interest to me because of my previous work among the pygmy hunters of the Congo. But it was not to be; for various reasons the Indian government refused permission, and with little time left I had to make an alternative choice.

Just then Elizabeth Marshall, author of *The Harmless People,* returned from northern Uganda where she had been gathering material on the Dodos, one of the great Karimojong peoples. She suggested that since I was so interested in hunters, why not visit the Teuso, who allegedly lived high up in the mountains above the Uganda/Kenya escarpment, and who had first been reported in a very brief note in an academic journal in 1931. She painted a delightful picture of a warm and friendly people, full of fun, whom she had met during their occasional visits to the administrative center of Kaabong, a tiny outpost near the point where Uganda, Kenya, and Sudan all meet in an incredible conglomeration of jagged mountains, arid deserts, and lush, gemlike, and isolated valleys. I reluctantly gave up the idea of a cool forest and prepared for the hills.

Here again anthropologists differ widely in the kinds of preparations they make. I think all of us read up on whatever literature is available, but in this case it amounted to no more than a few pages. Some then prepare as for any other kind of expedition, purchasing camping equipment and such supplies as cannot be bought locally in the field. Medical supplies have to be carefully assembled, and the necessary inoculations taken. It is all very matter of fact, and when the anthropologist arrives in the field all he has to do is to set up his tent, or tents, assemble all his camping equipment and stores, and then proceed to work much as if he were still in his office, but with an abundant supply of raw material all around. Such an anthropologist deliberately establishes himself outside the community he is studying; some even stay in nearby resthouses or hotels if a town is not too far away. They visit the "field" daily and pursue a diligent course of study, which they carefully plot as they go along, step by step. They are free from local involvement, emotional or otherwise, and can more easily preserve the intellectual detachment we all aim for. They necessarily miss a great deal by not living in the village with the people, but they claim that their vision, if limited, is clearer by being more objective.

There is no right or wrong way; it depends a great deal on the purpose, as well as the nature, of each individual case, and on the personality of the field worker. I prefer to enter a society as completely as possible, for although it becomes impossible to maintain as high a degree of objectivity at the time, one gathers much more material and in much more intimate detail, and this can be treated as objectively as you like when, once out of the field, the material is being analyzed. Of course, it is then too late to fill in any gaps that might result from being too immersed in the subject itself, but on the whole I find the rewards are richer. My previous two major experiences of this kind, in India and in the Congo, had both been immensely fruitful and, at the same time, immensely pleasurable. Minor physical discomforts were quickly obliterated by the constant excitement of discovery and the pleasure of companionship with people who welcomed my desire to learn their ways and were anxious that I understand them well. I saw no reason to think it could be otherwise with the Teuso. That was my first mistake.

The second mistake I made was to assume that the Teuso were hunters until I saw their intensive cultivation, and then to assume that they were farmers. My third mistake, and the greatest, was to assume that these gentle, smiling, friendly looking people who extended such a warm welcome were as gentle and as amicable as they appeared. It took a long time—almost a year— to convince me otherwise.

I arrived at Kaabong at a time when drought was beginning to result in famine. The famine struck the Turkana in Kenya even more heavily, and they were beginning to intensify their raids on the Dodos in Uganda, so that for two weeks the local administration was reluctant to allow me into the danger area. During these two weeks I stayed at Kaabong and met some of the Teuso who filtered down through the mountains in search of food. Two Teuso boys had, during a previous famine, decided to go to the mission school, where they were well fed, as well as well taught. They spoke their own language and Karimojong, which is the lingua franca in this area, and they also knew some English and Swahili. From them, I was able to work up a fairly respectable vocabulary and determine the basic grammatical pattern. I found it relatively easy on paper, but enormously difficult in practice, for the sounds were utterly unlike anything I had ever attempted to make, or had even heard, in a linguistic context. In the course of learning to splutter appropriately, I learned that "Teuso" is only a name applied by the Dodos, and that the tribal name is Ik. Their language is utterly unknown to any of the neighboring tribes, with whom they communicate only in Karimojong. It was unlike any African language known to me and did not seem to conform to the Sudanic classification it had tentatively been accorded. Perhaps it was the somewhat Bushmanoid appearance of the people that tempted me to see a possible linguistic connection in that direction, but from the outset it was quite plain that the Ik were a people apart from all others in the region, linguistically, physically, and culturally.

As soon as permission came through I spent a month visiting all the different villages, traveling by jeep as far as practicable, then simply walking or climbing. The effects of the drought had been disastrous. The fields, which had been planted with such evident care and labor, had received just enough rain at the beginning of the season to bring out the young shoots. Then the sun had come to stay in the cloudless sky, burning everything. It burned the crops of the Ik; it also burned the grass that the Dodos needed for their cattle, and it dried up the few water sources that both needed to survive. The outlook was bad, and I was impressed by the cheerfulness with which the Ik accepted the almost certain disaster.

Even after the grain that should have been reserved for next year's sowing had been consumed and when there was no longer any chance of rain coming in time to yield a harvest, the Ik, for a reason I could not then understand, remained optimistic. All, that is, except a few old people who were barely strong enough to crawl from their huts to talk. They simply said that they would die, since there was nobody to bring them food, and they were too weak to hunt or gather the wild vegetables that were still about. When I asked if they did not have children to help them, they just laughed—a laugh I quite misunderstood. It was a hollow, hopeless sort of sound that I have heard all too often since, and those who have made it have, as they predicted, mostly died. They did indeed have children, who remained obstinately optimistic and singularly well fed while the skin hung off their parents in long, wrinkled folds, leaving bones to stick out as though in angry protest.

The optimism of the youths, whose plumpness was perhaps comparative but who nonetheless could at least walk upright instead of having to drag themselves along the ground, lay in their knowledge that the drought, two thousand feet down below the escarpment, was even more disastrous for the Turkana. The Turkana, like all Karimojong, live by cattle. They drink the blood and milk of the cows and occasionally eat the flesh of their goats and sheep. The drought became so severe that raids on the Dodos were no longer sufficient remedy, for there simply was no food or water for the vast herds they possessed. Their only recourse, as the Ik well knew, was to climb up the escarpment, invade Uganda, and graze their cattle there.

By then I had decided to make my headquarters near the frontier police post of Pirre, on the side of Mount Morungole, overlooking the Kidepo National Park. There was a cluster of seven Ik villages there, and I had already seen a good deal of the remaining six villages to the east, along the top of the escarpment itself. It was, of course, into Kidepo that the greatest Turkana invasion came, with many thousands of cattle. They drove the Dodos from Pirre; this tiny police post, housed in about a dozen huts, was completely incapable of doing anything against such numbers. The track to Kaabong was barely passable even by jeep, the radio equipment broke down, and the local administration was in a quandary as to what to do, short of calling in the army and creating an international incident.

So the Turkana took possession of Pirre, and I confess that I found them a welcome change, wild and aggressive though they were. They said they had no wish to fight but only wanted to graze their cattle. They promised they would do no harm if left alone, and although they have probably one of the most unsavory reputations in the whole of Africa, I never doubted their word for an instant, nor did they go back on it even under provocation.

The Ik now displayed their talent for survival. They busied themselves making spears for the Turkana, who had recently been persuaded to surrender theirs as a peace gesture toward the Dodos. For this service they bled the Turkana much as the Turkana bleed their cattle, but with rather less consideration. The Ik began to grow fat again. They then persuaded the Turkana that the Dodos were a menace and began instigating raids between the two, acting as spies first for one side, then for the other, drawing pay in the edible form of cattle from both sides. Ik villages that had never possessed a single goat began to build *bomas* and to fill them with literally hundreds of cattle. They ate these as rapidly as possible, for they knew very well that any attempt to keep them would only result in their being stolen back. The youths continued to put on weight, but the old people remained as thin and emaciated as ever.

The Turkana were eventually forced out by the army, which left the Ik with only the Dodos to prey on, and the Dodos themselves were near starvation. The old people among the Ik began to die, and children, and even some of the youths. The selfishness shown over food was terrible to see, but seemed almost excusable under the circumstances. I myself was driven into hiding every time I wanted to eat, although I had barely enough for myself, since fresh supplies were unobtainable and I had given what I could to the old. Yet I was wary of even biting into a dry biscuit in case someone should hear the crunching and come and demand a share. When people knew anyone was eating, myself included, they came and sat around in a silent, hungry circle, knowing that nothing would be left for them, but hoping. I would have excused them anything during those days, just as I hoped they would excuse me.

The new year came, and with it the first rains in over twelve months. Work in the fields was slow to begin with, for few people had the strength. But the rains brought up edible grasses, wild berries and fruits appeared, and gradually the danger of full-scale starvation receded. Now the crops are well on the way to bringing in a fine harvest, and the wild foods grow in abundance all around. What has not grown, however, is any evidence that the Ik—even in such relatively good times—have any consideration for one another. Food is still the dominant thought; food getting the dominant activity. And, still, it is each individual for himself. At dawn, children flock out in a large, single, unruly band and scavenge the surrounding countryside for anything that might have come up during the night. The three- to seven- or eight-year-olds are too young to risk going any great distance, where they would stand a better chance. Their older brothers and sisters, having beaten the younger ones to get what they had not yet eaten, go farther out on hunting parties of their own. If caught by their parents, they, in turn, will be beaten and robbed. The adults steal from each other and angrily denounce each other, kinship affording not the slightest bond of mutual respect. A mother will leave her children, even one barely weaned, in care of the father while she goes off to gather for herself, sometimes staying away for a week. Meanwhile the father will go off and leave the children in care of grandparents too old to fend for themselves. To get water, for instance, may well involve a walk of three miles and a descent (and climb, in the reverse direction) of a thousand almost sheer feet. When someone dies, there is no wailing or mourning, merely a great deal of grumbling by the next of kin because of the obligation it places on them to provide ritual purification involving a feast for relatives.

I saw one father hurriedly bury his ten-year-old son by the door of his hut, so as to avoid the expense. The night before, he had beaten his wife to stop her crying when the child died, for by so doing she announced the fact he wished to conceal. All day he sat on a rock and grumbled at his son for dying, at his wife for crying, and at his relatives for demanding a proper burial, including the appropriate feast, to which they would have to be invited. It is, perhaps, at least comforting that the mother cried, but it is the only time I have heard it.

The old people tell stories of better times when, not so long ago, Kidepo Park was theirs to hunt in as they pleased; when the boundaries of the three countries were not subject to armed patrols; and when they could roam at will in search of food and game, instead of being restricted and compressed as they are now. They wonder why the animals in the Park are protected and allowed to live and flourish while they must die. They wonder why their children have abandoned them, for they remember how brothers would all join together, in the old days, to look after their parents. But even the old people, now, have only one concept of good. It is nothing that can be applied to an action, or to a relationship between one human and another; it is only a condition, clearly defined as "having a full stomach." This is the basis of their life, of their law, of their morality. It is a goal that justifies any action except killing, for the Ik never kill. Their legend of origin tells how God gave spears to the Karimojong, together with cattle, so that they have wealth but also the means to bring death. God gave the Ik the digging stick and told them not to kill. They don't, they just let each other die. Meanwhile they live a life devoid of affection. A woman's attitude to childbirth is that it is a nuisance, another mouth to feed for two or three years. A mother may be amused by her baby, but that is about as close as she seems to get to affection for it. When it is sick or hungry it is simply slapped and cursed as an annoyance. The most equable kind of interpersonal relationship, regardless of kinship, is that of mutual economic reliance, but this is temporary at best and inevitably ends in cheating and mutual recrimination.

The tightly stockaded internal divisions, which turn every village into a series of independent fortresses—each occupied by a nuclear family, each with its own single, sometimes booby-trapped private entrance—is sufficient evidence of the state of degeneration into which this society has been thrown by events it cannot understand. Youths have no concept of what their grandparents are talking about when the old folk grumble about the young deserting the old. One, wanting some food I was about to give to an old, old woman, said, "Why give it to her? She is going to die anyway." When I said it might make her a little happier meanwhile, he became angry at the waste, for such he considered it.

The economic noose that has been drawn around its neck may be enough to explain the condition into which Ik society has fallen, although even of that I am not yet convinced. It is difficult to understand how, even under such circumstances, a human society can exist and survive as successfully as this one does, devoid of nearly all those qualities that we consider raise us above the level of animals. And however well one may be able to explain the society as it functions at present, is that explanation valid without any understanding of the people themselves? For even simply as people, I cannot understand the Ik. I cannot bring myself to accept that a loveless society can exist, and constantly look for something I must have missed, fearing all the while that it is not there. The Ik are not a people one can dislike, as much as one dislikes almost everything they do, feeling that even animals would behave with more consideration for each other. One cannot dislike them because they themselves are without the ability to like or dislike, except with regard to the fullness of their bellies: in personal relationships there is a total hiatus.

At the moment it is impossible for me not to be largely subjective. There is always the hope that once I am out of the field, back in familiar and comfortable surroundings, with the leisure and strength to go over every detail in search of the truth, a different truth will emerge. Yet with all this in mind I fear that the truth has already been found. It makes me both angry and sad.

The Navajos

❖❖❖❖❖❖

OLIVER LA FARGE

[1948]

Recently the general public has become aware of the fact that we still have within the borders of the United States a tribe of Indians numbering over 60,000—a cohesive group, predominantly of full blood, retaining its language and a great part of its ancient customs. The public has heard of it; it has been photographed, described in newspapers and magazines, and made the principal subject of a major broadcast, for one unhappy reason—that this remarkable group, the Navajo tribe, has reached a condition of general ill-health, want, hopelessness, and hunger which is a national disgrace.

Those of us who knew and lived among the Navajos in the 1920s thought of them as the most hopeful of all the Indian tribes. We knew that they were the largest, although the highest guesses did not put their number over 30,000. They lived in a remote, semidesert country of great beauty—the greater part of it in northeastern Arizona, with a sizable segment in New Mexico and a smaller area in Utah. Their domain, about as large as the state of West Virginia, was difficult to reach. No important white settlements lay near it. Although not in any sense wealthy, the Navajos seemed to have a good, secure life, with their flocks of sheep providing their principal income. It looked as if they would absorb our civilization slowly and without destructive shocks, and as if the native culture elements of greatest value would have a good chance to survive. One could look forward to an evolutionary process that would result eventually in a large community of citizens of predominantly Indian blood, carrying with them a proud tradition and enriching elements of their ancient culture as they moved into the mainstream of American life.

This optimistic belief was strengthened by their past history. The Navajos are close relatives of the Apaches and with them form a southern offshoot from the area of the Athabaskan linguistic stock, the main center of which is in northwestern Canada and Alaska. Perhaps about A.D. 1000, bands of Athabaskans wandered into the relatively empty areas of the Great Plains. Probably from contact with more advanced tribes to the east, they learned a little farming and how to make crude pottery. Their culture was simple, their possessions few, their organization weak. Later, under the pressure of stronger tribes, they moved south and west until they entered New Mexico and came in contact with the sedentary, agricultural Pueblo Indians.

Most of the bands that later became Apaches drifted on, into the waste areas farther south, where they lived obscurely until in the eighteenth century they emerged as ruthless and deadly raiders. The future Navajos settled near the Pueblos. They learned farming on a new scale, irrigation, weaving, elaborate ceremonies. Their culture was profoundly modified, and yet, while they took over every element that they deemed useful, they did this selectively, fitting the elements into their basic pattern of individual freedom and the deep, psychological values of their original culture.

The coming of the Spanish led to changes. They acquired the horse. The men's costume changed greatly. They took up wool-weaving, developing an industry that has become nationally, even internationally, famous. They learned the rudiments of metalworking and by the middle of the nineteenth century were becoming skilled in this craft. It should be noted that many of the arts they borrowed from others, they developed beyond the skill of their teachers. Navajo silverwork put the local Spanish silversmiths out of business; Navajo blankets were more highly valued than those of either the Spanish or the Pueblo Indians; their dry paintings infinitely surpass those of their Pueblo teachers.

When the Spanish first encountered them, they numbered perhaps a little less than 2,000. By 1850, they had increased to about 10,000. With increasing numbers and the mastery of the horse, they made a further change. Farming became a secondary occupation, while herding sheep became primary—but it was not ordinary herding. They butchered their sheep whenever hungry and regularly replenished and increased their flocks by raiding the Pueblo and the Spanish settlements. They became as fierce as any of the other Apaches and were a scourge to the whole Southwest.

In 1866, Kit Carson broke them in a sharp, fierce campaign. The greater part of them surrendered and were moved to a sort of internment camp at Fort Sumner in eastern New Mexico, although a thousand or so diehards hid out in the wild mountains and desert. The government offered them a reservation in rich, grassy country in Oklahoma, but they would have none of it. Their one desire was to return to their beautiful, harsh homeland. At length, in 1868, a solemn treaty was made with them, and they received a part of their old domain as a reservation. At that time their numbers were estimated at 9,000. Many had been killed in the fighting; more had died on the "Long Walk" to Fort Sumner and during their exile there. Some who hid out were killed by tribes taking a fine opportunity to pay off old grudges. Thus it is safe to estimate that, in 1850, the tribe had numbered 10,000.

Now the Navajos changed again, becoming true shepherds, guarding and increasing their flocks and building up their crafts more intensively for commerce. The women abandoned a heavy, woolen costume adapted from that of the Pueblos (which in turn had replaced the earlier buckskin) and took up their present mode of dress. This consisted of a velveteen blouse and a full skirt of calico or velveteen, modeled after the dress of the officers' wives at Fort Sumner. More slowly, the men changed to the wearing of manufactured, standard clothes—but they have a way of wearing them, a preference in colors, a use of ornamentation, that makes them look anything but standard.

Their capacity for changing and yet remaining thoroughly true to themselves is one of their most interesting characteristics and one of the reasons why they have been looked upon as so hopeful. Their language gives a view of their characteristics. The studies of the Franciscan Fathers early in this century showed that Navajo then had a vocabulary of 18,000 words. By now it has been considerably enlarged. Most Indian languages today are loaded with words taken from the various European languages with which they have had contact. Not so the Navajo, in which loan words are rare. New things, such as the horse, the automobile, the airplane, in their turn, were given names compounded out of Navajo or newly invented according to the Navajo pattern.

The structure of Navajo is difficult; very few white men speak it at all competently. Yet it is so flexible that during the war the Marines recruited a special platoon of Navajos. At a school which was set up for them, they learned an enormous range of military and naval terms, all of which they translated into their own tongue. Then they were sent out as teams for landings in the Pacific, carrying on ship-to-shore communication over ordinary voice radio in Navajo, a code the Japanese could not break.

Such are the people who today are in a desperate plight. What has happened to them? In a sense, they are the victims of their own vigor, of their very success in adapting themselves to the ways of peace. In part, they are suffering from astonishing blindness on the part of white men. In many matters the Indians and the white men, represented by the United States Indian Service, have worked hand-in-hand to bring about disaster.

We can begin with a failure, a broken treaty. The Treaty of 1868 undertook to provide a teacher and schoolroom for every Navajo child between six and sixteen who could be "persuaded or compelled" to go to school. This has never been done, for several reasons.

The Navajos themselves, until recently, were not greatly interested in having their children educated. Some were outright opposed to schooling—from conservatism, from the need of having the children at home to tend the sheep, and because of the suffering and misery that were so common in the Indian schools of the old, bad days.

The Navajo country is difficult to travel in. It has virtually no all-weather roads. The Navajos live scattered all over it. No one knew for sure how many Navajos or Navajo children there were or where many of them were to be found. With the difficulty there was in filling the schools already in existence, the Department of the Interior never felt able to ask Congress for the constantly increasing appropriations that would have been necessary to offer education to them all. It is doubtful if there have ever been school facilities for half of them. Today, of some 23,000 Navajos of school age, by the exercise of the greatest ingenuity, barely 7,000 can be crowded into schools.

The blame goes further than the Navajos, the Indian Service, or the Department of the Interior. At least as early as 1930, senators were rebuking the Commissioner of Indian Affairs for not having asked for schools for all. Recently, several delegations from the tribe have begged the Congress for schools for all, and various congressmen visiting the reservation have heard the same plea. Yet Congress has initiated no action.

The vast mass of the Navajo population, inevitably, is illiterate and speaks no English. Very few have even a complete grade school education. Accordingly, when they face the outside world they are like blind men feeling their way. They are tied to their land, for when they seek opportunities outside, only the poorest, lowliest forms of labor are open to them, and even at such work they are the last hired and the first let go.

This ignorance is the first horn of the dilemma. As citizens of the United States they are in theory free to go where they please, but as primitive illiterates this freedom is meaningless.

The second horn is that their reservation, vast as it is,

cannot possibly support their present population. The dilemma should have been apparent long ago, but a curious and most unfortunate sequence of factors disguised it until it had reached its present extreme state.

It is difficult now to determine at what point the size of the tribe became too great for the "human carrying capacity" of the reservation. From 1868 to 1932, the Indian Service officials, as well as Indian traders and various private individuals and organizations, kept urging the Navajos to increase their flocks by all means. The Navajos responded well. In the 1920s, there existed a modest but genuine false prosperity among them, which arose from grazing upon the reservation more sheep, goats, cattle, and horses than the land could carry. The effects of the resultant overgrazing were apparent as early as 1921; by 1930, they were painfully obvious. The animals were still finding enough to eat, but the time was rapidly coming when it would no longer be possible to graze more than a small fraction of their number upon a ruined land.

Beginning in 1933, a newly awakened Indian Service began putting soil conservation measures into effect. Progressively the stock on the range was reduced until carrying capacity was reached. This meant cutting the number of animals approximately in half. The reduction of the sheep and goats threatened great hardships; the reduction of horses, many of them useless, struck deep at the pride and prestige of the men. Because so few Navajos had any real command of English, it was difficult to convey to them the realities of their problem. Many of them espoused a mystical concept of the relation of the sheep to the land, which precluded their accepting the idea that overgrazing could be harmful.

The Indian Service committed a number of blunders, not of principle but of method, in the course of reducing the stock. Added to the misunderstandings and emotions involved, these resulted in an alienation of the Navajos from the Service. Good relations were replaced by a hostility on their part which is still a troublesome factor. There was a change in their attitude toward white men generally. They used to be rather open and friendly, agreeable to strangers, good-natured. Now their behavior varies from guarded to sullen.

Nonetheless, grazing was brought down to carrying capacity, an essential move. The Soil Conservation Service was invited in, and some improvement in the condition of the land was made. In the face of unexpected conservatism on the part of the Navajos, improved methods of herding and better strains of sheep were introduced, bringing about a marked increase in the income per sheep from those remaining.

A great many families hitherto dependent upon sheep now were left with none, or with so few that they could not support a family yearlong. This was in part due to an inequitable, straight percentage cut which was put across by the small but influential group of Navajos who owned really large flocks. In some places it was due to the stupidity of local officials, in others there simply was not enough grass to enable anyone to have a flock that would guarantee subsistence. The increased income from the sheep remaining did not fill the economic gap, nor did the subjugation of a considerably larger area of irrigated land. Under normal circumstances, the stock reduction should have precipitated an immediate economic disaster.

Disaster was postponed by the very large amount of relief work and work on soil conservation projects obtained for the Navajos. The top officials of the Office of Indian Affairs, like most of the Navajos, allowed themselves to be lulled by this artificial source of income. There were only a few people who insisted that if a capital resource was removed, another must be provided, and that relief work was only a makeshift.

Relief ended with the war. Three thousand six hundred Navajos went into the armed services. This meant that not only was 6 percent of the population removed but that they were replaced by allotment checks which constituted an important increase in income. In the acute labor shortage that existed, thousands more got work off the reservation. Income went to a new high level. Everyone was happy.

The part of the Indian Service that administers the Navajos is known as the Navajo Service. The men at the top of the Navajo Service today, as well as many of their subordinates, are sincere, devoted, and intelligent. Issuance of ration books and other war measures provided the means for the most accurate count of the population ever made, resulting in the reliable figure of 62,000 members of the tribe. Studying the scene with this figure, these officials saw what was coming, and before the war ended they began belaboring the Indian Office in Washington with prophecies of what would happen when this third false prosperity ended. They were not believed.

The war ended; the men came home; once more it was hard to get work off the reservation. The money was spent. Then the situation that had been building up for decades was fully revealed. As the Navajo country now stands, and in view of the primitive condition of the Navajos themselves, not half of them can wring a bare subsistence from the land. For the remainder, there is only irregular labor of the most undesirable sort to stave off outright starvation. The population continues to increase, despite the highest infant mortality rate and tuberculosis death rate in the country, because the people are still prolific. With the weakening of chronic hunger, however, they may diminish.

The Navajos themselves have learned their lesson. They now set universal education above everything else and for several years, without result, have been pleading with Congress for schools and teachers that will fulfill the terms of their treaty.

In the fall of 1947, the full measure of Navajo destitution became apparent when it was necessary for the Red Cross and private individuals to rush to their relief until Congress could make an appropriation for that purpose. The Office of Indian Affairs and the Department of the Interior woke up. At last they accepted the representations of the Navajo Service and took up the rehabilitation plan it had developed in consultation with the Tribal Council.

After further consultation with various lay organizations working for Indian welfare and advancement, this plan was developed into legislation and introduced in the present session of Congress. It would set up a program extending over ten years for a major development of many thousands of acres of potentially irrigable lands, the full development of other resources such as coal and timber, a sorely needed network of roads, adequate hospitals, a vastly expanded school system, a strong employment and placement service. To the maximum possible degree all work would be done by the Navajos, who would receive on-the-job training and elementary instruction in English and literacy such as was developed by the military during the war. A thousand or so families would be resettled on extremely fertile, idle lands of the Mojaves' Colorado River Reservation on the Arizona-California border. The Navajos would be encouraged and assisted in setting up the industries which, with increasing education, they could profitably manage.

The program, which might cost as much as $150 million, would in itself carry the Navajos for ten years. At the end of that time it would have most of them established on a firm economic basis, with a large number trained in skilled and semiskilled work and ready to compete for good jobs outside. From then on, the adequate educational system would have to take over, producing graduates equipped to make their way in the great world or on the reservation with new enterprises not dependent upon the soil. Most authorities agree that the plan is sound and effective, and that for all its cost, it would be a long-range economy for the nation.

The Bureau of the Budget took a long time before it approved the legislation. The bill reached Congress in April. Hearings were held. Testimony was overwhelmingly in favor of the plan. Yet no action was taken, and the Navajos must survive on the hope that the next Congress will listen to their pleas.

The Navajos do not want to live on relief. They want

to support themselves. They are proud, they want to remain Navajos, and as Navajos they want to have true equality with their fellow citizens. They are ready to adapt themselves again, to take into the basic, free pattern of their life new elements of profound change. They can do it and still retain their fundamental values. They will become less picturesque from the point of view of the casual tourist, but to the anthropologist there will be fascination in the adaptations and selections they will make.

Without help they cannot select. Misery and sickness are causing their culture to degenerate. Family ties break down. Migratory labor undermines morale and morals. The attitude toward religion grows apathetic, while some in desperation turn to the drug-induced escape of the peyote cult, which is spreading among them. They will not die out, but they can become an utterly wretched group of disheartened paupers. For eighty years we have had them in our charge—a most hopeful and promising people—and this is our achievement to date.

To the Singing, to the Drums

❖❖❖❖❖❖

N. SCOTT MOMADAY

[1975]

It is a recurrent pilgrimage, and it is made with propriety, a certain sense of formality. I understand a little more of it each time. I see a little more deeply into the meaning of formality, the formality of meaning. It is a religious experience by and large, natural and appropriate. It is an expression of the spirit.

The Taimpe is an old society in the Kiowa tribe, dating back to the time of the Sun Dance. Not much is known of its origin; there are various accounts. An old woman, Ko-sahn, who knew many things and who is dead now, told me the following story:

"There was a young man who knew that he must go off by himself. It was necessary that he do this, for it was to be done for the people. He went out upon the prairie where it was very dangerous, for there were enemies all around. He came to a high place, a kind of little mountain, which was overgrown with sagebrush and mesquite—and there was one tree. The young man heard something, a voice perhaps, but strange and troublesome, and he was afraid. He climbed the tree and hid among the branches. From there in the tree he watched the approach of his enemy. The enemy was outfitted in the regalia of the wolf clan of his people. He wore the hide of a wolf, and he carried a bow and arrows. The wolflike man crept among the bushes, moving strangely, crouching and peering all around.

"By and by he came beneath the tree, and there he stood still. The young man in the tree dropped down upon his enemy and killed him. Then the young man

250

took up the enemy's arrows in his right hand and held them high and shook them. They rattled loudly like dry leaves in a hard wind, and to this music the young man danced around his dead enemy. The people heard the music and came to see what was going on. They were very happy for the young man, and they praised him."

This, said Ko-sahn, is how the Taimpe—the Gourd Dance—came to be, and she said it in the old, certain way, the way of the storyteller, nodding her head and speaking straightly, not to be in doubt or doubted.

Facets of the story flash upon me. I move toward the center with the others, dancing—yet not dancing, really —edging upon the music, that other, quicker element, fitting my motion to it slowly, waiting to enter wholly into it. The facets are the leaves of the solitary tree, glittering in the sky. I imagine the young, legendary man there, coiled. But I do not see him apart from the tree. His limbs are the limbs of the tree, his hair the splinters of light that pierce the shadows. His enemy is vaguely there in the mottled foreground, waiting.

The celebration of the Gourd Dance is performed on the fourth of July at Carnegie, Oklahoma.

From the window of the plane I can see to the horizon. Even at 25,000 feet there is a sense of vastness in the landscape of the Great Plains. I wonder that it always takes me by surprise. It is a mood in the earth, I think, suffered here only, a deep, aboriginal intelligence in the soil, deeper than the intricate geometry that I see below, as deep as ever ran the roots of that single tree or the blood of the buffalo.

I anticipate the air. It is warm and heavy in July; you seem to move against it, to spend yourself upon it; it confirms you. I watch the ground rise up to the window, feel for the touch of it. Space becomes lateral and infinite, faintly distorted—I think of seeing through a glass of water.

At the Will Rogers World Airport at Oklahoma City my father and my three daughters are waiting for me;

he spills the girls into my arms. Something now of the ritual proper has begun; generations have come together; the blood has begun to flow toward the center of time.

My children have an understanding of the occasion, rather a perception, not of what it is—that will likely come later in their lives—but *that* it is. It is a formality that gives shape to their lives.

From the time I was a small child I have heard stories from Kiowa tradition, and now so have my children, for I have seen to it. The stories are wonderful, engaging the imagination closely. They have a vitality that is peculiar to the spoken word; it does not exist in writing —or it does not exist to the same degree. This vitality informs the Gourd Dance, too; it is as if the dance is told in a story, imagined, realized in the force and nuance of an ancient language; there is that character to it, that quality of invention, of proportion, of delight.

The songs are torrential. They work a flood upon the afternoon. The sound is full of energy. Little by little I take it in, appropriate it to my mind and body. The sun beats down harder as the afternoon goes on. The dance ring is full of dazzling light. Banners move softly against the vague backdrop of the trees. Perspiration runs in my hair; my skin and clothing are wet with it. It is as if I am suspended between the music and the heat. I feel good, strangely exhilarated and strong, as if I could dance on and on and on, so long as the songs are alive in the air.

We drive westward on the freeway. The little girls chatter in the back seat. My father's hands are dark, large-veined, laid lightly on the steering wheel of the rented car. I used to stand beside him when he painted, watching him touch the brush to the paper, wondering how he could make such fine lines of color, how it was that his hand was so sure, so true to him. It occurs to me now that his granddaughters, too, must wonder at the same thing in the same way. Cael, the oldest, has gone to school at his easel. Certainly, she sees that his hand is an instrument that realizes the image in his mind's eye upon the picture plane. She will be a writer and a painter, she tells me. She will illustrate her own books.

At Chickasha we are on the edge of the old world that I knew as a child. We leave the freeway and proceed on Oklahoma 9, a more familiar and congenial way. At Anadarko we stop at the Southern Plains Museum to look at the arts and crafts exhibit there. This, too, we do each year, and always at the same time of day. It is where I complain that we are late, that the dance has already begun.

"How much farther?" asks Brit, the baby, who is six, when we are on the road again. "Oh, a few miles, not far," answers Jill, whose tenth birthday it is. "Oh, well then." Brit thinks it will be too hot at the dance. Nevertheless, she is looking forward to it; there will be children she sees just this one time each year; she will observe how they have grown; and perhaps there will be presents.

The earth is red along the way. There are escarpments like great gaping flesh wounds in the earth. Erosion is an important principle of geography here, something deep in the character of the plains. Nowhere else on earth, I suppose, is the weather so close at hand as it is here.

My father begins to recognize the landmarks of his growing up, and this excites the girls and me. "My dad and I used to come this way in a surrey," he says, pointing out a grove. "There we used to stop, every time, and eat. We ate watermelons. My dad loved watermelons." The girls look hard into the grove, trying to see the man and the boy who paused there in the other time.

Carnegie is a small, unremarkable town in the southern plains. It is like other towns thereabouts, essentially bland and tentative-seeming against the huge, burning landscape. In July the wide, glass- and metal-bordered streets not only reflect the sun, they seem to intensify it. The light is flat and hard just now in the early afternoon; the day is at white heat. Later the light will soften and colors will emerge upon the scene; the town will melt into motion, but now it seems deserted. We drive through it.

The celebration is on the north side. We turn down into a dark depression, a large hollow among trees. It is full of camps and cars and people. At first there are children. According to some centrifugal social force, children function on the periphery. They run about, making festival noises. Firecrackers are snapping all around. We park and I make ready; the girls help me with my regalia. I am already wearing white trousers and moccasins. Now I tie the black velvet sash around my waist, placing the beaded tassels at my right leg. The bandoleer of red beans, which was my grandfather's, goes over my left shoulder, the V at my right hip. I decide to carry the blanket over my arm until I join the dancers; no sense in wrapping up in this heat. There is deep, brick-red dust on the ground. The grass is pale and brittle here and there. We make our way through the camps, stepping carefully to avoid the pegs and guy lines that reach about the tents. Old people, imperturbable, are lying down on cots and benches in the shadows. Smoke hangs in the air. We smell hamburgers, popcorn, gunpowder. Later there will be fried bread, boiled meat, Indian corn.

My father is a man of great presence, a certain figure in the world. He is tall in stature, substantial, good-looking; there is a style to his attitudes, a quality most often called charm. Rather, I believe, it is goodwill. He simply enjoys society and is most closely realized in it. There is a deep-seated native vanity to him, an ethnic confidence, and it is attractive. It is good to see him here among our kinsmen. He has sure, easy access to the tribal spheres of being. The old people recognize him; they are drawn to him; they are delighted to see him and call him by his Indian name.

Mammedaty was my grandfather's name; it means "sky walker," one who walks in the sky. In my mind's eye I see him in silhouette, at evening in the plain, walking against a copper sunset; so he lives for me in his name. Fifty years ago, more or less, he was given a horse on the occasion of the Gourd Dance. My father says: "Oh, it was a beautiful horse, black and shining. I was just a boy then, Jill's age or Brit's. His name, Mammedaty, was called out, and he was given that fine horse. Its mane was fixed in braids and ribbons. There was a beautiful blanket on its back."

We greet Taft Hainta, the leader of the Taimpe society. He embraces us. Jill gives him a hundred-dollar bill. This, too, is traditional. Each year she has made the donation to the fund for the subsequent year's celebration. It is good that she gives a gift on her birthday. Taft sees that the girls are seated comfortably in view of the dance ground. It is not easy to find a good vantage point. There is a large crowd, and the shade is thickly populated.

Each year now it seems there are more and more young people in attendance. They come from far away, simply to be here, to be caught up in this returning, to enter into the presence of the old, original spirit that resides here.

For a time we stand on the edge of the crowd and watch, taking hold of the music and the motion. I see who is there, pick out friends and relatives. Fred Tsoodle is there always; he saw to my initiation five years ago. He counseled me, taught me how to take the steps, how to wear the regalia, how to hold the gourd and the fan properly. Now I look for him; it is a kind of orientation. My cousin, Marland Aitson, is across the circle. There is room next to him. I go there.

The sun descends upon the trees. There is a giveaway. People are standing in the circle, calling forth those to whom they will make gifts. I close my eyes, open them, close them again. There are so many points of color, like points of flame. The sun has drawn upon the place; it presses upon me. I feel the heat of it at my center. The heat is hypnotic—and the kaleidoscopic scene. It is as if I am asleep. Then the drums break, the voices of

the singers gather to the beat, the rattles shake all around
—mine among them. I stand and move again, slowly,
toward the center of the universe in time, in time, more
and more closely in time.

There have been times when I have wondered what
the dance is and what it means—and what I am inside
of it. And there have been times when I have known.
Always, there comes a moment when the dance takes
hold of me, becomes itself the most meaningful and appropriate expression of my being. And always, afterward, there is rejoicing among us. We have made our
prayer, and we have made good our humanity in the
process. There are lively feelings. There is much good
talk and laughter—and much that goes without saying.
Here and there the old people play at words with the
children, telling stories of this and that, of Creation and
of the good things and bad things in the world—and
especially of that which is beautiful.

The eagle is my power,
And my fan is an eagle.
It is strong and beautiful
In my hand. And it is real.
My fingers hold upon it
As if the beaded handle
Were the twist of bristlecone.
The bones of my hand are fine
And hollow; the fan bears them.
My hand veers in the thin air
Of the summits. All morning
It scuds on the cold currents;
All afternoon it circles
To the singing, to the drums.

Living with the Natives of Melanesia

❖❖❖❖❖❖

MARGARET MEAD

[1931]

In the cases of the South Seas Hall of the American Museum hang many specimens, pieces of costumes, ceremonial staves, ornaments, weapons, canoe models, the outer and visible symbols of the civilizations which have been built up by the patient brown peoples of the Pacific Islands. To the hall in the Museum it is only possible to bring these physical things, the carved float and net, the kava bowl with its opalescent tint testifying to the generations of kava drinkers which it has served, the child's grass skirt, tightly bound to preserve the carefully crinkled waves against the day when it was to be worn. But if these lifeless specimens are to be placed in their true setting, if we are to understand the uses to which they were put, the difficulties under which they were manufactured, the human needs which they satisfied, it is necessary to go to these island communities and learn meticulously those aspects of their lives which can never be enclosed within a wall case, nor caught more than superficially in a model. It becomes the task of Museum ethnologists to make expeditions into primitive communities just as those who are to prepare the great habitat groups of animals have to follow the elephant and the tiger into their native haunts.

We are accustomed to think of expeditions as large groups of scientists equipped to the teeth with scientific paraphernalia. Such expeditions carry preparators, cameramen, guides, shooters, beaters, in addition to the central quota of scientists. They march across deserts or into jungles, carrying their food and their tents with them, setting up a microscopic world of their own wherever they go. Such are the ideal conditions for an expedition in the natural sciences other than ethnology. But the ethnologist cannot march upon a native community like an invading army, for that community is going to be not only a source of labor and food, but also the very stuff of his investigation. He must slip in quietly, lower himself or herself as gently as possible into the placid waters of native life, make the unprecedented arrival of an inquiring white person as inconspicuous as possible. For such an expedition there are no cameramen, no preparators, no army of carriers, not even servants, because to take servants from another community causes friction and upsets the nice balance of native life. An ethnological expedition is limited to one, unless it be that a husband and wife or father and daughter can go together and take their place in native society. Two members of the same sex would work against each other, vying for the attention of the same informants, and the natives would not be slow to play them off against each other. Upon our last field trip my husband and I went together, a felicitous scientific arrangement, as there are such strong sex antagonisms in Melanesia that no member of one sex can hope thoroughly to win the confidence or understand the point of view of the other.

As one cannot take an army of helpers neither can one take too bulky an amount of equipment. Tents and pavilions would stand out too sharply on the native scene, tend to distinguish the investigator from the native at the very points at which the investigator wishes to blur the differences. We therefore took with us only a minimum amount of equipment, two stretchers, two tables, two chairs, a typewriter, camera, developing apparatus, and a shotgun. The rest of our luggage was packed with notepaper, drawing paper for the children —I took a thousand sheets and the supply ran out in the first month—baubles by the gross, beads, toys, balloons, paper flowers, etc., and large and bulky amounts of rice and tobacco. Everything had to be packed into cedarwood boxes with double locks, one of which sang when it was turned like a musical clock to warn the owner of the prowling thief, the other put on for safety, as there were many duplicate keys about. The tobacco had to be unpacked from the telltale crates in which it is shipped from Louisiana and repacked in ambiguous cedar boxes.

In Rabaul, the capital of the Mandated Territory, we had acquired a Manus boy from the village of Pere, who spoke excellent pidgin and would serve as an interpreter in his own village. As he was a government servant and therefore allowed by ordinance to wear a shirt, he was of no use whatsoever for any more menial tasks. In Lorengau, the seat of the Manus district government, we acquired a second boy from the village of Pere, and our insidious approach was by now well begun.

The next step was taken by the District Officer, who summoned Gizikuk, so-called headman of the South Coast Manus, because he was the one man who could make the ten independent little democracies cooperate to the extent of providing canoes when these were needed by the government. Gizikuk came, very proud and bedizened with beadwork, and was presented with preliminary "grease," no less than twenty sticks of tobacco. He looked over our luggage and decided that it would take nine canoes to transport it the day's journey to Pere. This proved to be just four and a half times as many canoes as would really have been needed. We agreed to pay five shillings a canoe, and Gizikuk went away to muster the fleet. Meanwhile, with the aid of Banyalo and Manawai, the two Manus boys, and through the medium of pidgin English, a start was made on the Manus language.

The fleet which Gizikuk had declared necessary arrived, and a box or so was allotted to each craft, slender dugouts built up with wide sidestrakes, the whole topped by a wide platform, upon which small dome-shaped houses are constructed. As it was impossible to foresee what the attitude of the natives would be concerning questions of food, whether they would expect us to share their meal, resent our eating in their presence, or tabu eating in mixed company altogether, we took no provisions but prepared to tighten our belts for the day. And so it proved, for with characteristic Melanesian manners, our boat's crew cooked messes of sago and coconut oil on the small fireplaces on the edge of the platform and feasted happily, completely ignoring our famished presence. Entrance into native life is always accompanied by just such delicate situations, into which the average white trader or government official can step without trepidation, making the native custom bend to his whim, but toward which the ethnologist has to act with the greatest circumspection. A misstep at the start may result in weeks or even months of delay. So on a Polynesian island, to take one's own food instead of relying upon the hospitality of the natives which is always tendered with the grand manner, would be to insult one's hosts irrevocably.

After traveling all day along the edges of the mangrove swamps, sometimes crossing the reef, more often poling our way through the shallow reef-bound lagoons, we arrived at about eight in the evening at Bunei, the village of Gizikuk. Here another situation arose. Gizikuk wished us to stay in his village; but Bunei was smaller than Pere—this had been ascertained from the census— and as I wanted particularly to study children, it was necessary for the village to be large. Furthermore, we had two boys from Pere who might be miserable in Bunei. But if Gizikuk were really a chief, as he claimed to be, to offend him by refusing to make his capital our headquarters would have been fatal. However, we bet on his authority being a mere matter of personality and government backing (a guess which subsequent experience proved to be correct), and we insisted, to his great disgruntlement, upon pushing ahead to Pere. At midnight the fleet of canoes, under full sail, swept into the moonlit lagoon village, between the rows of pile-built houses, up to the doors of the "House Kiap," the government barracks, where we took up our temporary abode.

The "House Kiap" is in the village, built by government order to accommodate traveling officials and other white men, but it is distinctly not of it. From its narrow walls, 14 by 12 feet, we again temporized, learned more of the language, tried to get an accurate enough picture of the social scene so as to know whom to trust and whom it was dangerous to displease. Meanwhile, through our two boys, and another and then another who were speedily added to our ménage, we let it be known that we wished to learn the language and witness all the important events in the lives of the people. For one to understand the onslaught to which we were subjected by such an invitation it is necessary to remember that these people have had only one kind of contact with white people, as inferiors, either as work boys or merely as native British subjects dealing with occasional government officials very much on their dignity. The house of a white man, any house in which a white man took up temporary quarters, was forbidden to the native, except in his servant capacity as cook or houseboy. Missionaries, who must use softer methods to entice the heathen into the fold, had never been among the Manus. Into this setting stepped ethnologists who could not work unless all these carefully constructed barriers for the peace of the white invader were summarily shattered. To the native it was as if we had hung up a shingle saying: "We want to be bothered. We aren't like other white people," and they responded to this chance of a lifetime with great vigor. All day the house was crowded and not until midnight was there any peace.

We set about having a native house built, and the clan of Pere proper courteously accorded us the privilege of building our house abutting on one of the two small bits of land which are used as village greens and dancing grounds. But obtaining a house site was not obtaining a house. The thatch had to be bought in lots of ten shingles each, from the land people. Payment had to be made in advance, then runners sent out to collect. It took two months before a large thatched structure on piles was almost ready to receive us. Before it was finished I came down with malaria, and within two days three of our boys were down also. In Manus, all sickness is due to the spirits, and an elder of the other end of the village, who was anxious to hasten our removal to his section, divined the cause of the illness as the malicious work of a dead police boy, appropriately domiciled in the "House Kiap." Very solemn, he sat on the floor and explained that neither the boys nor I would recover until we moved into the new and uncompleted house. I balked for twenty-four hours, as the prospect of moving with half the household sick was not enticing; then a fourth boy came down with the fever, and we moved to a doorless, stepless dwelling, where the cookhouse had no floor. Such intimate participation in the religious and social life of the community is inconvenient and wearing, but it is the only way in which the necessary knowledge of native society can be obtained. And the way is full of pitfalls. I shall never forget the panic caused among a group of visitors, early in our stay, when my husband complied with one person's tentative request that he pronounce my name. Several people almost fell into the sea in their horrified retreat from such blasphemous behavior.

The endless tabus upon mentioning the names of any relative-in-law in a person's presence make it necessary to know the social organization of the village by heart, all the past marriages, the present marriages, the contemplated marriages. In addition it is necessary to know each person's three or four names. Even then one is continually trespassing, as when I inadvertently sneezed in the presence of a woman whose daughter was engaged to a youth named "Sneeze." There are relatives-in-law who may not look at each other, and it was necessary to construct a house with several exits, so that mothers-in-law could depart as sons-in-law entered, for it is always the women who have to do the running away. On one occasion, when I was alone in the village and had added to my household of six small boys and two girls, a man and his wife, there were so many complicated relationships that the only place where Ngaoli, my seventeen-year-old girl, could eat, without transgressing, was huddled in a corner behind the bed. And the linguistic confusion which resulted from getting a new cook boy who was the brother-in-law of three of the other boys was terrifying. One could not say his name in front of them but must refer to him grandiloquently as "the husband of Pondramet" (their sister); if he were also in the room, even this would not serve, as his wife's name could not be mentioned in his presence.

A large part of one's time in these remote villages is taken up with doctoring, as there is no doctor within a day's journey and often not one as near. Here again there are many dangers. To give medicine to someone who may die is to risk crippling one's fieldwork, as the natives may blame one for the resulting death. The children were continually fainting from malaria; a fact which was advertised to the entire village by the wails of the mother. The prescribed method of bringing the child around was for a hundred people to collect in the house, all the female relatives of the child gathering close about it, wailing, for which expression of affection they were subsequently paid, while some important man, or possibly two, stirred bowls of water with long sticks and invoked their guardian ghosts' aid in returning the child's purloined soul stuff. It was a simple matter to thrust a bottle of aromatic spirits of ammonia under the children's noses, but the natives never admitted that this brought them to, insisting that the spitting and coughing were signs that the spirits disliked the horrid medicine.

Sometimes, however, my doctoring brought rich rewards. There was one tall, shaggy-headed sorcerer, with one injured eye and a bad case of ringworm, who sought my aid to cure his disfigured skin. Day after day he came to be treated, while I supervised the application by one of the small boys of a stronger lotion than the natives were allowed to have themselves. After about two months Pataliyan was cured and made me the confidant of his projected elopement with a widow. The wrath of the ghostly husband shook the village and killed an unfortunate woman go-between, and the whole village was thrown into confusion—which was priceless to the ethnologist—all from a steady application of ringworm medicine to make the lover beautiful and desirable to a much-wooed and most excellent maker of pots.

The children were my chief concern, as I was trying to add to our knowledge of child psychology at the same time that I worked on the general ethnological background of the people. By selecting the oldest boys of the adolescent group, youngsters of about fourteen, as houseboys, we were able to attract all the rest of the children to our little patch of backyard. Each fourteen-year-old had a ten-year-old slavey, who in turn delegated the disagreeable aspects of his task to a six-year-old. Dinner was often prepared by some dozen small hands, one small boy tending each pot, faithfully blowing up the twig fire underneath it. The little girls were enlisted to pluck the wild pigeons and to fetch the firewood. I was making a collection of drawings by these savage little youngsters who had never seen paper or pencil before, and this practically disrupted the household. Every available square inch of table, box, or trunk surface was pre-empted by children engaged in drawing. They would have drawn all night happily, had I permitted them, and they came to wake me before dawn with requests for "paypa." Getting meals prepared or floors cleaned in this general nursery-school atmosphere was often difficult and always accomplished in the midst of a terrific din of happy insistent voices.

Photography demanded more organization. In that climate films have to be developed at once; there is no packing them off to the darkroom of a commercial photographer. This meant working at night. Water had to be brought from the mainland almost a mile away, and the only water fit for photography came from a "place of blood" where some of the ancestors of the village had been slain. Such blood lingers and has a bad habit of entering the bodies of the descendants who are foolhardy enough to approach within its death-dealing atmosphere. So it took many sticks of tobacco to obtain a large enough supply of water for washing films. If the water ran out, there was no remedy, for no one would venture into that fearful place after dark. As there were many films to be washed, we trained a squad of native children as helpers, retaining two extra children, one to watch that no torchlit canoes came near the house and one to scratch the backs of the other children so that they wouldn't drop the films which they were washing.

By such devious means and amid such peculiar surroundings, we worked our way into native life, until our house was known generally as the "kamal" or clubhouse, because it was always so crowded. From the native children which I had assembled into a household, it was possible to reach out into their respective homes, and to follow the details of the ceremonies, quarrels, and reconciliations which went on within the thatched walls of other houses. By oneself assuming the tabus and duties, the privileges, and obligations of a native woman, as much as possible, one receives in return the confidence of the women and learns the carefully guarded secrets which have been hidden from twenty generations of husbands and fathers. The temper, the emphasis of native life, from the woman's point of view, gradually unfolds before one's eyes, as do the moods, the thought processes, the interests of the group of children who sleep on one's floor and eat one's rice day after day. The native language becomes more and more a familiar idiom. One learns to joke in it, perhaps even to pun a little (although I knew that I was never permitted to swear, as both of my parents are living and profanity is only permitted to the orphaned). One learns to shudder when tabus are violated, to meet the news of a misfortune with the immediate question "Which ghost is responsible?" The personalities of all these alien people who press about one all day long become as clearly realized as those of the members of a family.

Only a six-weekly or less frequent mail breaks this long detailed identification with native life, from which one finally emerges wearied with the continuous restraint, the continuous reevaluation of experience, but bearing, as a field trophy, a knowledge of the native customs and the native thought attainable in no other way.

Twenty-fifth Reunion at Manus

❖❖❖❖❖❖

MARGARET MEAD

[1954]

And what is it like to come back, after twenty-five years, to the same village, to a people who have traversed centuries in that short space of time? Well, for one thing, it gives one a new kind of understanding of what has happened in our own past. You see what it must have meant to our own ancestors when they first learned to write, first heard about a calendar, or first heard about roads and laws.

If one goes to study a group of primitive people who are just being affected by civilization, one is almost sure to be *against* the changes that are bound to come. The old native culture seems like a beautiful, finely woven texture into which cheap trade goods have introduced an ugly and alien note. Since one's task is to rescue the old, one usually becomes so attached to the old that the new can only be viewed with hostile eyes.

Here in Manus, however, it is different. For one thing, I didn't think the old culture, as I saw it twenty-five years ago, was very attractive, although it was picturesque to look at—the thatched houses standing like long-legged birds in the water, the strong, lithe women in their crinkly grass skirts, the children tumbling in the shallow lagoons, canoes skimming over the water with square spread sails. But their way of life was a harsh and coercive one, which turned jolly, curious, generous children into grasping, driven, quarrelsome adults, always seeking to add one dog's tooth to another, while unrelenting ghosts presided over every household, driving each house-owner on to bigger economic enterprises.

267

It was a society in which there was rhythm but no melody, vigor and intelligence but little happiness, activity but no rest. People died young, worn out from trying to meet their endless obligations. The village lay open to the moonlight, but there was no dancing—only quarreling about debts.

I have come back to find the people whom I knew as young people and children and babies still the same community, with sons and adopted sons following in their fathers' footsteps. "You remember his father never was one for going about much," someone would say. Or "You remember when she was born and they thought her mother would die," or "He lived in the back of my uncle's house when you were here." With faultless exactitude each person put himself back twenty-five years so as to remember where a house would have been, how old a child was, or by what name I would have known someone. Perhaps it is because I know them as individuals and remember the wistfulness, the violence, the patience, and the bumptiousness of individual children that it is easier to sympathize with what they feel today. At any rate, their attempt to span centuries within a few years—to move from an illiterate people having no form of government and owing allegiance to the recently dead ghosts of each household to become a literate, responsible, self-governing community—appears as a small-scale model of man's effort to take on, from groups of other men, forms of social organization and civilization higher than those he knows.

This little village is now built on the land, and only the posts of the old lagoon village remain to show its ground plan out on the water. There is a school. It is not a school to which the children are lured or dragooned into coming, against their own and their parents' wishes, but a school that is their own. The self-taught teacher sets up sums on an old piece of blackened plyboard, while the children sit on rough benches with clipboards on their laps, writing on the backs of old army forms—all the abandoned bits of World War II turned to a new use. Late at night, one will hear a strange kind of chanting, but it is no primitive magical ceremony. It is a group of boys, sitting around a lamp made of an old tin can with a small sputtering cloth wick, reading English aloud in chorus. Twenty-five years ago, the men, naked except for bark cloth G-strings and with elaborate ornaments of shell and bone, danced defiance at each other with obsidian-tipped spears. Today their sons, now grown, ponder slowly how to adapt Robert's *Rules of Order* to village purposes. When voices are raised and the old tendency to shout and stamp asserts itself, the young clerk, just literate, whose grandfather used to terrorize the whole South Coast, rises and slowly and painfully reads the rules about majority and minority behavior!

The native medical assistant says he is ready to go and see the patient. He walks with empty hands, but the thermometer is stuck securely in his hair (where pencils also are kept). Today the people can read and interpret thermometers and keep records of births and deaths. Twenty-five years ago there was an eclipse of the moon, and I explained it to them. This summer, there was a similar eclipse, and the people remembered the explanation and did not give it a magical and threatening interpretation as some of their neighbors did.

The Manus people, the people who are the true saltwater people, have persuaded some of the cannibal landspeople to come down "inside," and now the children of cannibals sit and discuss whether carrying children spread-eagled on the back is a desirable method of child rearing.

Today I went to a ceremony. A man from the next village had come to inspect the money that his kin here will exchange with him for bags of rice and flour and sugar. Instead of strings of dogs' teeth and long strands of shell money and bands of beadwork, Australian paper and silver money lay on the pandanas mat—ten shillings ("the red one"), a pound ("the green one"), and a five-pound note ("the blue one"). Esthetically, it is far less picturesque, but one has to have seen the old system to appreciate what the people feel when they say: "Our money was only something that could buy what we ourselves made; your money can buy things from all over the world." In the old days, the competitive exchange of property put a heavy burden on every self-respecting man. Recalling this today, they say, "Now it is against our rules to pay more than five pounds for a wife, and we have forbidden the big, continuous exchanges of property, which were very hard and caused our strong men to die young. What we did once in earnest, we now do only for fun, just a little, freely and without coercion." And, acute in their realization of what is happening, they say, "The men 'in the middle' remember the old quarreling ways and bring some of them into the new, but the young men will be able to really play."

Clear-eyed, proud, self-reliant, they say: "Yes, we have seen what you have learned to do. Inside your country, things are straight. Your children do not die and die and die. Your old people live to a real old age. People do not work so hard that they are destroyed. People are regarded as nonreplaceable, whereas you have so many things that you can always get more if some are lost." And so the people who once ruined the coolness of the tropical night with drummings and fury over a broken pot, learned from the way the American Army dumped tons of equipment that people matter more than things.

By the freak of circumstance that caused them to be selected for intensive study twenty-five years ago, they and their new experiment in civilization now stand on a lighted stage. During the long evening meetings, in which men, women, and children all vote (for no one has told them that children aren't fully people), they jack up each other's morale by conjuring up visions of what "All America" will think of them if I have to report deficiency in the orderliness with which they conduct their affairs. One may argue that they have drawn a Utopian and nonrealistic picture. That may be true, but then you hear them say, "You have learned the things we want to learn: how to keep babies from dying, how to keep roads in repair, how to make the sick well, and how to make people take their quarrels to court." Of all our institutions, the court is the one that fascinates them most. In court, threats and fear are relegated to some lower order of existence, and law reigns; so people sometimes dress for court, putting on their upper garments.

This afternoon there was a long meeting about repairing houses and working a supply of sago for Christmas. It ended with the statement: "If you don't pay attention and learn how to do things, you and I, ourselves, can ruin ourselves. If we want to walk over the land, the road will be closed. If we want to go inside the ground, the road will be closed. If we want to fly up in the sky, the road will be closed. But if we all pay attention, we yet ourselves can make our village *gerup.*" Gerup is a pidgin English term which came from "get up," but it has no English equivalent. The word means to awake, to start up, to leap up, and—in this case—to lift oneself by one's own bootstraps.

PART FOUR

On Floods, Famine, and the Future

The ecological perspective is a handy tool. It is not as novel as its current position in the news might suggest. Some naturalists in past centuries thought of wildlife and man in terms of interaction with the environment and other populations through time. Ecology, in some ways, is simply yesterday's natural history with numbers.

Yet there is a change in emphasis today. Scientists not only measure as many important variables as they can find, they also make models of interacting populations and changing environments. With their models they make projections, and the results are often frightening. But these are frightening times.

Richard M. Klein's ecological analysis of floods in Florence—both recent and past—reveals how little man learns from painful lessons. Arthur H. Westing's first-hand look at the ecological damage in Indochina shows how modern technology is capable of mass ecocide.

Ecologists have an annoying tendency to be right. They long ago predicted the food and energy crises that are the news today, and Marvin Harris's conclusions about the so-called Green Revolution and George M.

Woodwell's analysis of energy limitations indicate that food and fuel problems will persist.

Yet ecology is not a dismal science, capable only of dark projections. In the last three articles in this book, Lewis Thomas, Kenneth E. F. Watt, and Marston Bates all argue in their own special ways for individualism and diversity. In a sense they have evolved from scientists to prophets. For the future of all life on this planet, I hope the modern world will hear their message.

The Florence Floods

❖❖❖❖❖❖❖

RICHARD M. KLEIN

[1969]

As it did to other presumably educated Americans,
the announcement of the Florentine flood of November
4, 1966, aroused in me the immediate reaction of horror
felt by most people when they hear of a natural catastrophe. Fragmentary stories on the wire services were
followed by detailed descriptions of specific paintings
damaged or destroyed, books soaked with water and
oil, and accounts of death, hardship, and personal
heroism. I shuddered at the evoked word picture of
the odors of sewage, rotting animal and human flesh,
mold and mud and oil. In the succeeding days, as is
usual in our overcommunicated world, the stories receded into the back pages of the newspapers and
fresh stories of other tragedies took over my attention.

Yet, there remained a nagging feeling that this flood
should never have happened at the level of intensity
and with such severe loss of the treasures of Renaissance Italy—indeed of Western civilization. As I read
more about the history of the Florentine region, I began to realize that the 1966 flood was an almost classic
example of how to ensure that floods will recur.

The area known as Tuscany is a well-marked and
fairly compact geologic unit, which rises gradually
from the western coast of Italy to the heights of the
Apennine Mountains. It is a harsh land of hills and
valleys, of winter rains and summer droughts. The
valley of the Arno lies on the northern margin of the
African trade winds and on the southern margin of the
prevailing westerlies that bring rain from the Atlantic

Ocean. In winter, the warm air above the sea forms a low-pressure cap that draws winds over the water. As these warm, moisture-laden winds flow up the hills to the Casentino mountain range, they cool, and the rain may fall furiously for several days in succession. Of the 25 to 40 inches of rainfall that Tuscany receives annually, over 80 percent falls between October and January—much of this from late October through the middle of December. In the summer, there may be no rain for several months, as the hot, rapidly moving winds from Algeria simply do not pick up enough moisture from the sea to supply rain.

Today, the hills surrounding Florence can scarcely support olives and grapes. There are occasional patches of scrub, including lavender, myrtle, rosemary, and thyme: aromatic, romantic, lovely to look at in flower, and completely useless as ground cover. The soil is leached-out clay with pockets of stone and sand. The sun beats down on impoverished and badly worn soil, changing it into cement-like hardpan. In spite of, or perhaps because of, its aridity, the land above the city of Florence has a very real beauty. From the surrounding hills, one can take in the peaks of the Casentino mountain range, bared and gleaming in the summer sun. First in abrupt descents and then more gently, the highlands fall away to the foothills. Sere, brown, and rocky, the hillsides catch the early morning or late afternoon sun, leaving the hollows in deep shadow. From a distance, it seems a landscape devoid of plants.

The present city of Florence stands on land that has been a part of the civilized world for more than 3,000 years. Excavations have unearthed artifacts dating back to the Bronze Age, and there is some evidence that Neolithic cultures flourished there even earlier. And well they might have, for the Tuscan valleys and hills were fertile and wooded, the climate then was generally mild, with just enough seasonal variation to stimulate, but not debilitate, the people, and there was reasonable protection from marauders from the north. The major river, the Arno, was a freshwater stream, apparently abounding with fish, that flowed throughout the year and was broad enough to permit travel, and hence trade, with the coastal peoples through the delta that is now the city of Pisa.

The earliest complex civilization about which we have reasonable information is that of the Etruscans. Apparently they settled in what is now Tuscany about 800-600 B.C., coming from northwest Asia Minor via the Caucasus. In addition to being farming peoples, they were experienced merchants, and much of our knowledge of them is derived from their commercial activities. The Etruscans found, settled, and exploited a land of some natural beauty. The Arno and its tributaries were clean, clear, fishable, and navigable. The hills were completely forested. In the valleys were found the Aleppo pine and two evergreen oaks, the Holm oak and the Valonia oak. These formed fairly open forests, with understories of various small trees and shrubs. The mid-mountains contained excellent stands of beech, Spanish chestnut, and deciduous oaks, and the upper mountains were clothed with black pine and several species of fir. There was an abundance of animal life, for figures on Etruscan pottery depict deer and bear hunts. In the fourth century B.C., Theophrastus mentioned the beech groves of Tuscany as being of such excellent quality that the wood was bought from the Etruscans for the construction of ships' keels. Some records suggest that they also sold fir lumber to Carthage. Even by 300 B.C. the forests in the hills were so dense that the Roman legions hesitated to invade. The plant cover was still notable several hundred years later when Strabo reported that the central Apennines and the hills of Etruria provided wood for the construction of Rome. The Sila hill range yielded "fine trees" and pitch for shipbuilding activities centered near Pisa at the mouth of the Arno.

The Etruscans were a vigorous people who attempted to use their land for many activities related to commerce. They planted olive trees and grapevines on the hillsides and farmed the valleys for wheat and barley. They mined some copper, zinc, and tin to make bronze for tools and weapons, and they probably also smelted mercury and some iron. Sheep were grazed on the lower hills to supply the white, black, and brown wools that were much prized for their softness, fineness, and natural colors. Thus, some deforestation and grazing injured the land, but the populations were too small to severely damage the fragile hills. By the end of the Etruscan hegemony, the Romans were lavish in their praise of this still-wooded, fertile, and well-watered land.

The first adequate records of floods date from the twelfth century A.D., actually 1117, when the Ponte Vecchio, then the only bridge over the Arno, was swept away. These records show clearly that the Tuscan hills were denuded, the Arno was a seasonal stream, and the land was plagued by drought. If we date the demise of Roman rule at about A.D. 300, and we know that the land was ruined by 1117, we are left with approximately 800 years to account for in terms of physical geography. What happened to the forests, the clear streams, the good soil, and the fine climate? Can we use the meager records to fill in the details of man's rape of this land?

The primary city of the Etruscans was not the area of present-day Florence, but was the now small hill town of Fiesole. Present-day Florence was a lower suburb about 15 miles downstream on the Arno. The plain of the Arno is broken into a succession of old lake beds, which filled with debris and in which beds of travertine were deposited. Florence itself was initially situated where the Arno issued from the mountains at about 180 feet above sea level, a few miles upstream from its present location. The upriver location was determined by a simple fact—the site of the present city was a marsh. Indeed, when the winter snows melted in February, the river was not easily forded. Livy noted that in the late winter of 217 B.C., Hannibal and his armies floundered for four days in the muck of the valley floor. Yet the river bottomland was very fertile, producing an excellent crop of hard wheat, some millet,

and good barley. The snowmelt served to supply nutrients, and the water moved out to sea by March, leaving
enough time to plant. There was a second reason for
the lowly political position of Florence, one related to
the defense of the area. The Etruscan military wanted
its citadel on the heights, not on the nearly indefensible
valley floor.

Fiesole, as the political and defense center, tended to
gather the greater share of the population, but it soon
became apparent that this small, hilly area could not
provide an adequate living for the populace. The hills
about Fiesole had to be intensively cultivated and the
only practical way to do this was by terracing. The
technique was certainly not invented by the Etruscans;
the Greeks and other peoples of Asia Minor had been
cutting horizontal ridges into their hills for eons. In the
Tuscan context, terracing was necessary more as a
means of fully utilizing all land within the protected
reach of the fort than as a conservation measure (although it certainly served well in this respect). Cereal
crops were not planted on the terraces but were grown
on the Arno Valley floor, and the crop was stored in
the granaries of Fiesole. Vines were planted on the
terraces, particularly on the drier, stony, south-facing
slopes of the hills. Typically, the vines were festooned
from tree to tree. Initially, the trees were native species,
but these were replaced by the olive prior to the advent
of the Roman invasions from the south. Thus, even
before the rule of Rome, some of the plant cover on
the hills had been removed. Since the Romans left no
records of flooding, we can assume that the major
portion of the Tuscan hills was still covered with plants
that sopped up the water and prevented the destructive
run-off that resulted in floods.

Tuscany, being on the route from the lands of the
Franks and the Goths to that of the Romans, served
as a staging ground for many armies. The mountains
were no longer an effective barrier from the north as
logistics and disciplined armies replaced wandering
bands of military plunderers. Records are hazy and

contradictory, but it seems that the Romans defeated the Etruscans several times between 300 and 200 B.C. and that about 200 or 150 B.C. Roman rule was firmly established. The Roman road system was extended through Tuscany, and during its construction the engineers tried to stay in the piedmont except where there was a necessary valley river crossing. The Via Julia Augusta crossed the Arno at the site of the present Ponte Vecchio to connect with the Via Cassia going to the north. Even then, the Roman legions knew it as a bad crossing because it was muddy and tended to flood in the spring. There are no records of massive winter floods, however.

Under the protection of the legions and the Roman governor, Sulla, the population of Fiesole began to move down the Arno to where life was easier. When Sulla was defeated by invading Franks, Florence was leveled and burned, and again the people retreated to the hills. By 59 B.C., Florence was restored under the auspices of Julius Caesar to its present location and given the name Julia Augusta Florentina, the latter word apparently being a good omen rather than having any botanical allusions. The city was a typical Roman city-fort with temples, baths, aqueducts, and an efficient sewage-disposal system. There was a central marketplace, now the Piazza Vittorio Emanuele, and the city was walled. Apparently there was some attempt to drain the swampy area then outside the city walls. Although flooding in winter did not assume sufficient importance to record, the Romans were well aware that snowmelt was a danger, for they did erect levees on the banks of the now contained but still free-flowing Arno.

The ancients knew the value of woodland as flood protection. Plato deplored the reckless cutting of the Greek forests and pointed out the cause-and-effect relationship between forest destruction and the rapid run-off of rain from bared hills. Pliny quoted Plato when he admonished the Romans to maintain and to replenish their forests, and while we have no direct evidence, it seems likely that some form of forest conservation was practiced in the Tuscan hills.

With the population increasing, terracing also increased, but this stopped rather abruptly. Malaria, which had been introduced into Sicily from North Africa during the fourth century B.C., moved onto the continent during the Second Punic War of 218–204 B.C. By the beginning of the Christian Era, it reached Tuscany, where it became endemic in the lower valleys and in the city. Within less than a century, Florence and the hill towns had virtually been abandoned. The terraced farms, no longer cultivated, were subjected to erosion that washed away the precious soil. Lacking stability, it is easy to visualize the stripping of the soil from the hills, the mud slides, and the consequent silting of the tributary rivers and, eventually, of the Arno itself. Although no records exist, we are fairly safe in saying that minor flooding occurred in the Arno basin from about the middle of the first century A.D.

During the subsequent 300 years, the town of Florence continued to decline, local trade decreased, and the once relatively important Roman city became little more than a village. As the Roman Empire began to fall apart during the third and fourth centuries, tilling declined and the plowed land and terraced lower hillsides were subjected to direct erosion. The upper hills, however, began to restore themselves, and flooding probably decreased.

The fortunes of the city took a turn for the better by the end of the fourth century as the malaria began to disappear for reasons that are not known. The Lombards made Florence into a military center, and when the Franks replaced the Lombards in 774, the entire region assumed an increased role as a trade center. By then Fiesole had declined to the level of a town, a condition that has never been reversed.

As the population grew, there was a greater demand for wood to be used for construction and for fuel. The hills were rapidly stripped, so that by the end of the seventh century wood had become so scarce and expensive that stone became the primary construction material. From the perspective of the art historian, this had some importance. The artisans of the time were both good craftsmen and good architects. These early stone buildings served as models for the Renaissance master builders, who made Florence a place of enduring beauty and, incidentally, laid out a city especially suited for flooding. As the city began to assume its present shape virtual bathtubs were created there—piazzas and squares with a single inlet street and one or a few outlets. Water rushing into one of these squares could not easily pour out the other side and the whole area filled up. Most of the listed highwater marks of the 1966 and earlier floods occurred in these piazzas.

Although the Etruscans and the Romans engaged in the wool trade, and Florence had been a weaving center for many centuries, the increased use of wool cloth by peoples less exalted than the aristocracy resulted in a great increase in woolen mill activity. As the woodlands were decimated, the cleared land that resulted became pasture for goats and sheep. Now, both these animals nibble forage to the root level, effectively killing the individual plant. The overgrazing became so severe that by the eighth century the Florentine mills could no longer depend on local wool and hair but were forced to import it from England and Spain. Parenthetically, it is likely that the denuded Spanish hills are partially the result of overgrazing by sheep to supply wool to Florence.

The effect of land clearing on the climate of Florence is not easy to document. Modern ecological and ecophysical studies show that forested areas serve as natural air conditioners. Heat is collected by trees during the day and released slowly at night. Modified by the cooling power of evaporation, the heat never builds up as it does when captured by stone and paving; a walk from a city street into a park at dusk illustrates this dramatically. The presence of nothing but baked clay on the hills above Florence served to perpetuate its summer heat and drought. The forests served, as the Etruscans and Romans knew, to ameliorate the heat of the summer. Not incidentally, the absence of the forests with their water-holding capacity resulted in loss of scarce summer moisture and the rivers and brooks ceased flowing in the summer.

By the beginning of the ninth century Florence had about 30,000 people, and the old walls had been breached and built farther out several times. The region had many different rulers, none particularly firm or effective. The weak rulers gradually let power slip from their hands, and authority, power, and ownership of the land became divided among the Roman Catholic bishops and a few wealthy landowners. These interlocked concentrations of land ownership led steadily toward the development of a feudal system in which relatively large areas were tilled by serfs for the production of a few economically important crops and products. Goats and sheep continued to graze, and meadowlands were cut from the forests farther up the hills. With the removal of the sparse grass, the summer droughts baked and caked the clay soil to the consistency of rock, and natural seeding in it became virtually impossible. Bound to squeeze the last florin of profit from the country, the church and the landowners made no attempt to replenish their land. Tuscany, a land noted for good water, forests, and fine agricultural bottomland, inexorably declined into the arid, bare, and impoverished country that we see today. The greed of the church, the avarice of the aristocracy, and the ignorance of the people have given us this legacy.

The remainder of this sad tale can be told rather quickly. The first complete record of a major flood was provided by Giovanni Villani for the flood of November, 1333. There was an average of 4 feet of water, the city walls collapsed (never to be rebuilt), and three of the then four bridges over the Arno were destroyed; the Ponte Vecchio stood firm. Quoting Villani: "Wherefore everyone was filled with great fear and all the church bells throughout the City were rung continuously as an invocation to heaven that the water rise no farther. And in the houses, they beat the kettles and brass basins raising loud cries to God of '*misericordia, misericordia*,' the while those in peril fled from roof to roof and house to house on improvised bridges. And so great was the human din and tumult that it almost drowned out the crash of the thunder." Not unexpectedly, the flooding was worse in the low-lying districts nearest the Arno. Three hundred people died in the hard-hit districts of San Piero Scheraggio and the Porta San Piero. On the Via de Neri the flood crest was 13 feet 10 inches, only 14 inches lower than during the 1966 flood. Villani carefully listed the losses of grain and casks of wine, and in quite modern fashion he noted the cost of bridge repair, as well as municipal outlays for cleaning the streets and for minor compensations to citizens.

Villani noted the extraordinary rainfall over the Arno watershed but then wrote: "On May 15 there was an eclipse of the moon in the sign of Taurus . . . and then at the beginning of July there followed a conjunction of Saturn with Mars at the end of the sign of the Virgin." The church had the last word, stating that "by means of the laws of nature, God pronounced judgment on us for our outrageous sins." There was slight consolation from the King of Naples, who told the Florentines that "whom God loveth, He chasteneth." The Florentine Renaissance had opened with a bang.

A tiny note of biological intelligence was, however, struck by Gianbattista Vico del Cilento, who recommended a government-sponsored reforestation plan. Two hundred years later—the plan never having got off the ground—Guistino Fortunato dismissed Vico's plan, stating that trees were ugly and useless.

We need not detail the economic and biotic history of Florence beyond 1333. In spite of accurate information on causes of floods and adequate technical information on flood control, nothing was done. Vico was probably not the first, and he certainly was not the last, to chastise the Florentines for their laxity. Giovanni Batista Adriana said that the severe flood of 1547 badly disturbed the people who demanded that something be done. They were told that God wanted, with this act, to signify that worse calamities would occur, so they decided to wait. In 1545, Michelangelo cautioned a nephew about buying a house in the Santa Croce district, "every year there the cellars flood." His warning was apt, for the flood of 1547 was followed by another in mid-September of 1557, when the entire Santa Croce district was under several feet of water. Lorenzo de' Medici warned the population about the Arno: "Its arrogant anger splits and beats away at the weak banks." But in spite of his authority to order new construction, he did nothing, and there is no evidence that the people heeded the warning.

Leonardo reported that the streams of Tuscany were muddier when they passed through populated districts and suggested that the mud was washed-out soil that clogged the streams and leached the soil of the hills. He conducted surveys and designed projects to develop water impoundments in the hills, to dredge the tributaries of the Arno and the Sieve, and to develop chambers under the city to hold excess floodwaters. These, too, were ignored.

The Tuscan flood situation had only one useful effect. In 1861, President Lincoln appointed the Vermonter George Perkins Marsh as first American minister to the kingdom of Italy. Marsh's travels in Tuscany and his reports on the relatively minor floods of 1861 and 1863 undoubtedly contributed to his thinking in the preparation of *Man and Nature or Physical Geography as Modified by Human Action*, published in 1864. As a result of the interest (indeed the controversy) created by this book, Marsh was asked to help compile the irrigation laws of Italy, laws never adequately enforced, which could have alleviated the floods that have occurred during the past seventy-five years. It must be noted that Marsh's book so stimulated Gifford Pinchot that he persuaded President Theodore Roosevelt to set in motion the legislation leading to the conservation policies of the United States.

For what it is worth, the statistical picture is gloomy. Since 1333, there has been a moderate flood in Florence every 24 years, a major flood every 26 years, and a massive flood every 100 years. Of the massive floods, those of November, 1333; November, 1844; and November, 1966, have been the worst. Since 1500 there have been more than 50 floods qualifying as moderate and 54 qualifying as major.

In 1797, a French engineer, Fabre, announced that the alpine torrents that flooded the lowlands were a direct result of deforestation of the heights. One hundred years later, in 1890, the French government undertook the job of reforestation in the Hautes-Alpes. Engineer Surell reported that as reforestation continued, floods decreased in number and severity. This report was widely distributed in Europe, was acted upon in Germany and Switzerland, but was ignored in Italy.

Apparently no one in Florence could believe that water could cover their city in the twentieth century. But they, themselves, place marble markers on their homes and churches "commemorating" previous floods. They, themselves, proudly indicate the high-water marks of floods dating back 500 years. They, themselves, speak of their dry, bare hills, which shimmer in the summer sun, and they cannot fail to see that their "ribbon of shining silver," their Arno, is a muddy, silted-in, malodorous stream that almost stops flowing during the summer.

The New York Times of January 2, 1969, reported that during the week preceding Christmas of 1968—two years after the most damaging flood in Florentine history—the Arno crested toward the flood mark. "Only after the river began to subside at 9:00 P.M. did the crowds move homeward." The bed of the Arno is still filled with the debris of the 1966 flood and has never been dredged. It is now estimated that the silt from 1966 alone is 6 feet thick.

There are two dams on the Arno, the Levane dam at

Livorno, 35 miles upstream from the city, and the Penna dam, yet higher into the hills. These are power dams and do not provide for flood control. No money has been (or apparently ever was) appropriated for reforestation as recommended in 1334 by Vico, for the construction of water impoundments and for dredging the Arno as recommended by Leonardo, or for caring for the land as recommended by Plato.

It is beyond the scope of this article to discuss the storage of irreplaceable books and art treasures in the basements of Santa Croce, noted by Michelangelo as the district where the cellars flood every year. It is beyond the scope of this article to discuss the reasons for the lack of coordination between the two damsites. It is beyond the scope of this article to discuss the lack of retaining walls bordering the Arno; even Lorenzo did nothing about them. As George Santayana warned in his *Reason in Common Sense*, "when experience is not retained . . . infancy is perpetual. Those who cannot remember the past are condemned to repeat it."

Lightning Water

❖❖❖❖❖❖

JOSEPH WOOD KRUTCH

[1968]

Flash floods, those wildly beautiful desert hallmarks, serve as a healthy reminder that nature on the rampage can quickly reduce to utter helplessness the careless individual or the person who naïvely assumes that the whole of the natural world has been "conquered." Strangers to the desert cannot believe that a sandy gully, which looks like a good place to camp, may become, without warning, a raging flood—a wall of water several feet high plunging forward with enormous speed and force.

Reclamation engineers, operating under a variety of names, are making a concerted effort to tame or conquer these floods—along with everything else that is free and natural. Their rationale often alludes to the fact that people have sometimes been drowned in them, but people have been killed rather more often in highway accidents, and no one talks about the necessity of eliminating automobiles. Perhaps the real reason for the often intemperate enthusiasm of the reclaimers is that the projects they dream up will provide them with jobs.

Like the road builders, the reclaimers are inclined to see needs where no one else can, and their consequent boondoggling threatens to destroy a large portion of the remaining natural environment. When every stream has been dammed and all the countryside has become a mere network of roads, their triumph will be complete— America the Beautiful will have become America the Conquered.

If we would only begin to question our naïve faith

that the road and dam builders "must know best because they are experts"; if, instead, we would only realize that the first concern of all of them is their vested interest in their own jobs, rather than in the public good, then their pointless vandalism of our countryside might be stopped. But this realization is likely to be too late in coming.

It doesn't rain often in the desert and the total annual rainfall is small. But when it does rain, the water often comes down in torrent proportions. This is one reason why the flash flood is primarily a desert phenomenon. Death Valley in California furnishes an extreme example. It is the driest spot in the United States. Average rainfall is about 1.5 inches and more than a year has been known to pass without a measurable trace. Yet in July, 1950, a cloudburst (a convenient but not very meaningful term) produced a flood which cut a 6-foot-deep gully across the main road and rolled along boulders 5 feet in diameter. In Arizona more than 5 inches of rain has fallen in a twenty-four-hour period; as much as 11 inches in the course of one storm. These are exceptional figures, but very heavy downpours within a short time are usual.

The other principal reason why the flash flood is almost exclusively a feature of the desert is that nearly all the water that falls in a torrential rain runs off. Vegetation ground cover is sparse or nonexistent. The surface of the ground is often baked to an almost bricklike consistency. Very little water is absorbed. Most of it runs off into the dry riverbeds cut by previous floods. These gullies are among the most characteristic features of arid lands and are called by a variety of names—dry wash or draw in Arizona, arroyo in California, wadi in the Near East. Some of the floodwaters that periodically rage through an arroyo sink into its usually sandy or rocky bottom. A few feet below the surface, the soil may be damp, while that of the surrounding desert floor is completely dry. The difference in moisture creates a special environment for plant life. Near the borders of the dry wash there may be cottonwoods that cannot survive the desert and a special species of palo verde trees, which needs just a bit more water than the easily distinguishable species that grows in more arid situations.

Another geomorphic feature created by the flash floods is the alluvial fan—characteristic of desert regions bordered by mountains. These are delta-shaped accumulations of sand and rock, deposited at the point where mountain ravines open onto the desert floor. Torrents arising from storms in the mountains plunge down these ravines, finally dumping their debris when their speed is reduced by emergence onto the flatness of the desert. Especially striking specimens can be seen in Death Valley. They look rather more like glaciers than like the flood deltas of moister regions, and they are among the most graceful of land forms.

Most paved roads in the desert are crossed at frequent intervals by dips that conduct the water across the roadbeds. These dips, too, may be dangerous in flood season. Neither the pedestrian nor the motorist can quite believe the force of the water that occasionally rushes through these dry beds. But the presence of automobile-sized boulders in the arroyos attests to the carrying force of the water which increases enormously with an increase in speed.

It is said that the carrying power of a stream varies as the sixth power of its velocity. But whether or not this figure is entirely accurate, all the lay traveler needs to remember is that an increased speed of flow increases manyfold the stream's power to sweep heavy objects along with it. He must not assume that because the flood doesn't look much swifter than it did when he crossed it safely a short time before, it is probably still safe. If he makes that assumption, he may be in for trouble. Flash floods are dangerous only if you don't take the trouble to know what they are and why they exist. But to some of us it seems that it would be better to teach people how to travel or live in the few remaining natural areas than to destroy their unique characteristics.

The ultimate endeavor of the reclaimers is to homogenize the American earth, which today presents an infinite variety. The more it is crossed by freeways and the more its streams and lakes are regularized by engineers, the more every part of it will look like every other part. It will no longer be worth taking the journeys from one region to another that the superhighways are supposed to make so easy and so quick.

The Southwest without the flash floods would be no longer recognizable, no longer unique, no longer beautiful in its own way. We have begun to hear some talk about preserving a few wild rivers, and the flash flood is the wildest of all wild rivers. On the other hand, the reclaimers seem determined to tame everything capable of inspiring awe and to put everywhere in its place the tame, the uniform, and the convenient. They are making this a far less interesting world.

Ecocide in Indochina

❖❖❖❖❖❖

ARTHUR H. WESTING

[1971]

All wars raise havoc with the land on which they are fought. However, our war in Indochina has been, and continues to be, particularly disruptive of the environment.

The country is largely rural, and the enemy is dispersed in the fields and forests, in the mountains and swamps. This enemy matches his numbers and concealment and persistence against our wealth and technology and persistence. They hide and we seek.

In an attempt to cope with that elusive enemy, dispersed and hidden in the wild stretches of Vietnam, the United States military employs two major tactics: bombing on a staggeringly unprecedented scale and laying bare vast stretches of terrain. Both tactics are enormously disruptive of the ecology (and economy) of Vietnam.

When an area is found to contain—or is even suspected of containing—Vietcong, it is subjected to intensive aerial bombardment. Hundreds of bombing sorties are flown each day. Some 3 million bombs are dropped annually, for a total now of more than 10 million tons, and the program is being intensified daily. In flying over the country, as I did not long ago, one is overwhelmed by the endless craters, each 20 or 30 feet deep and 30 to 40 feet across. These ubiquitous craters are (at least during the rainy season) usually filled with water and provide an ideal breeding habitat for malarial mosquitoes. The long-term ecological effects, possibly for centuries, of this massive intrusion of the environment have attracted little attention.

292

The other massive ecological disturbance is our program of defoliation: the destruction of vast stretches of vegetation in order to deny cover and sanctuary to the enemy. This is done in two major ways. One rather straightforward approach is to bulldoze the countryside. Using giant tractors equipped with sharpened Rome-plow blades, we have now cleared a 1,000- to 2,000-yard strip along most major transportation routes. Most of these swaths—often scraped down to the infertile subsoil—are barren and subject to erosion. The remainder are largely weed-choked wastelands. They will be difficult to reclaim and rehabilitate after the war.

In addition to roadside clearing, large contiguous areas of countryside are Rome-plowed to deny them to the enemy. At least half a million acres of forest were cleared through 1969, according to information released by the Army. This program continues unabated. In the words of the commanding officer of this operation, "The B-52 bomber is the battle-ax of this war, and our plow is the scalpel."

The second and much more extensive means we have devised for denying wild land cover and sanctuary to the other side is the aerial application of plant poisons, or herbicides. This aspect of the war drew me to Indochina twice, most recently in August, 1970, as director of the Herbicide Assessment Commission of the American Association for the Advancement of Science (AAAS). There is no precedent for the massive use of herbicides in a tropical environment and thus no way of reliably predicting the full extent and seriousness of the damage being inflicted upon the ecology of Vietnam. The likelihood of serious long-term damage to the environment has been a major concern of many scientists in this country and elsewhere. In December, 1970, the Council of the AAAS resolved to urge the United States to renounce the military use of herbicides.

War against the plants of Vietnam began in late 1961 and, according to a recent Department of Defense news release, was inflicted upon some 5½ million acres through 1969. Since the program continues to this day, the current figure can be estimated to be in excess of 6½ million acres. (A half million or more acres classified as agricultural have been sprayed.) All told, one acre in six in South Vietnam has now been sprayed.

To illustrate the extent of environmental disruption more graphically: South Vietnam approximates the size of New England; the area sprayed is larger than Vermont; the area bulldozed almost that of Rhode Island. While none of Vietnam's forty-three provinces has escaped, some have been attacked herbicidally with particular intensity and frequency. Among these are the Rung Sat region in Gia Dinh Province southeast of Saigon, Tay Ninh Province (War Zone C), which is northwest of Saigon, and Long Khanh Province (War Zone D) northeast of Saigon—the last previously contained major stands of South Vietnam's magnificent virgin tropical forest.

Most forest spraying has been done with a 1:1 mixture of 2,4-D and 2,4,5-T, Agent Orange in military terminology; some with a 4:1 mixture of 2,4-D and picloram, or Agent White; and small amounts with dimethyl arsenic acid, Agent Blue. The use of Agent Orange was discontinued in early 1970, largely in favor of Agent White. Agent Orange was applied at the rate of 25 pounds of active ingredients per acre; Agent White at 8 pounds; and Agent Blue at 9.

When an upland forest is attacked with herbicide, the leaves drop after two or three weeks and the trees remain bare for several months. Sunlight, able to reach the forest floor following defoliation, promotes the growth of a luxuriant understory in which certain herbaceous grasses and shrubby bamboos dominate. A tropical forest has an enormous diversity of species, some more sensitive to the spray than others. When refoliation of the trees occurs, about one out of ten trees fails to survive the treatment, perhaps more. This has occurred on more than 5 million acres in Vietnam. The repeated spraying of an additional million acres or so of upland forest has caused even more serious damage. In such areas the proportion of trees killed rises dramatically, as much as 50 percent to 80 percent or higher, depending upon the number of applications, the type of spray, and the local mix of species. An estimated 6½ billion board feet of merchantable tropical timber have been destroyed, plus an indeterminate amount of fuel wood, charcoal wood, and other forest products.

In flying over these hard-hit areas, I was impressed by the widespread invasion of cogon grass (*Imperata*) or, even worse, a variety of low-growing scrub bamboos. These species are aggressive colonizers and prevent the reestablishment of the former high forest. The resultant grass savannas and bamboo brakes have a reduced biomass and an impoverished fauna. Commercially worthless, they will be extremely difficult to eradicate. These vegetational wastelands will remain one of the legacies of our presence for decades to come.

Additional, less obvious ecological damage is likely to occur in a sprayed upland forest. In a tropical forest ecosystem (unlike those of temperate zones), the major fraction of the total nutrient budget is in its biotic component (largely in the leaves and small twigs). Following defoliation, a significant fraction of the leaf-stored nutrients is probably lost permanently in the water run-off. It takes decades for a tropical ecosystem to restore its former productivity following such nutrient dumping.

Herbivorous insect, bird, and bat populations are bound to decline markedly and with them, their pollinating function, which is so important in a tropical forest where individual plants of the same species are usually widely scattered. In the replacement community, particularly following multiple herbicidal attacks, the original set of animal populations will be replaced by a less diverse set. A large number of species will be eliminated and the replacement community will have higher numbers of fewer species, many of them new to the area. In addition, the miles of borders (or ecotones) between divers vegetational types is being greatly increased. Such a fringe habitat supports its own animal community. For example, the scrub typhus mite appears to be restricted to such a niche.

The chemicals used for defoliation missions (largely 2,4-D, 2,4,5-T, and picloram) are potent herbicides but are supposedly not toxic to animals. These chemicals have their main effect on terrestrial animals (both large and microscopic) indirectly, via the dependence of these animals on plants for food and shelter. However, at least one of the herbicides, 2,4,5,-T, contains dioxin as an impurity. Dioxin is both highly toxic and enormously teratogenetic (causing birth defects) to mammals. Vietnam's countryside has been drenched over the years with some 47 million pounds of 2,4,5,-T, with an estimated dioxin concentration of 25 parts per million. This means that more than 1,000 pounds of dioxin have been introduced into Vietnam's environment. Dioxin's environmental stability, mobility, and possible points of concentration in the ecosystem are not yet known.

In a different ecological situation, more than 1 million acres of Vietnam's southerly coastal regions are subject to daily flooding at each high tide. This tidal zone supports a characteristic biotic community known as mangrove swamp. It is an inhospitable region used mainly as a source of charcoal and as sanctuary for the ubiquitous Vietcong. More subtly, it is a crucial breeding and nursing ground for a great variety of ocean fishes and crustaceans and some river fishes.

To date, more than one-quarter of Vietnam's mangrove association has been sprayed and killed. I say *"killed"* because, through some quirk of nature, one herbicidal attack of this tidal zone literally kills all the plant life that grows there. Moreover, for unknown reasons, the plants do not regenerate. The utter devastation that results is eerie to behold and also frightening because I could find no indication of how soon, if ever, recovery would occur. Tens of thousands of acres sprayed years ago still have no sign of green on them. The web of life on these vast stretches has been destroyed, with ecological ramifications—and even geologic ones via marine erosion—not yet possible to fathom. Whether or not the recent disappearance of the freshwater tarpon, which breeds among the mangroves, from the Mekong Delta is the result of this destruction remains to be determined.

My focus has been on the strictly ecological impact of the military use of herbicides in a tropical setting. What must be left for another time is the impact of this program on human ecology—on the 17 million semi-destitute Vietnamese peasants and primitive hill tribesmen inexorably enmeshed in the vagaries of the war. This unfortunate aspect of the problem has incredibly serious economic, public health, and social welfare dimensions.

Whatever one's political and moral views may be toward the war in Indochina, one has to assume that the war will end some day and that the surviving population must have a natural resource to support itself. The natural resource is the base upon which an under-developed country must build its future.

In December the White House announced a "phasing out" of the use of herbicides. It is my hope that a second statement is imminent announcing the immediate cessation and abrogation of such use of herbicides. I hasten to add that I have little against the discriminate civil use of many herbicides; I am only against their massive and indiscriminate use by the military. One cannot destroy a nation in order to save it.

Down on the Commune

❖❖❖❖❖❖

ARTHUR W. GALSTON

[1972]

Most recent American visitors in China follow a well-worn path—from Canton to Shanghai to Peking—with a visit to historic Sian and Yenan, or some other city of special interest, thrown in for some. They are all put up in Western-style hotels such as the Peking or Hsin Ch'iao in the nation's capital or the Hoping in Shanghai (the splendid old Victor Sassoon Cathay Hotel), where they sleep on Western beds in luxurious suites, eat Western-style food, and talk almost exclusively with other visitors from the West.

When they visit factories, schools, apartment houses, or communes, they are driven in commodious limousines, which move swiftly through the streets, honking pedestrians, buses, and slower traffic out of the way. At their destinations, they are usually met by official delegations from the relevant Revolutionary Committee and then whisked through the establishment on a carefully worked-out and busy schedule. I think it is fair to say that their view of China is at best fragmentary and selected. It is not at all surprising that their reports have been remarkably uniform.

When I was in China for fifteen days last year, I insisted on being allowed to walk about by myself part of the time, so that I could observe and photograph whatever came my way. This was valuable and enjoyable, but still limited and selective, since I could perforce walk only in the cities in the vicinity of the hotels where I was staying. My ability to profit from my experiences was further hampered by my complete lack of knowledge of the Chinese language.

This year I have returned to China with my wife, Dale, and daughter, Beth, aged 23, and the experience is proving quite different in many respects. We are staying for two months rather than two weeks. Almost from the moment of our arrival, we protested against the restriction of our activities to lodging in luxury hotels in big cities, attending formal banquets, and riding around in chauffeured limousines. After a bit of argument, we won a series of small victories that culminated in our being allowed to move, by ordinary bus and walking, to a people's commune for an indefinite stay. And at this writing, we are living in a typical (but fairly well-off) peasant's home, eating ordinary fare, and within the limits of physical endurance, participating in the regular *lao dung,* or manual labor, that consumes the larger part of an average commune member's life. It is a life common to the almost 80 percent of China's population—about 600 million people—who live in rural areas.

We have visited schools, nurseries, clinics, hospitals, and stores and are even being permitted to sit in on the biweekly political discussions required of almost all workers in China. We are enjoying a view of China quite different from what I was able to observe last year, one that is probably unknown to all but a few foreigners.

The Lu Gou Chiao Jenmin Gungsha (Marco Polo Bridge People's Commune) is located a short distance from Peking. It comprises an area of about 18 square miles and a population of about 46,000 people, living in 10,700 households. This is not extraordinarily large; the Malu People's Agricultural Commune outside of Shanghai, which I visited last year, has 75,000 people.

Our commune is divided into 21 brigades subdivided into 143 production teams. The latter are the true functioning units of the commune; their members plan, work, discuss, and criticize together. They also share the problems and rewards of their joint agricultural effort.

My wife, daughter, and I are staying with a production team of 97 families. The team is closely knit, and in two weeks we have come to know many of the members. In addition to its primary agricultural activity, the commune manufactures farm tools, motors, lime, and bricks and has facilities for the repair of trucks. Its children attend its own 19 elementary and 5 middle schools under a Committee on Culture, Education, and Sanitation.

Each brigade is led by a Revolutionary Committee (RC), nominated and elected by its members. The Syau Tuen Brigade, of which our Mei Shih Kou production unit is a part, has an RC of nine members, one from each of its six component production teams and three chosen at large. Although only one of the RC members of this brigade is a woman, it was emphasized to us that the head of the commune itself is a woman, and that women play a large role in the commune as a whole.

When we arrived with our interpreter, Li Ming-teh, we were met by two leaders of the production team, a man and a woman. Chang Chung, a muscular man of 44, has had no formal education, but he is a skilled farmer and excels at getting along with people. He has six children, four boys and two girls. Chang Shu-men, a 27-year-old woman, is married, has no children, and is completely devoted to her role as a "responsible person" in the commune. We quickly learned to refer to them as "lao" Chang and "syao" Chang, for "old" and "young" Chang.

They led us to the home of our host, Shih Chen Yu, a 73-year-old patriarch with three sons and two daughters. Two of his sons live and work on the commune in close proximity with their parents, the other son and one daughter are mill-workers in nearby Peking, and the younger daughter is a teacher in the commune.

The extended family, twenty-three people, occupies a brick-walled compound of 90 by 84 feet, subdivided into an outer courtyard 30 feet wide by 84 feet long and an inner courtyard 60 feet wide by 84 feet long. Two two-room houses, each about 21 by 40 feet, form an L at one corner of the inner court. At the opposite end is the toilet, a walled-in "one-holer" of concrete, open to the sky. Family waste is collected regularly and allowed to ferment for two or three months in an airtight concrete tank. Then, odorless and disease-free, it is used for fertilizer, especially on the vegetable plots, which are the primary concern of this production team. The remainder of the periphery of the inner compound is occupied by cooking sheds, storage sheds, rabbit hutches, chicken coops, and a small vegetable plot.

Near the houses in the central courtyard is a hand-operated pump in almost continual use, which yields large quantities of apparently pure fresh water. Water heated on coal stoves is brought to each house in a kettle and stored in insulated jugs to provide abundant hot water for tea making or washing up.

The courtyard floor is earthen, but there is one concrete path down the center to the main house. This courtyard is swept and sprinkled frequently and is as scrupulously clean as conditions permit. The outer courtyard has an enclosure for a pig at one end, flanked by a shelter for a tethered sheep and her lamb and a pile of storage wood. The corners near the entrance to the lane contain a pile of coal and a pile of straw.

The house in which we live is divided into two rooms, one about twice as long as the other; about one-third the area of each room is given over to an elevated *k'ang*. This is an earthen bed platform built over a heating unit. It is covered by straw mats, sometimes also by rugs or thin mattress pads, and affords a spacious and comfortable, if firm, bed. The pillows, stuffed with chaff and covered with a finely woven straw mat, are also surprisingly comfortable.

Our days start at about 4:30 a.m. Fires are rekindled, water boiled for tea and wash-up, and children tended to. By 5:00, we are washed and dressed and sipping tea outside in the courtyard. Seated on low footstools around a low, square table, we are frequently joined by our hosts, interpreters, or lao and syao Chang. By 5:30 we are off to work, which moves at a good clip until breakfast at 7:00 a.m. At this time, the community loudspeakers, which have been playing inspirational music, switch to the news. Breakfast, rest, and true wash-up follow until 8:30, when work recommences and continues until noon with a break between 10:00 and 10:30.

Lunch is the big meal of the day and is followed by a long rest in the heat of the day, until 2:30 or 3:00 p.m. Then work continues until 7:00, with a break from 5:00 to 5:30. It is a long, hard workday, but always sociable, never frenetic. During the busy harvest period, some workers return to the fields after the evening meal, served at about 8:00 p.m. But we fall exhausted into bed at about 9:00 or 9:30 every evening.

We share a fair sampling of the work of the commune, which in the case of our team is two-thirds vegetable and one-third grain production. We tie up and weed cucumber plants, harvest beans, debud tomatoes, remove and bundle rice seedlings for transplantation, haul harvested wheat to the thresher, pitchfork the once-threshed material into piles for further winnowing, cart chaff to the piggery, gather the straw into stacks, sweep the grain into giant piles, shovel it into bags, help haul the bags to the warehouse, and sweep and tend the large, open threshing area.

We are finding muscles that we haven't known for years and marvel at the strength and endurance of the men and women who work the fields constantly. Their labor is continuous, graceful, and cheerful and frequently accompanied by much chatter and ribbing and music from the community loudspeaker. We especially respect their ability to squat on their heels for hours on end without fatigue; we can last only about five minutes, and in harvesting beans and removing rice seedlings, this is a distinct disadvantage.

Our reaction to this hard work regimen after one week surprises us. We are exhilarated by it; we enjoy working together with a group engaged in a mutual, productive effort. We find our appreciation for small things, like tomatoes and cucumbers, heightened by our familiarity with the problems associated with their production. We also feel that the distressing problems of the world, in which we were so recently immersed, have receded and that what is really important is getting the wheat harvested before the rains come, getting the vegetables irrigated before the drought damages them, and increasing the welfare and happiness of our friends on the commune. In short, the brief exposure has worked; we are hooked and have become truly emotionally attached to the commune.

Each production unit has several "barefoot doctors," that is, regular workers who have received from one month to one year of special medical training. They can administer first aid, dispense routine prescriptions, assist at childbirth, and handle some inoculations and small surgery such as stitching up a wound. Each brigade (about six production teams) has a clinic staffed both by regular and barefoot doctors; the regular doctors can be either Western- or traditional Chinese-trained. Each clinic building has rooms for examinations, inoculations, minor surgery, and a pharmacy. It is open, with someone on duty, twenty-four hours a day.

The commune operates a large hospital, complete with all modern medical facilities and a staff of doctors, including Western, traditional Chinese, and barefoot. It is prepared to handle all but the most serious medical emergencies, for which patients would be sent to nearby Peking. Under this system, all commune members receive complete medical care for the sum of 2 yuan (roughly 80 cents) per year.

Both my wife and daughter developed colds during the third day of our stay, and in my wife's case the complications of coughing and fever were enough to warrant some medical attention. So we were visited by a team of four medical people: a Western-trained doctor, a traditional Chinese doctor, and two barefoot doctors, all of whom had a hand in the diagnosis.

The traditional Chinese doctor, the senior member of the delegation, started the proceedings by taking my wife's pulse and then telling her that she had a cold, her throat was dry and sore, her stomach was upset, her head hurt, and her joints ached. He was right on about

80 percent of these statements, but he didn't ask, he *told*.

Then the Western-trained woman doctor took my wife's temperature, blood pressure, and pulse, looked inside her throat, and listened with a stethoscope at various spots front and back. She ended by palpating the abdomen. Both doctors then consulted with each other and the barefoot doctors and jointly wrote Chinese- and Western-style prescriptions, both of which were promptly filled and delivered to our house. This treatment was probably rather special, because we were foreign visitors and VIPs, but it was impressive nonetheless. Whether because of the treatment or because of the passage of time, my wife rapidly improved.

Furthermore, it does seem that all commune members feel secure medically, no matter what the emergency. This notion is reinforced when we hear many older members refer to the preliberation era when no peasant could expect medical attention for any illness.

Schooling, too, is self-contained within the commune, with each brigade operating one or more primary schools, and the commune operating the lower and upper middle schools for all. The primary school we visited has slightly over 500 students and 22 teachers, 7 male and 15 female. The teachers (usually more than 20 years old) are themselves graduates of upper middle schools and have studied some educational technique and a special subject. Their salaries are in the 50–60 yuan per month range, the median for workers generally. The school is governed by a three-man Revolutionary Committee under the close supervision of the Communist Party. The chairman of the RC, for example, is secretary of the local party branch, and the vice chairman is also a party member; the third member is a teacher. Yet we were told that these three are all chosen by election; we still cannot resolve this logical inconsistency.

The students go to school from 8:00 a.m. to 11:45 a.m. or from 2:00 p.m. to 5:45 p.m., double sessions each divided into 45-minute periods. During the first three years (ages 7–9) they study Chinese literature, mathematics, music, sports, drawing, and politics (largely Maoism). During the second three years (10–12), the program is extended to include industrial knowledge (practical work on the commune or at nearby factories) and "fundamental knowledge," which we gather is a general world view.

We visited an abacus lesson in a fourth-grade arithmetic class, which seemed well run and lively, though quite strict and rigid by our standards. The teacher had firm control of his 36 students, who raise their hands, wait to be called upon, recite crisply, and sit down promptly. We also witnessed tumbling on the athletic field, group singing in the music class, and reading aloud and a question period in the literature class. This modest building, in which many of the rooms have dirt floors and peeling plaster, is producing a well-drilled and educated youth, but there is much political indoctrination, uniformity of thought and action, and little allowance for individual divergence from the norm.

All primary school students go on to the lower middle school, which engages them until age 15–16; about 20 percent of the lower middle school graduates can go on to upper middle school in this area; the remainder must go to work. The lower middle school we saw was an impressive red brick building on a large piece of land containing extensive athletic fields. It was founded in 1968, in the midst of the Great Proletarian Cultural Revolution, and already enrolls about 1,000 students in twenty classes with 43 teachers and 10 staff members. Almost all students are from peasant families.

This lower middle school is run by an RC of nine members nominated "by the masses," whose election, after discussion, is approved by the Party Committee of the People's Commune. We were told that no nominated individual was ever disapproved by the Party Committee and that no person who had failed to be nominated ever complained or tried to run on his own initiative. The teachers are chosen by the Revolutionary Committee of the commune and the books are supplied by the Educational Department of nearby Peking Municipality. Courses offered include Chinese language and literature, mathematics, physics, chemistry, agriculture, politics, history, geography, foreign languages (seventeen English classes and three Russian classes), music, painting and drawing, and physical education.

To go on to the upper middle school, students must be recommended. Selections are made first by the students, then by their teachers, and final approval, as usual, is given by the Revolutionary Committee. There are examinations and grades, but we were repeatedly assured that there is no competition; students aid one another and special attention is given by the group to those having difficulty.

We visited a chemistry class in which a spirited and able woman teacher was explaining solutions, solvents, and solutes to an eager and attentive class of 48. After laying out the basic principles, she posed questions. Students responded by raising their hands, speaking loudly and clearly, and sitting down smartly after completing their answer. By contrast, the English language class was stiff and formal, and the stories in the readers were propagandistic, nationalistic, and frequently anti-American.

In the courtyard, we witnessed vigorous basketball, Ping-Pong, volleyball, and gymnastics. While competition between opposing teams was keen, it was maintained in a spirit of friendly rivalry. The major problem of this new school, according to three members of the Revolutionary Committee that we interviewed, is fulfilling the requirements for cultural reformation set by the Great Proletarian Cultural Revolution. To help adequately train teachers for this task, special seminars are held during the summer months.

Our overall view of the elementary and middle-school facilities we visited was complicated, and, in fact, my wife and daughter reacted in one way and I in another. While all three of us agreed that the extension of universal education to age 16 is bound to raise literacy and increase skills and further educability, we differed on the effects of the strict rote learning and political indoctrination from the earliest ages. My wife and daughter felt that the children, taught unquestioning reverence for their "great leader and helmsman, Chairman Mao," would have limited desire and ability to deviate from any political or ideological line handed them in the future. If the successors to Mao and Chou En-lai turn out to be aggressive leaders out for world conquest, such regimented children could turn into willing and obedient soldiers, willing to follow wherever they were led.

While I acknowledge that these are real dangers, my experience with university people leads me to believe that their early training had damaged neither their critical faculties nor their ability to look at their leaders and party in a realistic light. Which of these points of view is more correct is impossible to say now, but the years immediately ahead ought to give us hints. I am also struck by the fact that even in a relatively open society like our own, the military forces can find enough soldiers willing to fight and bomb in Indochina that our operations there have continued for more than a decade, even in the face of determined opposition on the part of a growing number of citizens and congressmen. Thus, I feel that the danger lies, not so much in the early education of the children, but in the policies of the leadership of the country.

Rounding out the self-sufficiency of life on our commune is a line of shops near the schools. They offer foodstuffs, cloth and notions, agricultural implements, stationery supplies, and some toys. A commune worker receives an average of 500 yuan per year in addition to almost all the food he needs (some grown in his private plot). His living quarters and utilities are virtually free, and medical care and education are almost without cost, which enables him to use the better part of his allowance for the purchase of clothing, bicycles, household utensils, wristwatches, fountain pens, electric fans, and transistor radios. Since almost all adults and mature teen-agers, both men and women, work and receive salaries, the family income may well exceed several thousand yuan per year, much of which is saved or spent for consumer goods.

In China, there is no income tax or sales tax and no internal or external debt; the government gets all its income from the controlled price structure. A government agency buys all farm produce from the communes and then sells it at a sufficient markup to guarantee receipt of the differential required to sustain governmental operations. This system must employ a small army of economists, but it seems to work well. Prices in China are stable, the people have access to all the necessities of life, and the government is able to function and to improve life by construction of public works, housing units, roads, railways, etc. (During our overnight trip from Shanghai to Peking by train, the punctuality and cleanliness of the train, plus the cheerfulness and efficiency of the employees, made us feel that Amtrak should send some observers to see how they do it.)

In the matter of income distribution, individual differences are both recognized and rewarded. Each production team shares the fruits of its labor; thus, two production teams growing the same crops on the same commune may earn quite different returns for their labor. Within each production team, outstanding workers receive more production points than less able workers. Thus, within this system of total communal ownership of the productive process, there is adequate incentive for individual initiative.

Entertainment, too, is provided within the hardworking communal regime. There are mobile movie teams, traveling actors, acrobats, and musicians, and "home talent" activities. As we work in the fields or take a break, we find the workers eager to exchange songs with us. Especial favorites with them are "Old Mac-Donald Had a Farm" (they crack up on the animal imitations), "Yankee Doodle," and "Clementine." We have also introduced several brightly colored Frisbees with great immediate success, especially among the boys and girls.

So, there is our commune—outside Peking in China —an incredibly hard-working, cooperative assemblage of dedicated people, sharing all the worries, plans, and profits of a collectively run, diversified enterprise. They enjoy levels of health, security, and material rewards undreamed of just a generation ago. They sense their growing prosperity and power. They support their present regime enthusiastically and virtually unquestioningly.

And in this resides the one aspect of life on the commune, and in fact in all China, that deeply disturbs us—this complete control of all that is taught, learned, and read. The news gives a partial, slanted view of the outside world. School routines foster rigid adherence to one point of view. Social or political deviation is met with criticism, usually followed by public self-criticism and frequently an enforced "re-education" process. The pressures to conform are well-nigh irresistible. What is this doing to individual mentality, creativity, and basic happiness? It will take many more months of experience in China before we can begin to analyze problems such as these.

The Coming Famine

❖❖❖❖❖❖

PAUL R. EHRLICH

[1968]

I read Arthur Hopcraft's *Born to Hunger* while flying to Washington to address the Second International Conference on the War on Hunger. I could not help but be impressed with the contrast between the hopelessness, malnutrition, failure, and death described in his compelling narrative, and the air-conditioned, overfed opulence of the first-class section of our 707. A day later, in our nation's capital, I was impressed by another contrast. First I had the pleasure of meeting William C. Paddock, co-author of the tough-minded *Famine 1975!* Then I sat through a long day of speeches at the conference, many of which were compounded of wishful thinking and political platitudes—albeit given in support of what the participants thought was a good cause. The conference was, in essence, a political rally for the Food for Peace Act.

If there is a "war on hunger," then Hopcraft's book is a report from the front. On a 45,000-mile trip through Africa, Asia, and South America he recorded his personal impressions of what it is like to be on the losing side. He tells of Dr. Lema's survey of the vicinity of Dar es Salaam, which listed 30 percent of the children under five as malnourished. From this area 65 children entered the hospital suffering from severe kwashiorkor, a disease caused by malnutrition, and 14 of them died. Farther to the west, in a less fertile region, the death rate of children under five is nearly 50 percent. This situation is similar in India. Hopcraft quotes Dr. Shah of Ajarpura, India, to the effect that in the Ajarpura area the infant mortality rate of 125 per 1,000 births was caused by gastroenteritis, respiratory diseases, and malnutrition. And Ajarpura was considered a progressive village, although the majority of the people were malnourished.

In Colombia, Hopcraft reports 100 infant deaths per day from malnutrition, and in Turkana, Kenya, he reports 6,000 people still living on handouts in famine camps established in 1961. But his reporting is not just of hunger and malnutrition in the underdeveloped world. He deals with a vast maze of related subjects: agriculture, agricultural training, urbanization, public health, cultural attitudes toward food, communications, and, above all, the root cause of the entire problem— overpopulation. *Born to Hunger* does not deal with most of these systematically, but rather area by area in an informal travelogue style. And in this lies the great strength of the book, for it gives immediacy to the problem; it makes you feel you are there. It would serve as a wonderful treatment for those stunned by the statistical avalanche that inevitably buries whoever seeks to understand the plight of the underdeveloped world. Hopcraft finishes his book with a rather good discussion of the need for population control—especially effective in pointing out that even the most optimistic demographic predictions make a strong case for tight population control. His short chapters on "aid" are somewhat marred by the optimistic view that the developed world has all of the means to help the underdeveloped out of its predicament. I wish it were true, but I am afraid it is not. Especially in the area of tropical agriculture we lack expertise that could have been developed over the past few decades had the need been widely recognized. But this flaw is slight, and *Born to Hunger* can be recommended as a good piece of war reporting.

Famine 1975! would make interesting reading after *Born to Hunger*. William and Paul Paddock have written a book of strategy for minimizing our losses in the war on hunger. They claim that massive famines are now inevitable, and that the United States cannot hope to feed all of the hungry. The essence of the Paddocks' strategy is to reserve our food aid for those nations it will help the most. The Paddocks say we cannot save everyone from starving, so we must decide where our limited food supplies can do the most good. They suggest, for instance, that sending more food to India, as will be done under the Food for Peace Act, is a waste. They say we cannot prevent massive famines there, and that our limited food can be put to better use helping countries that have a chance of becoming self-sufficient. It is not a point of view designed to please Indian or American politicians, who have reacted strongly to it.

Whether or not the Paddocks are right is a matter of great debate. The Indian Government, for instance, claims that the country will be self-sufficient agriculturally by 1971, barring further droughts. Knowledgeable people doubt it (biologists may remember that the same government claims malaria has been eradicated—news which has not yet reached the plasmodia!). For instance, Louis H. Bean, international economic consultant, told the War on Hunger Conference that he expects the present gap between Indian food production and population will widen over the next decade. Another expert, Dr. Raymond Ewell, recently summed up his view of the Indian food situation in an address to the Synthetic Organic Chemical Manufacturers Association. He stated:

"In 13 years India is going to add 200 million more people to their population. In my opinion, as an old India hand, I don't see how they can possibly feed 200 million more people by 1980. They could if they had the time, say until the year 2000. Maybe they could even do it by 1990, but they can't do it by 1980. It's a matter of time, of learning new techniques and doing all the various things that need to be done. They all take time.

"Even the United States would be greatly pressed to provide for 200 million more people. Say we had 200 million more people dumped on the United States in 13 years. We'd have an extremely difficult time feeding them alone, to say nothing of providing housing and education and transportation, parking spaces for all the cars, etc. It would be an enormous problem for the United States, and yet the United States has a superb industrial plant, very productive agriculture, a good educational system, excellent natural resources, lots of natural gas, petroleum, coal, mineral ores of all types. India has none of these things. And yet India is going to have 200 million more people in the next 13 years."

Difficult as it is to make sense of the vast "numbers game" of population-agriculture statistics, my guess is that the Paddocks' assessment of the situation is the most accurate. But then, concerned biologists recently have been tending more and more toward a new version of Pascal's wager. Pascal said that the best strategy was to believe in God. If there was one, you were saved. If there wasn't, you lost nothing. Similarly, believing in the Paddocks' predictions can only help us. Everyone admits that more than half of the world is undernourished, with many starving. We clearly already have too many people—what conceivable reason can there be for further increasing the population? People such as Karl Sax have been warning of the consequences of overpopulation for decades. Their views were widely contested by the technological optimists and the superstitious. Now we know that Sax and others were right. But the same kinds of people who opposed Sax and population control now condemn the Paddocks. They want to focus their attention on producing more food, perhaps giving lip service to population control. Or if, like the Indian Government, they finally have committed themselves to population control—perhaps too late or ineffectually—they want well-intentioned efforts to be considered successes. Few people, inside this country or out, want to face the cold, hard facts.

These facts are really quite simple, and only three in number. The first is that, by the elementary standard that most people are going hungry, the world today is overpopulated. And we expect the situation to get worse. At present the population of the world is growing at a rate of slightly less than 2 percent a year. Doubling times (the time required for the population to double) range from about 20 to 30 years in the underdeveloped countries; in the developed world, countries mostly lie in the 50- to 120-year range—with the United States one of the fastest (about 63). Some demographers see reason to hope for a substantial reduction in population growth rates in the last quarter of the century. But even those more optimistic than I, such as my colleague Dudley Kirk, are pessimistic about the short run. And I admit to extreme pessimism about population control with the current level of effort. Reports from India are not very cheering—low level acceptance of vasectomy, rejection of the intrauterine devices (IUDs), removal of IUDs in order to collect again the small monetary reward paid by the government for insertion. Bernard Nossiter gives a very depressing report of the failure thus far of the birth control campaign in rural India. The following sample statements will give the flavor of the article:

"They are afraid that the sterilizing operation will destroy their male power and make them docile, like castrated animals. Mostly, they are afraid of interfering with God's will."

"A Hindu father of three blurts out 'It is a sin to prevent children from being born.'"

"A grizzled farmer breaks in angrily and says 'You must practice self-control.'"

"Nagoan's crew is responsible for 59,000 persons in more than 100 villages. In the 10 months of active campaigning only 47 vasectomies have been performed, 27 loops inserted, and very few free condoms accepted."

Unhappily, the establishment in the developed world is mesmerized with the concept of "family planning"— an approach that has so far been a failure in the area of population control. This failure has been brilliantly outlined by Kingsley Davis. As he says, "the things that make family planning acceptable are the very things that make it ineffective for population control. By stressing the right of parents to have the number of children they want, it evades the basic question of population policy, which is how to give societies the number of children they need. By offering only the means for couples to control fertility it neglects the means for society to do so." Justin Blackwelder of the Population Crisis Committee put it differently: "Family planning means, among other things, that if we are going to multiply like rabbits, we should do it on purpose. One couple may plan to have three children; another couple may plan seven. In both cases they are a cause of the population problem—not a solution to it."

People in the underdeveloped areas of the world *want* large families—sizes that promote demographic catastrophe. "Family planning" is used mostly to lock the barn door after the horse is stolen. For instance, Davis reports that of 5,196 women seeking assistance in rural Punjab, India, two-thirds were over thirty. Since many were married before they were fifteen it is hardly surprising that more than half of them already had six or more children. Conservative groups, such as the Committee on Population of the National Academy of Sciences, cling to the idea that family planning programs foster their own further acceptance. It is too bad for the world that wishing won't make it so! Their commentary on Davis's fine article, which the Committee on Population published in *Science* (February 23, 1968), makes instructive reading for those concerned with reasons for the lack of effective population control measures in the world today. This committee states that a "zero rate of population growth may be essential in the long run, but as a goal within the time horizon of current policy it has little support in either the developing or the developed world, certainly not among governments." What a pity that the committee does not use its prominent position to attempt to change governmental goals.

So the first fact is that there are too many people, and more arriving every day. The second is that food supplies are inadequate. Even most optimistic food "experts" think that agricultural production will at best be enough to maintain today's standard of misery over the next decade. Many informed people believe that a monster food-population gap will appear in the next decade, and that massive starvation will occur. Most of the "hope" in the line of food production comes from two areas. The first is the hope of a good harvest this year —potentially an extraordinarily good one because of superb weather. If this hope is met when the harvests are in, then the world will pretty much be back where it was before the 1965–66 disaster years. A second cause for limited optimism is the spreading and acceptance of new varieties of rice, wheat, grain sorghum, and corn. These are being rushed into production, but their actual potential under field conditions and over the long term is largely unproved. We can only hope. And if we are intelligent, we will base our plans on somewhat less than optimal results.

Finally, and even more critical, is a fact not discussed by the vast majority of writers on the population-food problem, including Hopcraft and the Paddocks. That is, we are rapidly destroying our planet as a habitat for *Homo sapiens*. The warnings of eminent ecologists such as Lamont Cole continue to fall on deaf ears. The War on Hunger Conference was started with a filmed Esso commercial promoting the use of oil, asphalt, and pesticides for short-range productivity gains, with no consideration of long-term environmental consequences. While technological optimists dream of more pesticides, fertilizers, and farming the sea, the ecologically sophisticated are concerned about the poisoning of the sea, the air, and the soil. They are concerned about chronic poisoning of people by pesticides, and the poisoning of children by nitrates (from fertilizers) in baby food. They are concerned about the reduction of photosynthesis on land and in the sea, leading to a serious reduction in the oxygen in our atmosphere. They are concerned about the possibly fatal interruptions of delicately balanced ecological cycles. They are concerned about hundreds of unplanned acts despoiling our environment. They are concerned that an insane preoccupation with an ever-growing gross national product could lead in the not-too-distant future to no national product at all.

It is quite possible that the penalty for frantic attempts to feed burgeoning populations in the next decade may be a lowering of the carrying capacity of the entire planet to a level far below that of 1968. But, of course, too few people in the developed world seem to care about the fate of their less fortunate fellow passengers on the spaceship Earth today. Mass concern for future generations seems too much to ask.

Mankind may be facing its final crisis. No action that we can take at this late date can prevent a great deal of future misery from starvation and environmental deterioration. The dimensions of the programs that must be mounted if we are to survive are awe-inspiring. To ameliorate the "time of famines" I have suggested that the developed world, through the United Nations, set up a multivalent program of area rehabilitation. This program would involve simultaneous population control, agricultural development, and, where resources permit, industrialization of selected countries or sections of countries. Population control would be the *sine qua non* of area rehabilitation, and careful consideration and monitoring of environmental consequences would be an absolute requirement. The program would involve the establishment of TV networks (with distribution of sets for communal viewing in villages) to help people understand population control, public health, and agricultural measures. It would include a worldwide renaissance of agricultural-ecological research and the promotion of a "county agent" network for the underdeveloped world.

If we can get population growth halted without unprecedented catastrophe, then we must turn to the question of the "carrying capacity" of the earth, although this is a question that we can begin to consider now. What is an optimum population size, from the point of view of man's physical and psychological welfare? What is the maximum level of material affluence that can be supported worldwide for an indefinite period of time without destroying the earth? No doubt this will prove to be a considerably lower level than Americans are accustomed to. Perhaps the concept of "the good life" needs reevaluation, with less emphasis on material things. There is some evidence today that college students are less concerned with affluence than are their parents. The earth's energy budget and resources are limited. We must recognize that and learn to live within them. But changes in the quality of life for people can only be achieved when their quantity is under control.

Are the necessary programs possible? Possible, yes, but their realization seems hardly probable. Much will depend on whether the United States, as the most influential superpower, can be made aware of its grave danger. Can Americans learn the grim lesson that considering the population explosion a problem of the underdeveloped world is like saying to a fellow passenger, "your end of the boat is sinking"? Most of our citizens do not realize, for instance, how totally we depend on imports for our material affluence. After all, we use well over half of all the raw materials consumed each year. Think of it! Less than one-fifteenth of the population of the earth requires more than all the rest to maintain its inflated position.

Many Americans may be willing to help the rest of the world for humanitarian reasons. Can other Americans be convinced that to help is in their own selfish interest? We are willing to spend many billions for ill-advised military-political interventions. Is it conceivable that this power can be diverted into projects of greater use to ourselves and the rest of mankind?

Unfortunately our government has its attention focused elsewhere and is not aware of the true gravity of the situation. The likelihood seems nil that tens of billions of dollars a year will be spent to meet a threat most politicians cannot perceive. Could the biological community sound the warning and force the politicians to face reality? Unhappily, most biologists are involved in biomedical research leading to lowered death rates. They do not have the background, and often lack the inclination, to recognize the threat. And, of course, the degree of change in national attitudes and policies required to meet this challenge would be viewed as a threat to their position. After all, to save future generations we might have to change our pattern of research support! The answer will not come from the scientific and political establishment. The establishment must be forced into action by the concerned public.

The "concerned public" is already large and will soon be drastically increased in size as riots tear cities apart, fishermen find they can no longer eat their pesticide-loaded catches, smog disasters become common, famine pre-empts the headlines, and the international situation continues to deteriorate. Everything possible must be done to mobilize American public opinion and to mobilize it fast. If the connection between growing population at home and abroad and the steady deterioration of the quality of life can be made apparent, then perhaps successful action can be instituted before our planet is irreversibly ruined.

The Starving Roots
of Population Growth

❖❖❖❖❖❖❖

ROY E. BROWN and
JOE D. WRAY

[1974]

Most people accept the concept that the population explosion is based on a decline in death rates, not on a rise in birthrates. The literature concerning developing countries is replete with arguments by economists, demographers, sociologists, politicians, and public health officials that, by substantially lowering death rates, public health techniques are responsible for the population crisis.

Although this remains a controversial issue, health professionals, who not long ago were placing increased emphasis on saving lives in areas infected with communicable diseases, now find that their budgets are being channeled into family planning programs. Alarmed by population increases, medical people are now becoming increasingly interested in the technology and mass distribution of contraceptive techniques.

This may not work. Family planning programs are only effective in conjunction with cultural, medical, and personal factors and, paradoxically, may fail totally in achieving zero population growth if adequate public health and nutrition are not available. Furthermore, it seems logical to assume that if modern medical technology is responsible for the population explosion, then the withdrawal of such services will reverse the trend, but just the opposite may be the case. Certainly, the assumptions need further examination.

Is there, in fact, a causal relationship between public

health measures and population increases? The development of immunization techniques, antibiotics, and anti-tuberculosis drugs, the eradication of malaria, and improved public sanitation have all been held responsible for declining death rates. There is, however, little evidence to support this; if anything, in many parts of the world such public health measures have made a negligible contribution.

In the late eighteenth century, for example, England and Wales experienced a decline in death rates and a corresponding population upsurge, a shift historians have attributed to medical improvements. True, there were larger hospitals, more clinics, and more health practitioners, but aside from vaccination against smallpox, the eighteenth-century physician had little technology to offer his patients.

Recently, a malaria eradication program in Ceylon was followed by a dramatic decline in the death rate and an increase in population. Yet falling death rates in Ceylon go back as far as 1905 and show an accelerated downward trend in the late 1940s, completely independent of malaria eradication programs. People who have studied this program conclude that, based on the available evidence, malaria control was not the sole major cause of a population explosion in Ceylon. The global effort against malaria began in the 1950s, after death rates began falling throughout the world; in fact, as of 1967, only eleven countries had eradicated malaria.

What about antibiotics? Certainly, it is the popular opinion that the development of the so-called wonder drugs has played a crucial role in lowering mortality rates. Penicillin was first used in 1944 and broad-spectrum antibiotics became generally available after 1948; in the Western world, however, death rates had been falling since the 1850s, while from 1920 to 1949, death rates in eighteen developing countries fell about 35 percent, indicating no causal relationship between the development of antibiotics and lower mortality. Similarly, in the case of tuberculosis, mortality rates were declining sharply long before an effective antituberculosis agent was developed in 1945.

Furthermore, antibiotics are not widely used in the developing countries. Although available, they are greatly restricted in use owing to their cost, to lack of public knowledge, and to the shortage of health personnel and services. In contrast to the spread of technology and science in the West, the developing world has not yet felt the comprehensive impact of modern medical or health institutions. Yet mortality is declining.

As for improvements in sanitation, they have been found to affect both morbidity and mortality in early childhood. As of 1968, however, the World Health Organization concluded that "safe adequate water was not available to 90 percent of the population of the developing world," which strongly indicates that such improvements have not been important in the declining global death rates.

How is the decline to be explained? Probably the single most important factor is improvement in the standard of living, particularly raised nutritional levels. Over and over in a given population, we find that when death rates start to decline and the number of people increases, there has been a change in the quality and availability of food. It is important to remember that although a given country may be poor, with thousands of its children suffering from malnutrition, overall, the citizenry may still be better nourished than 50 or 100 years ago.

Conversely, in areas where childhood mortality rates are still high, malnutrition is widespread. Of the world's 60 million annual deaths, 30 million occur in children under the age of five years, and approximately one-half, or 15 million, of these deaths result from the combination of malnutrition and infection.

A study sponsored by the Pan-American Health Organization showed that, in thirteen cities and five rural areas in Latin America, malnutrition was an associated cause in from 30 to more than 60 percent of all deaths occurring in children under five years of age. When certain specific illnesses were considered, diarrheal disease and measles, for example, more than 70 percent of the deaths occurred in children who also were suffering from malnutrition.

Improving the general nutrition of a population has a much more marked influence on infant and young child mortality than does increasing the number of physicians or, by implication, improving the medical services. Dr. Harald Frederiksen studied data from twenty-one generally well-developed countries for the period from 1950 to 1960. Examining the relationship between changes in birth and death rates with other changes, he found a strong negative correlation between infant and early childhood mortality rates and increases in animal protein and caloric consumption and a weak negative correlation between these rates and an increased number of physicians.

Additional evidence comes from the Cornell University health care project in the Many Farms Navaho Indian community. Despite carefully planned and executed efforts to improve medical care among the Navaho, there was little effect on infant mortality. The children were suffering from weaning diarrhea, which seriously interferes with nutritional status. If it were possible to eliminate such infections, the nutritional status of many children would improve.

Unfortunately, despite assumptions to the contrary, feasible medical methods for controlling infections in these children are not readily available at the village level. Summing up the situation at Many Farms, Walsh McDermott of the Cornell Medical School was explicit in his description of the situation: "The . . . well-named 'weaning diarrhea' . . . has a nutritional component, the precise role of which is unclear. It is definite, however, that while antimicrobial therapy may be helpful in some instances, it does not predictably and decisively alter the disease."

Finally, a five-year study of two Guatemalan villages showed that moderate improvement in the nutrition of preschool children produced improvements in morbidity and mortality equal to, or better than, those produced by an extensive and expensive medical care and public health program that did not alter the children's nutritional situation.

Improvements in nutrition can only be achieved in association with other changes. In Western countries, nutrition has been improving and death rates falling for the past two centuries; during this same period, we find the beginnings of stable government administration, reduction of destructive warfare, the improvement of internal security, the reduction of catastrophic famines, the encouragement of food production, and the expansion of road and railway development, which improved food availability. Simultaneously, irrigation programs were developed and communication and trade routes grew. As elementary education was expanded, literacy increased; not surprisingly, recent studies show that there is significantly less malnutrition among the children of literate mothers.

During the three decades from 1900 to 1930, infant mortality fell dramatically in New York City, from 140 per 1,000 live births to slightly more than 50. This was before there were any significant antibiotic drugs or specific vaccines for diphtheria, pertussis, and tetanus, among others. The period, however, was characterized by intensive economic and community development, social reform, and educational expansion.

Whether caused by political squabbles, lack of roads, or insufficient storage facilities, inadequate food distribution plays a significant role in malnutrition. With the construction of a new road, the redrawing of political boundaries, or a substantial increase in yearly crops, improved nutritional benefits may result.

The introduction of a new food source can be crucial, and historically, food changes have been associated with rapid population growth. Within 100 years after the introduction of the white potato in 1750, Ireland's population nearly tripled. The recent introduction of enriched flour in Scandinavia was followed by a decrease in childhood mortality, and the Chinese population explosion in the sixteenth century was related to the expanded use of corn, sweet potatoes, and peanuts.

But if improved nutrition means that more children will survive, won't increased population pressures ultimately lower nutritional status? On the contrary, as nutrition improves, infant and childhood mortality rates decline; as mortality rates decline, parents respond by having fewer children. Parents are not enthusiastic about family planning in the presence of high infant and childhood mortality rates. Family planning implies that planning will be successful, and parents should be able to plan that their existing children will survive to adulthood. Intrauterine devices cut down on births but provide no insurance against dysentery, pneumonia, or malaria.

There is, in fact, evidence from Bangladesh showing a direct relationship between the death of a child and the probability of a birth in the family during the subsequent year. A study in an Egyptian community showed that a mother who has lost at least one child will desire a larger number of surviving children and will actually have more births than women in the same community who have lost no children. In the Philippines, too, a report shows that total fertility is lower in couples who have lost no children; it is also lower in communities where mortality rates are lower. According to Dr. Harold Taylor of the Population Council, "A basic dictum is that parents will not stop having children until they believe that those they already have are going to survive."

In developing regions, children are highly valued. Not only do they play an important economic role, helping with farming or other jobs, but by supporting their parents in their old age, children also represent a form of social security. Just as important, children are also desired for themselves.

The relationship between mortality and fertility has been called the "demographic transition." In the West, mortality rates began to decline slowly in the mid-nineteenth century; birthrates followed, also slowly. Over a period of many decades, these countries underwent a transition from high mortality and high fertility to low mortality and low fertility, with net population growth never becoming excessive. Today, however, mortality rates in the developing world have fallen rapidly and birthrates continue to remain at high levels. As a result, the demographic transition has not occurred and we have the population explosion.

It should be emphasized that fertility rates declined in the West long before contraceptive technology had approached the convenience or effectiveness demanded today, long before family planning services were readily available, when, in fact, publication of information about contraception could bring imprisonment. At a time when national population policies were unheard of and few were concerned with the long-term effects of population growth, birthrates were falling almost as rapidly as death rates.

This can only be interpreted as indicating that thousands upon thousands of families wanted fewer children and somehow managed to achieve their goal. Their decisions were so successful that the aggregate effect resulted in declines in fertility at national levels.

Given the available methods of limiting family size at the time, there must have been powerful and sustained motivating forces at work to produce such unprecedented declines in fertility in large population groups. Such motivation must have emerged from the everyday life situation, from the awareness of problems felt at the family level, such as "having another mouth to feed."

The same has been true in the developing countries; in many instances in which fertility followed mortality downward, there were no formal family planning programs. People were on their own, just as in the original demographic transition. In addition, the time lag is shorter, approaching several years.

When infant and child mortality rates fell rapidly in Singapore after World War II, birthrates were not far behind. In rural Turkey, where infant and child mortality rates declined sharply when a comprehensive medical program, including family planning services, was established, fertility rates held steady for several years, then dropped, reducing the net population growth. Analyzing his data from Ceylon, Harald Frederiksen concluded that "[there is] such remarkable correlation between previous levels of the death rates and current levels of the birthrates that low death rates merit consideration as contributing factors, if not prerequisites, for low birthrates in the less developed, as well as the more developed, countries."

There is no question that increased family size is associated with increased incidence of illness, and thus mortality, which in turn keeps birthrates high. This has been documented among Indians in the Punjab, as well as among all social classes in the United Kingdom. As families get larger, there are greater economic limitations, more crowding, and poorer sanitary conditions. Children from larger families are also more likely to be malnourished than those from smaller families. In developing countries, as laboring men get older, their earnings rise very little, while family size may be increasing steadily. They attempt to compensate for this by spending a larger proportion of their income for food, but in fact, their per capita expenditures for food actually fall, and malnutrition in the children increases.

In addition to family size, child spacing plays a large role. Mortality, both among infants and mothers, is lower when the birth interval is longer. Repeated pregnancies followed by prolonged lactation produce sustained needs for high-quality protein in the maternal diet. Since these needs are poorly met in many parts of the developing world, we find the "maternal depletion syndrome," which contributes to low-birthweight infants, poor performance in lactation, and, often, early death among women.

Obviously, in the absence of effective family planning, the mother who has children at frequent intervals is likely to have more of them. The more young children in a household, the greater the demands upon the mother's energy and skills to provide adequate care for them. Dr. Benjamin Biel of International Planned Parenthood Federation describes "unconscious infanticide" —a mother attending less and less to each successive child and infant mortality rising with increasing birth order.

The continuing high burden of disease and death in some parts of the world is an effective obstacle to the rapid acceptance of family planning services. To expect people who are faced with high levels of morbidity and mortality in their own environment rapidly to accept family planning is to discount the reality of experience.

For these reasons, it is difficult to check birthrates until better child-health care has been established. Economic development and the production and adequate distribution of more food will reduce mortality, even in the absence of any medical input whatsoever. Provided with a constant food supply, each individual will have more food available, thus increasing his chances of survival.

As long as demographers and economists seek to solve the population problem by emphasizing birth control exclusively, success in limiting population growth will prove elusive. Integrated programs of nutrition, sanitation, and public health services must be incorporated into a country's overall program for family planning.

If we wish to limit population growth, the primary thing we must do is to lower infant and childhood mortality rates. When these remain at high levels, fertility will remain high, but when mortality rates decline visibly, fertility will fall within a few years. The most effective way to lower infant mortality rates is to improve nutritional levels. Therefore, the best birth control program is, simply, to feed the children.

The Withering Green Revolution

❖❖❖❖❖❖

MARVIN HARRIS

[1973]

"You have to be brutally frank with some governments; you have to push them into using it," remarked plant geneticist Norman E. Borlaug during an interview shortly after he won the Nobel Prize. Dr. Borlaug was talking about the introduction of the high-yield, semi-dwarf wheat, the so-called miracle seeds of the Green Revolution. It was for the development of those seeds that he had won his prize. He was also deeply involved in promoting their use throughout the world.

At the same time that Borlaug was being interviewed, in January, 1971, U.S. government food experts were claiming that the battle against hunger and malnutrition in the underdeveloped world would soon be won. High-yield varieties of rice and wheat had provided four consecutive years of record harvest in India and Pakistan. The miracle seeds had ended the need for rice imports in the Philippines, and President Suharto was predicting self-sufficiency for Indonesia.

"It doesn't do any good to get 10 or 15 percent yield increases," Borlaug continued. "They won't listen to you. You have to throw the long bomb. You have to make a 100 or 200 percent gain to change their old worn-out practices."

As I predicted a year ago, the Green Revolution has not brought any significant respite from hunger and malnutrition in Asia. Despite a total of more than 50 million acres planted in high-yield varieties of rice and wheat, grain production fell to dangerously low levels throughout Asia in 1972.

In the Philippines more than 50 percent of the acreage devoted to rice was planted in high-yield varieties, yet output last year fell 5 percent below 1971, which was already down 3 percent from 1970. Following typhoons, floods, and civil disorders, Ferdinand Marcos instituted a dictatorship. The rice shortage was one of the fundamental causes of this crisis.

India also may be on the verge of a disaster. By the end of 1972, news sources in Delhi, Calcutta, and Poona were reporting crop failures and famines in four states: Maharashtra, Rajasthan, Gujarat, and Mysore. Some 33 million people were already affected. Speakers at the eleventh regional conference of the Food and Agricultural Organization in New Delhi in November, 1972, bluntly declared that the high-yield varieties had not solved Asia's food problem.

India's plight can be seen in figures recently presented by Kenneth Murray and Emanuel McNeil of the Grain and Feed Division of the U.S. Foreign Agricultural Service. Total Indian grain production went from 68.5 million metric tons in 1960–61 to a high of 92.8 million metric tons in 1970–71. The forecast for 1972–73 was 84.0 million metric tons. In the meantime, India's population has grown from 440.3 million to 570 million.

On a per capita basis, therefore, India's grain production has fallen below the levels of 1960–61, which was before the Green Revolution began. India produced 0.1556 metric tons per person then versus 0.1473 metric tons per person now. Even comparing 1972–73 with the worst drought year in past decades, total per capita grain production has improved less than 10 percent.

In each of the affected regions, government experts are blaming the deficits on unusual weather conditions —either too much or too little rain. But erratic monsoons, tropical storms, floods, and droughts are nothing new. These are precisely the conditions that must somehow be met and overcome to improve on the "old worn-out practices."

The main problem with the miracle seeds is that they are engineered to outperform native varieties only under the most favorable ecological conditions and with the aid of enormous amounts of industrial fertilizers, pesticides, insecticides, fungicides, irrigation, and other technical inputs. Without such inputs, the high-yield varieties perform no better—and sometimes worse—than the native varieties of rice and wheat, especially under adverse soil and weather conditions.

Even when the technical inputs are applied in sufficient quantities, certain ecological problems arise, which seem not to have been given adequate consideration before the seeds were "pushed" out onto the vast acreage they now occupy. Conversion to high-yield varieties creates novel opportunities for plant pathogens, pests, and insects. The varieties also place unprecedented stress upon water resources. In the Philippines, for example, tungro rice virus, which was never a serious problem in the past, reached epidemic levels in 1970 and 1971, when more than half of all the rice acreage had been planted with high-yield varieties. I suspect that the modification of natural drainage patterns to provide extra water for paddies with high-yield plants contributed to the severe flooding that accompanied the typhoons in the summer of 1972.

In Pakistan tens of thousands of electrically operated tube wells have been drilled to provide water for high-yield wheat. Tube-well irrigation is already lowering water tables and increasing the salinity of the soil. One might think that a tube-well farmer would at least be able to come out ahead during a drought. But this has not necessarily been the case. Reduced water flows in the major rivers have led to cutbacks in hydroelectric production. Without electricity the tube-well farmers cannot pump water up to their fields. Moreover, the loss in hydroelectric output has impaired chemical fertilizer production.

Of course, every man-made technological disaster has its man-made technological solution. But the peasant smallholders of Asia cannot meet the costs of spiraling technical inputs needed to avoid disaster. The Green Revolution inevitably widens the gap between landowners who have the credit and the know-how to keep up with the technological solutions and the peasant smallholders who stand to lose their land when the unanticipated ecological side effects appear.

The Green Revolution in Indonesia is a case in point. According to Professor Richard Franke of the Department of Anthropology at Montclair College, that ricegrowing country has already had three distinct phases of Green Revolution, all of them failures. In Green Revolution I, the government gave loans to individual peasants for the purchase of high-yield seeds and expensive fertilizers. Not knowing what the price of rice would be at the end of the year, many peasants calculated that they would do better selling the fertilizer on the black market rather than putting it on their fields. They also skimped on the insecticides, hoping to save some for future use. Some farmers had no choice but to sell the entire high-yield packet because it arrived in their villages after the planting season. Corruption and mismanagement among officials charged with distributing the packets created additional problems. With large numbers of peasants defaulting on their loans, the government abruptly halted the program in 1968.

Green Revolution II began in 1969. Having lost faith in its own ability to control the distribution of the technical inputs, the government contracted with large international corporations to use their know-how to push the high-yield seeds in the villages. The government agreed to pay $54 for each hectare that the corporations converted to miracle rice. The corporations proceeded by subcontracting with Indonesian firms. Peasants were given loans that had to be repaid with one-sixth of the rice harvest; the army was supposed to collect this one-sixth and use it as a salary supplement for government employees.

To make certain that the prescribed amounts of insecticides were applied at the scheduled time, the corporations hired planes and pilots to spray from the air. The principal insecticide used was Demicon 100, produced by CIBA, a chemical corporation that happened to be the program's largest contractor. In 1969–70, CIBA, Mitsubishi, Hoechst, and other corporations were bringing Green Revolution II to about 2,471,000 acres in densely populated areas of Java, where the average farm was an acre in size and where 30 percent of the population owned no land at all.

The schedule for aerial spraying was fixed at regional headquarters, and it was up to the individual farmer to make sure that he was ready when the plane came over. Some peasants who did not want their lands sprayed kept moving the ground markers around to decoy the planes. Although CIBA denied charges that Demicon 100 was responsible for the death of children and water buffalo, everyone seems to agree that the spray was killing off the fish in the fishponds. The Indonesians rely on these fish for most of their protein. (Demicon 100 had already been implicated in a great Rhine River fish kill.)

Human duplicity finally put an end to Green Revolution II. Peasants underreported their harvests in order to lower the amount of rice they would have to hand over to the army. At the same time, local army officers in charge of collecting the rice overestimated how much had been produced in order to enlarge their personal cut of the one-sixth due the government. No one could determine if production had actually increased or decreased. The government soon discovered, however, that it was paying CIBA more than two dollars for every one dollar's worth of rice that the army said it was getting from the peasants. According to Gary E. Hansen, a research associate at the Technology and Development Institute, East-West Center, Honolulu, rice produced with CIBA was costing the government $305 a ton when the world market price was only $130 a ton. Now that's what I call a "long bomb."

Green Revolution III began in 1970 and is still going on. The government ships the seeds, fertilizers, and insecticides to local warehouses. Peasants take out low-cost loans and use the inputs as they see fit. Franke studied the effects of this program in a village where ecological conditions were optimal for the success of the high-yield varieties and found that actual yield increases of up to 70 percent over native varieties were being achieved.

Yet Franke discovered that only about one-fifth of the farming households had joined the program. As predicted, the chief beneficiaries were the households that were already better off than average and that had no labor debts to pay off. For the majority of farming households, the 70 percent productivity increase was not sufficient to make any real difference in their class position since they did not own enough land and would have to continue working for somebody else in order to get through the year. Traditionally, poor families in Franke's village make ends meet by working for well-to-do patrons who lend them money to buy food. The patrons are not eager for their clients to get out of debt because they need cheap labor for their large paddy holdings; on the other hand, the clients are afraid to break off relations because they fear being left on their own during a drought or family crisis.

Elsewhere in Indonesia, Green Revolution III is encountering ecological problems. A combination of political, economic, and ecological factors must be at work in the latest crisis. Whatever the precise cause, rice prices have trebled in recent months, and the government has already imported 1.5 million tons of rice and is looking around for more.

You have to be brutally frank with some experts, you have to push them into realizing it: the Green Revolution is a hoax.

The End of an Energy Orgy

❖❖❖❖❖❖

KENNETH E. F. WATT

[1974]

The United States, particularly the northeast, is in continuing danger of economic strangulation because of the fuel shortage. How could we be so ill prepared? The answer is that we are the victims of a defective pattern of thinking that originated in a series of historical accidents in the nineteenth century. The ultimate consequence of this erroneous thinking was inevitable; the Arab export embargo merely hastened the arrival of a crisis that would have arrived by 1979 at the latest.

In the nineteenth century we consumed wood, whale oil, and buffalo at astonishingly high rates. This pattern of resource use had profound implications on our later development. By 1850, 91 percent of our energy came from wood, and Americans were consuming fuel wood at an annual rate equivalent to the burning of 7,091 pounds of coal per person. To put this into perspective, in 1969 the total consumption of energy in all forms, in pounds of coal equivalents, was only 6,993 pounds per capita in Switzerland, and 6,235 in Japan. Thus, by the mid-nineteenth century, and perhaps even earlier, the United States—by cutting down the trees that surrounded its population—had attained a level of energy consumption that two of the most technologically sophisticated nations on earth would not reach until about 120 years later.

Wood did not decline significantly as an important source of fuel until 1880. It was replaced by coal and some oil, which had been used for over two decades. Long before wood ran out, other sources of energy became available. This pattern was repeated three times;

coal became important before wood ran out; oil became important before coal ran out; and gas became important before oil ran out.

Two other resources, now almost forgotten, led the United States early in its development to a very high level of resource exploitation. By 1847, we were using 313,000 barrels of whale oil per year, or about 0.014 barrels per person per year. This got the United States into early and heavy use of oil for lubrication and illumination and set the stage for heavy use of crude petroleum shortly thereafter. To indicate the magnitude of forward momentum in oil use, by 1928 the United States consumed 7.62 barrels of crude oil per person, while in the rest of the world, average per capita use in the same year was only 0.19 barrels.

The sperm whaling industry collapsed from overexploitation in 1881, but by then crude oil in quantity was available to replace whale oil. As in the case of the shift from fuel wood to coal, the United States never got the chance to learn an important lesson: that the conversion from one energy economy to another takes a long time. Historically this country has taken from forty to sixty years to get a new source of energy to the point where it could supply 10 percent of the national energy needs.

We acquired a taste for meat early. By 1872 we were killing seven million buffalo a year. A meat-eating society requires more land per capita to produce food than a largely plant-eating society. This is because of the lower efficiency in solar energy use, which must pass through one extra trophic level in the food pyramid, from plants to herbivores, before it reaches man. A superabundance of buffalo, combined with a greater availability of space per capita relative to other countries, taught us to ignore land or food as critical limiting resources. The ultimate result has been that farmland has been cheap compared to the same land converted to urban purposes. Even in the last few decades the value of land used for farming has declined relative to the value of that same land used for urban purposes.

The consequence has been a trend toward incredibly sprawling cities with no real urban center. Only in Canada and Australia have similar cities developed, and in those countries, too, the temporary superabundance of farmland has deceived the population into thinking it did not matter if cities grew by spreading out, rather than up. In countries where farmland is at a premium, the typical city building is seven or more stories. Indeed, in many old European cities, it is difficult to find a building less than seven stories high, and new buildings on the outskirts of cities are often ten to thirteen stories high.

Unconsciously, we learned several lessons from our experiences with resources in the last century; unfortunately, they were incorrect, the result of temporary situations in which we managed to get by because of extraordinary luck. One conclusion we reached was that resources are limitless, so there is no need to conserve them. This produced an economy characterized by low unit costs for resources relative to the cost of labor. Since there is no historical precedent for high resource prices, politicians today hesitate to permit prices to increase sharply in the interests of conservation. We were also taught that it doesn't matter if anything runs out, because there is always a substitute. This is one basis for the widespread and unshakable belief that atomic energy will arrive in the nick of time. Also important, because there was always a substitute ready in time, we have come to ignore the great importance of time itself as a critical limiting resource. Thus, we are unaware of the enormous time required to get new technologies working.

Our experiences in the nineteenth century led us as a nation to acquire excessive faith in "Yankee ingenuity." Because of our superabundance of resources, our ingenuity never encountered an insoluble problem. Thus, we overemphasize what we can accomplish and naïvely believe that nuclear energy, solar energy, wind, or gravitational fields will produce another miracle for us.

Each nation does what it can and what it must. Other countries have the same ingenuity as ours: the airplane, airship, automobile, and many other inventions were developed in several countries almost simultaneously. But lacking our resource base, other countries evolved in the direction of more efficient energy use. This meant trains and buses instead of cars; it also meant compact cities and different diets. Thus, while we instinctively used energy to solve all our problems, always deluding ourselves that high energy use means high technology, many other nations tended to equate high technology with great efficiency of resource use.

For a long time, advertising and our natural instincts to acquire goods have led us to use up much of our resources. Because we came to believe that our wants were insatiable, we never worried much about the possible consequences of market saturation. But wants can be satisfied, and the simultaneous total satisfaction of a wide variety of wants is having a profound effect on our economy. Even without the Arab oil embargo, we would have discovered that economic growth was slowing because we had a glut of cars, planes, luxury resort hotels, upper-class housing, and electronic goods.

Our most serious problem, however, is our selection of an erroneous set of national goals, which were based on our luck in the nineteenth century and which we have advertised with great vigor internationally. Rather than being concerned with the quality of life, we are committed to maximizing gross national product by maximizing the flow of matter and energy through the economic system.

Our current national goals maximize resource depletion, increase pollution, reduce life expectancy, destroy our city centers, and give us a slow, inconvenient, unhealthy form of travel. Shifting our goals to maximizing the quality of life would lead to less resource depletion, less pollution, higher life expectancy, more pleasure (more culture, more entertainment, and less haste), and a faster, more convenient transportation system less detrimental to health.

What happens to us if we don't change? We are in real danger of simply running out of everything, while still expecting substitutes for soon-to-be depleted resources to show up, as they did many times before. The authors of *Limits to Growth* alerted many people to a series of difficulties that can befall us. This book, however, was based on a highly aggregated model in which much detail was omitted by design (to expose the essential features of the big picture). But an interesting thing happens when we disaggregate to determine the impact of additional mechanisms on limits to growth. We discover that the timetable for troubles resulting from excessive growth is moved closer to the present.

A highly aggregated global model tells us that given present trends, a particular resource will be gone in thirty years. A more detailed model that deals with the 175 nations on earth reveals additional difficulties because the nations placing the heaviest demands on the resource may not be those with the greatest supply. And a nation with a supply surplus may not allow all of that supply to go to another nation with excessive demand. The Arab oil embargo is the first major example of this phenomenon, but we will undoubtedly see many similar occurrences involving many critically important minerals.

Less highly aggregated models reveal additional sources of difficulty when we divide the population into age classes. Rapid growth leads to very large imbalances in the age structure of the population, which quickly become so severe that, in reaction, birthrates drop in developed countries. This is currently leading to a situation in which only 69 percent as many children will be born in the United States in 1975 as were in 1960. No comparable decline over a fifteen-year period has ever occurred in U.S. history, not even from 1920 to 1935. What will happen to U.S. economic growth by about the year 2030, when the fifty-five-year-old class of 1975 will be trying to support the seventy-year-old class of 1960? Imbalances in year-class strength alone can bring an end to excessive economic growth.

We have deluded ourselves because of a set of historical accidents that were never perceived as unusual.

Now we must quickly unlearn some erroneous lessons so that a future sequence of incidents such as the one that led to the Arab oil embargo will not catch us by surprise.

We should not perceive the energy crisis as a problem, but rather as a glorious opportunity, ripe for exploitation. Our history with wood, sperm whales, buffalo, coal, oil, and gas leaves little doubt about our ability to exploit glorious opportunities. We can do this in two ways: by converting to more efficient use of resources and by shifting a higher proportion of the labor force from manufacturing and transportation into service occupations. The improved efficiency would lead to more sophisticated, convenient technology for everything: transportation, communication, entertainment, and appliances. Shifting the labor force would bring better medical care and a cultural renaissance. Anyone for modern mass transit and community art centers? The more immediate problem is the transition period. The transition can be facilitated by community-organized car pools, dial-a-grocery delivery services, small companies marketing solar-powered home heating and cooling units, and aggressive organization of community theater, dance, music, and art groups. Also, now, when we are in danger of an explosion in unemployment, is the opportune time for massive political pressure to get cradle-to-grave, guaranteed comprehensive health care for everyone. This would certainly take up some of the slack in employment.

The time has come, in a sense, for America to grow up. For some two centuries we have lived luxuriously off the energy-rich land, like a spoiled child off wealthy parents. Now, crises are forcing us into a period of maturity, to an awareness of the consequences of high energy consumption. The development of this maturity could bring a style and richness of life that Americans have never known. But it will take all our Yankee ingenuity—and more—to reach such a golden age.

The Unavoidable Limits to Energy Growth

❖❖❖❖❖❖❖

GEORGE M. WOODWELL

[1974]

Energy drives our world. Energy from oil is sending me eastward at 600 miles per hour in a giant airplane flying 30,000 feet over the Wyoming desert. Energy from oil was used to smelt the aluminum to build the plane: more energy from oil was used to make the plastic tray I'm writing on, the plastic fiber of the seats; still more to freeze the ice in my lemonade, served in a plastic cup. Most of my world is fossil fueled—but not quite all.

A hitchhiking fly tickles my hand. I flick it away. It moves to the window, attracted by the sunlight reflected from the plane's wings. The fly's source of energy is, of course, the sun. This solar energy flows to the insect through green plants somewhere far away. And the energy I use in flicking my hand also comes from the sun, fixed in photosynthesis somewhere recently, perhaps in the great green circles of western Nebraska's irrigated farmland now passing below me. Outside my silver capsule, the sun dominates: warming the land, evaporating water, heating the air, circulating the oceans, making the weather, causing the winds—and providing the energy for all life.

These are the two sources of energy used by man. The first, principally fossil fuels—but also including water power, nuclear power, and geothermal power, among other minor sources—drives our technology. The other source, the sun, drives the biosphere. A small fraction of the total energy from the sun, perhaps 0.1 percent of all the solar energy reaching the top of the atmosphere, is fixed in photosynthesis and becomes available to support life. Most of the balance is reflected immediately back into space. Both sources—energy in the technological segment and energy from biotic resources —are currently in short supply, locally and around the world. In addition, shortages of fossil fuels have profound implications for all biotic resources, including food.

The immediate problem is a decline in the rate of increase in oil production in the United States. Total production appears to have reached a peak just when worldwide demand is soaring. The decline in resources means that the United States no longer holds a dominant role in bargaining for oil elsewhere. As a result of this squeeze, prices are rising and gross changes are occurring in the relative costs of different sources of energy. What are the implications of these changes for biotic resources?

We should base our answer on a consideration of the size of these two energy flows, one through technology and one through life. Two recent studies are of help. The Energy Policy Project, financed by the Ford Foundation, issued a preliminary report not long ago that summarized the various uses of nonbiotic energy. According to the report, the total energy use in 1973 from all nonbiotic sources, including fossil fuels, hydropower, geothermal sources, and nuclear power was about 66 trillion (66×10^{12}) kilowatt-hours. The United States consumed about one-third of this. Use has been increasing rapidly in recent years. It now takes about twelve years for total energy use to double; the U.S. doubling time has recently been estimated at about eighteen years.

The second study, by R. H. Whittaker and G. E. Likens of Cornell University, is a comprehensive appraisal of the total amount of energy fixed on earth by green plants. That total is thought to be equivalent to about 840 trillion kilowatt-hours per year. This is net primary production, the energy available to support animals, including man, and the organisms of decay. About two-thirds of this total is fixed in terrestrial ecosystems, mostly forests. Agriculture supplies about one-twentieth of the total. Contrary to popular belief, agriculture is not a cornucopia of new resources in support of man; it is simply a diversion of net primary production from one form and place to another. The diversion is made by lavish use of energy in technology. Recent estimates suggest that several units of fossil fuel energy are required to produce each unit of food energy. This ratio demonstrates the importance of society's energy flows in maintaining modern agriculture.

The energy available worldwide as net primary production was probably ten to fifteen times the amount of energy used in the technological segment of society in 1973. How much of this solar energy is used to sustain human life? Direct use includes all the energy fixed in agriculture for food production. Cultivated land supplies net primary production approximately equivalent to 40 or 50 trillion kilowatt-hours annually. We must add to that estimate the harvests of food from natural systems, including the harvests of grazing mammals. The magnitude of this entire segment might be as much again as the flow to man from cultivated land.

We also harvest fish from the oceans. The total yield of fish is about 70 million tons annually; it has not increased in recent years despite intensified efforts in fishing. While better management of fisheries might increase the yield somewhat, at present, fish are probably being harvested at about the maximum rate possible.

In addition to these uses of food, we harvest large quantities of lumber for fuel, pulp, and construction purposes from natural or lightly managed plant communities around the world. The total current harvest of forests probably exceeds the annual growth, since massive inroads are being made in this decade on old-growth forests. Such a drain on natural ecosystems cannot be sustained, of course. A conservative estimate suggests that as much as 30 to 50 percent of the net primary production of the earth is being diverted to direct use by man for support of the current population.

This estimate of the use of the biota does not take

into consideration what I call the "public service functions of nature." These include the stabilization of water flows through river valleys, the purification of air and water, the amelioration of local climate, the control of plant and animal populations, the stabilization of soils, and the retention of nutrients in biotic cycles. These functions are commonly assumed to continue no matter how intensively biotic resources are exploited, but there is powerful evidence that these services performed by nature are now being lost.

The losses are due to two types of biotic changes. First, there has been an unprecedented decrease in numbers of species. We are living in a period in which the numbers of different plants and animals are being reduced more rapidly than at any other time in the history of the earth. Second, the losses of species are coincident with a systematic reduction in the structure of natural ecosystems around the world, especially in forests. Clearcutting of old-growth stands reduces not only the standing crop of trees but may also reduce the capacity of the site for photosynthesis. Losses of nutrients, changes in the physical conditions of soils, erosion, and other changes in the site frequently reduce its capacity for supporting vegetation of any type. The spread of an impoverished Sahara southward in Africa, the reduction of tropical rain forests and their replacement with scrub, and the destruction of large areas of temperate-zone forests all reduce the capacity of the earth for sustaining human life, the arguments of exploiters notwithstanding.

The net effect of these changes is the gradual, cumulative, and largely irreversible biotic impoverishment of the earth. The extinction of species is an irreversible change. The loss of nutrients normally held in the biota of the uplands is irreversible in a time span that is of interest to us. The destruction of natural communities in lakes, streams, and coastal oceans by eutrophication and pollution, and the heedless redistribution of species by man, also constitute irreversible change. In the Great Lakes, for example, the combined effects of human actions in changing drainage basins, modifying patterns of water flow, causing pollution, and carelessly introducing alien fish have grossly impaired the ability of the lakes to supply food and other services for man. The question is, how do we recognize the small steps that lead to such major changes?

The structure and function of natural communities follow clear and well-known patterns of change. The patterns of biotic impoverishment have been known in many cases for hundreds, even thousands, of years. One of the best modern examples is an experiment at Brookhaven National Laboratory, where for more than a decade the effects of ionizing radiation on a forest have been examined. A large source of ionizing radiation was set up in the center of a uniform stand of oak-pine forest. The radiation source was 9,500 curies of cesium 137, a radioactive by-product of the atomic energy industry that emits gamma radiation similar to X rays. The source was large enough to provide a gradient of radiation intensity ranging from several thousand roentgens per day within a few yards of the point of emission to about 1 roentgen per day at 400 feet. The experiment was started in November, 1961, and has continued to the present.

Within six months of the start of irradiation, the pattern of damage to the vegetation had been established. There were five clear zones of effect. In a zone close to the radiation source, no higher plants survived. At slightly lower radiation exposures, only certain hardy herbaceous plants of the forest floor survived, principally the sedge *Carex pensylvanica*. At lower exposures, the carex was joined by the shrubs of the forest: blueberries and huckleberries. At still lower exposures, about 160 feet from the source, certain trees survived, forming an impoverished oak forest zone. At exposures below a few roentgens per day, all of the higher plants of the forest survived, including the indigenous pine *Pinus rigida*. The pine, which is the most sensitive to ionizing radiation, was removed by very low exposures, leaving a forest that appeared otherwise intact.

This form of biotic change is not unusual. While the

cause of the change in the Brookhaven experiment was an extraordinary exposure to ionizing radiation, parallel changes also take place where no such experiment has been conducted. A pattern of systematic change of structure occurs in forests exposed to wind, salt spray, and extremes of pollution. Similar changes in vegetation occur additionally around smelters that emit oxides of sulfur and heavy metals into the atmosphere. As human influences spread around the world, we find various stages of ecological impoverishment characteristic of regions that have long been inhabited by man. The vegetation of the Mediterranean region and the Levant is characterized by impoverished forests, reduced by the effects of human habitation over thousands of years.

The common assumption is that industrial energy has freed man from dependence on biotic resources. Nothing could be further from the truth. The real effect of industrial flows of energy has been to allow the transformation of net production from less useful to more useful forms. The transformations are maintained, in turn, only at considerable effort and expense. The replacement of forests by agricultural communities of various types is one such transformation. The use of energy in technology also allows the transport of net primary production around the world to convenient places for man.

But there are limits. In the fifteen years between 1951 and 1966, a 34 percent increase in food production was accompanied by a 146 percent increase in the use of nitrates and a 300 percent increase in the use of pesticides. There is every reason to believe that the further intensification of agriculture will require similarly disproportionate efforts as less fertile lands are put into production. Moreover, there is reason to fear that toxification of the environment over large areas will aggravate this problem. As food becomes more and more expensive, driven up in price by scarcities born of increasing population, the pressures on agriculture can be expected to increase. Because ever larger amounts of nitrates and pesticides are required to produce an improved agricultural yield, the intensification of agriculture will require additional energy. This energy will be applied less efficiently in the future than at present. Just as we appear to have reached the limits of oceanic fisheries so, in many instances, we may also have reached the limits of terrestrial agriculture, unless remarkable further advances are made in management techniques.

The problem is even more complicated. As demand for energy to feed the economic and technological segments of the still-growing industrialized nations mounts, there is increasing pressure to lower the standards for pollution control. Nuclear power is widely heralded as one important part of any possible solution to the energy squeeze. Advocates of nuclear power hope to find sites for power plants where there is abundant water for cooling. Nuclear power plants now in existence produce about 1,000 megawatts each and require cooling water in volumes of 30 to 50 million gallons per hour. There are few bodies of water or rivers in the continental United States that can supply this amount of water for once-through cooling to such power plants. The present hope is that these plants can be placed along the coasts, perhaps not on the shore at all but in the ocean, where there is abundant salt water for cooling. The plants, however, must necessarily be located in fairly shallow waters and will hence affect coastal fisheries. There is no possibility that these establishments will improve the fisheries; there are many reasons for believing that they will diminish them, perhaps greatly. The principal problem is the large volume of water that nuclear reactors use, pasteurizing it with heat.

Reactors also release toxic substances used to kill organisms that might foul their cooling coils. In addition, there is erosion of toxic metals from the reactors themselves in quantities that may approach several tons annually, as well as the continuous release of radioactivity. This latter problem is more severe in the oceans than on land because there is little possibility of cleaning up any offshore radioactive spill. Once radioactive nuclides are released into coastal waters, they will circulate in biotic systems and have the potential for affecting humans. This latter fact alone is sufficient reason to give serious pause to those who advocate offshore reactors. One large radioactive spill from such a reactor could render a segment of the coastal fisheries unfit for human consumption. Would the gain in energy be worth adding such a risk to other certain costs? Far from appearing as a boon, nuclear power looks more and more like an unacceptable burden.

Another example of the interrelationships between technology and natural systems helps to clarify this apparent dilemma. Rains over much of the eastern part of North America have become extremely acid. The acidity presumably comes from oxides of sulfur and nitrates formed in the combustion of fossil fuels. Apparently the burning of sulfur-containing oil and coal and the use of internal combustion automobile engines that fix nitrogen as a by-product have turned precipitation into a dilute mixture of sulfuric and nitric acids. The acidity is in the range of 3 to 4 on the pH scale, sufficient to leach nutrients from leaves and, over a period of years, from soils. Soil scientists recognize that continued leaching with a weak acid will reduce the productivity of agriculture and of other vegetations.

A 10 percent reduction in agricultural productivity is difficult to measure and might be recognizable only over a period of several years. Yet a reduction of that proportion in the productivity of forests and of agriculture in New England seems to be a realistic prediction if acid rains continue for ten years or more. A 10 percent reduction in the net primary productivity of natural vegetation and of agriculture in the New England states would represent a loss of energy equivalent to the power produced by fifteen 1,000-megawatt reactors.

The segments of society that are most closely dependent on natural resources, such as farmers and fishermen, would feel this loss most, but all of us would feel it to some degree. A reduction in the yields of forests and agriculture would raise the prices of all forest products and of food. Effects would extend to estuarine and coastal fisheries as well. This is simply another instance in which the use of nonrenewable resources has been, and continues to be, allowed to destroy renewable resources.

We cannot separate the squeeze on energy used in support of technology from the squeeze on biotic resources; nor can we separate the squeeze on these resources from the growing squeeze on food and the quality of life. Despite the dreams of technologists, the availability of cheap energy has not created new basic resources for human use; instead, the net effect has been a reduction in the net primary productivity of the earth and a concomitant and now soaring increase in the rate of loss of species. These facts taken together suggest that we have reached a point in the development of our current civilization where further increase in flows of energy through technology will cause a significant reduction in the capacity of the earth to support mankind. The world cannot use more energy safely. The arguments for relaxation of controls on pollution or for the further diffusion of the deleterious effects of technology around the globe are clearly and simply wrong. So, too, are the dreams of continued economic growth in the patterns of past decades, using abundant new supplies of energy. We have reached the point where biotic resources are crashing—limits are with us now. Technology may alleviate some of the problems at present rates of energy use, but another doubling of energy consumption in the United States may be impossible—and a worldwide doubling is frightening.

My glistening aluminum capsule—low on fuel, empty of food, its tasteless movie spent—is sinking through the smoke and fog of New York City toward the concrete strip that was formerly part of Jamaica Bay, once one of the largest salt marshes in the world. We have just crossed the Hudson River, passed the towers of Manhattan, and are gradually descending over mile after square mile of brick tenements in Brooklyn. Energy makes this city possible—the same energy and technological genius that produced my plane, plus energy from natural systems, from the green of those irrigated plots in western Nebraska, the green of the forests of New York State's Catskill and Adirondack mountains, the greens and browns and reds of the ocean out beyond Far Rockaway.

The earth's surface—the land and the oceans—is an energy-fixing machine. From this point of view, what is the real cost of this city, measured in total space on a finite globe? No one knows for sure, but the cost reaches far beyond the city or the state or even the entire country to include a large segment of the North Atlantic and a large portion of the atmosphere. It includes, as well, a share of problems that are worldwide in scope—the energy crisis, the use of DDT and other poisons, the control of acid rains, the management of world fisheries, and the impending worldwide crisis of biotic impoverishment. The earth is overpopulated and overdeveloped; the important problem now is ecology, not energy and not economics.

Sensuous Symbionts of the Sea

❖❖❖❖❖❖

LEWIS THOMAS

[1971]

One's first reaction to a close view of the life of the sea is confusion, unease. How can things be so beautiful, with such intricate balance and symmetry in their infinitely varied forms and, at the same time, seem so hostile, so threatening, ready to lunge, to snatch life from each other? So many of the moving parts of sea life seem to be designed, exquisitely tooled, for nothing but destruction and devouring. It is disconcerting, almost as though we have had the wrong idea about beauty and harmony; living things so evidently aimed at each other's throats should not have, as these things do, the aspect of pure, crystalline enchantment.

Perhaps something is wrong in the way we look at them. From our distance we see them as separate, independent creatures interminably wrangling, as a writhing arrangement of solitary adversaries bent on killing each other. Success in such a system would have to mean more than mere survival; to make sense, the fittest would surely have to end up standing triumphantly alone. This, in the conventional view, would be the way of the world, the ultimate observance of nature's law. It was to delineate such a state of affairs that the hideous nineteenth-century phrase "Nature red in tooth and claw" was hammered out.

What is wrong with this view is that it never seems to turn out that way. There is in the sea a symmetry, a balance, and something like the sense of permanence encountered in a well-tended garden.

To be sure, individuals die—in such abundance that

a permanent shower of organic fragments descends through the layers of the ocean—but the whole system survives and thrives and remains in balance. The creatures flourish, in vast surfeits. They feed on each other; it does not distort the arrangement to say that they are feeding each other.

On another level, they can be seen to be connected to each other. Once this view is opened, the extent of their interdependence and connectedness is astonishing. Nothing lives alone. One cannot find a genuinely solitary form, uncoupled from everything else. Instead, life is a dense, shimmering matrix of live tissue, in which the creatures of the sea spring to view as working parts, like cells in tissue or organs in an organism.

For all their appearance of readiness for combat, the animals tend to move out of the way of a battle, especially when the circumstances stipulate that someone has to lose. The coelenterate species of *Gorgonacea* illustrates how an individual organism may simply bow out when necessary. Gorgonians tend to grow in closely arranged masses, but they do not fuse. Jacques Theodor has shown that when two are placed side by side, pressed against each other, the smaller will always undergo disintegration. It is the smaller partner that turns on and governs the lytic enzymes. The smaller gorgonian is not done in by the antagonist, but simply retires, totally.

Many of the negotiations between marine antagonists are conducted discreetly, by chemical mediators, with the adversaries keeping at a suitable distance, beyond grasp much of the time. Starfish release a substance that will set any nearby scallop in violent, fleeing motion, clacking like agitated dentures. Fish communicate by a diplomacy of chemical signals. Bullheads, for instance, release substances that enable other members of the species not only to identify each one as an individual but also to discern the order of rank; a retiring bullhead, recently defeated in a contest for leadership, will have a different smell from the one that has just become chairman.

The threatening gestures, the wild declarations of hostility, often turn out to be signals, warnings, pronouncements of individuality and territory. The creatures of the sea are marvelous in their ornamentation, their embellishments of selfness. They flag each other off, send chemical information to each other announcing the inviolability of their various households.

Thus far, this is familiar territory. This is much the way our body systems work; we have immunologic mechanisms that detect foreign creatures, and we prevent bacteria, fungi, and viruses from overrunning our tissues by mobilizing our reactions of inflammation and immune defense. Our mechanisms are efficiently designed to engulf and eject anything that does not belong. To be sure, it is precisely this kind of defense that often gets us into the difficulties we recognize as disease, with inappropriately violent inflammatory reactions or sometimes, due to misinformation, with the kinds of destructive tissue lesions called autoimmune disease. Nevertheless, we place solid reliance on immunologic recognition as our protection against everything outside ourselves.

But the recognition systems used by creatures in the sea appear to have an altogether different function, at least some of the time. There are multitudes of animals with the most exquisite and precise mechanisms for identifying the surfaces of cells and tissues other than their own, and these are used, not for defense or aggression, but to get together. They are not immunologic in our sense; indeed, they do not involve the formation of antibodies and antigens. In their net effect, they enable one creature to locate the special animals of other species with which it forms advantageous partnerships. Somehow, the phenomenon of symbiosis has evolved in the life of the sea with the same degree of specificity and accuracy that has characterized the emergence of immunologic mechanisms in other forms of life.

Take, for instance, the hermit crab, which lives in symbiosis with an anemone perched like an ornament on its shell. The crab will seek out and can find its partner in a crowd. The anemone, for its part, can identify its particular kind of crab by chemical markers on the shell surface—a molecular recognition of a high order of sophistication. The anemone may attach itself, or the crab may pick the anemone up in its claws and fix it in place. Certain crabs will carry their anemones around permanently attached to their claws, using them as a sort of dining implement. The food is caught by one partner, sampled, and passed along to the other.

There are barnacles that live only on the surfaces of certain whales, and there are other barnacles that then attach, selectively and with the same specificity, to the backs of those barnacles. There are fish that live out their lives amid the lethal tentacles of Portuguese men-of-war, shielded by the nematocysts and fed whatever comes their way. Other fish, like the damselfish, are always found in association with specific anemones; early in life they must learn their way into the tentacles by swimming tentatively around the borders, until they become somehow labeled so that the anemone no longer recognizes them as nonself.

The life of the sea is filled with the most fantastic arrangements for partnerships, condominiums, communities. There are the narrow, elongated arrowfish, designed to live poised forever between the sharp spines of sea urchins; the serpentine fish that live, for reasons of their own, inside sea cucumbers, into which they swim gracefully, tail first, through the cloaca. Some fish are adapted to life in the immediate vicinity of larger fish of a different species; some have developed suction disks so they can be carried by their particular host. Fish of all kinds are able to recognize the extraordinary species of cleaner-fish; they will queue up to have their surfaces, and even the insides of their mouths, picked at and cleaned.

Sometimes there are inventive adaptations that seem to be in the process of being worked out, like preliminary sketches for future evolution. Several years ago some Australian surf bathers were stung by what felt like jellyfish but turned out to be *Glaucus,* small nudibranchs, which had fed earlier on Portuguese men-of-war. These mollusks had edited their meal, permitting the stinging cells to migrate intact through their bodies to their surfaces and preserving for the time the essence of jellyfish in a kind of limited partnership.

Sea creatures tend to live together, not because they lack the mechanisms for self-discrimination or the ability to discern the differences of others, but rather because their associations are so highly selective, and their discriminatory properties are so extraordinarily sensitive and accurate. The distinctions we make between organisms have a different meaning, almost the opposite kind of meaning, for these creatures. Some of them even overlook the doctrinal separation of animals from plants that we take so seriously in our taxonomy, and they put members of the two kingdoms together in the same tissues, sometimes in the same cells. The giant clam, for example, contains in his siphonal tissues a green pasture of algae. The clam, dependent on the photosynthetic contributions of the plant cells, lives with the green tissue always facing up toward the sun; there are small lenslike structures, adapted from visual organs, arranged over the algae to focus sunlight on them. It is an amiable, bucolic accommodation, but it comes as a shock to us to learn that algae are sheltered and encouraged to multiply inside the clam's phagocytic cells. We have become used to the idea that these cells are our primary lines of defense, the most fundamental of the aggressive mechanisms in the human system.

A coral reef is a universe of symbiotic relationships. It is like a giant organism, with various working parts made up of polyp, fish, worm, plant, crab, mollusk, plankton, all interdependent. When disease occurs, as in the ulceration of a reef by the crown-of-thorns starfish, you can count the many different life forms bound together in one reef by the number and the variety of casualties.

The tendency to live together in close partnerships may represent the most ancient habit of all living things. Perhaps it is most conspicuous in the sea because life began there and the habit has hung on in undisguised form. When you consider what the earliest stages were probably like, the pattern of symbiosis has a certain consistency. There was, according to current theory, a first cell type, probably a very first single cell, put together by a lucky aggregation of polymers formed from basic ingredients in the broth that covered the cooling earth. Lightning may have launched the final process. The progeny of that first cell have been replicating ever since to mold the living parts of the earth, in a process rather like the morphogenesis of a stupendous embryo.

Variation and the elaboration of species have been imposed by modifications and embellishments of DNA during the long, continuous process of replication from the first strand; some of these have occurred spontaneously, some by radiation, and very likely many have been carried from one genome to another by viruses. The fusion of different sorts of primitive cells may have developed more complex types of cells. Perhaps in such a fusion the mitochondria became the main source of oxidative energy within cells; originally they were probably bacterialike cells, and they still retain their own specific DNA and RNA. The chloroplasts of plant cells, responsible for photosynthesis and hence the source of the oxygen in the earth's atmosphere, also seem to have started out as small organisms before they became incorporated as organelles in plant cells. In both cases, these essential structures can be viewed as symbionts in modern cells, and there are probably other organelles with similar origins. Our cells are no longer the pure, primary building blocks they once seemed; they are a sort of organism, and as more is learned we may realize they are ecosystems as complicated as Jamaica Bay.

The parts of cells do not seem much concerned about their individuality. In his laboratory James Danielli discovered that amoebas can be taken apart like small watches and then reassembled, using cytoplasm from one amoeba, the nucleus of another, and the membranes of a third, and the final refabricated creature swims away untroubled.

The ultimate challenge to the notion of separateness is the phenomenon of cell fusion. When cells from different animal species are placed together under the right circumstances, their membranes will join, form bridges, and fuse, and the cytoplasm will flow across to produce a single, hybrid cell—half-kangaroo, half-mouse—capable of multiplying for generations with its combined heredity intact. Perhaps it is the nature of cells to fuse, given the chance. A currently attractive theory has it that this is the way metazoan, multicellular forms of life may have been put together in the first place, combining in the single genome of a new organism the genetic information required for assemblies of different cells with different functions.

With this kind of family history in the background, it is not surprising that the habit of symbiosis remains so strong. Were it not for the formidable arsenal of weapons and the inventive displays of markers of individuality, of entity, that have evolved at the same time, we might have ended up as a mass of invariant, interliving, undifferentiated life, missing all the fun.

Man's Efficient Rush Toward Deadly Dullness

KENNETH E. F. WATT

[1972]

Is diversity of concern to people interested in natural history, conservation, and the environment? To answer the question fully, one must understand the exact meaning of diversity, the ubiquitous loss of diversity in the world today, and the reasons for the value of diversity.

An argument for preserving anything, particularly something rare, often turns out to be an argument in disguise for diversity. Thus, it seems worthwhile to provide natural historians with a handy kit of powerful arguments for variety because all too often they feel defenseless when confronted with the arguments of developers, which are clearly supported by short-term economic benefits, at least for a few investors.

The rapid loss of diversity in the world is a serious and pervasive phenomenon. Everywhere we look, we see examples of a large number of diverse entities being replaced by a small number of similar entities. We all know about endangered species such as birds of prey and large mammals, including all species of whales. Most of the world's commercial fish stocks are in danger, shell collectors are depleting tropical beaches and coral reefs, and pollution will annihilate commercial shellfish populations, resulting in simplification of our diets. But progressive environmental simplification is far more widespread than this. Half the butterfly species have disappeared in Holland in the last few decades. Conversion of the Russian steppe from wild plants to wheat fields has cut the number of insect species there by 58 percent.

In the economic sphere, there has been a tremendous reduction in the number of manufacturers (think of the number of automobile manufacturers in the United States in 1910). Our numerous corner grocery stores have been replaced by a small number of huge super-markets. In many fields, large numbers of small busi-nesses have been replaced by small numbers of large businesses, to the point where we now have close to a monopoly in the manufacture of automobiles, aircraft, and computing equipment. Similarly, in agriculture large numbers of small farms have been replaced by small numbers of gigantic farm corporations.

Textural and cultural diversity has declined in our cities, whether you compare different parts of the same city or different cities in different countries. Driving from an airport to the downtown section of a city, the signs tend to be in the same language (English) and to advertise the same products, whether one is in Rome, Beirut, or Singapore. Stores and banks seem to be stamped from a common mold.

Remarkably, the same process has occurred in the human population. An extraordinarily high proportion of the world's population is now very young. The variety once found when many human age classes coexisted in approximately equal numbers has gone.

There are too many examples of the decline of di-versity for this situation to have come about by chance. There is indeed an underlying explanation: we live in an age, and a culture, that puts tremendous emphasis on efficiency and productivity as desiderata for mankind. Since variety is inimical to these goals, variety has suf-fered and will continue to suffer. Unless powerful and compelling arguments can be offered to stop this loss of diversity, we will soon be living in a homogeneous —and boring—world.

The large number of specific arguments for main-taining the diversity of particular sets of plants, animals, or other items, all fall into four categories: (1) diversity promotes stability; (2) it insures against risks; (3) it utilizes more completely the sun's energy; and (4) it promotes the mental well-being of humans.

There are only two basic elements in all theoretical arguments as to why diversity promotes stability. The first is the idea of spreading the risk (the same idea applies when you buy insurance from the largest insurance company). If an organism feeds on many different species, the chances of all its food sources being wiped out in some catastrophe are less than if the organism feeds on a few, or only one, species. The second idea is that a system functions more harmoniously if it has more elements because it then has more homeostatic feedback loops.

This abstract language can be translated into concrete examples. The greater the variety of foods the human population has available for harvesting, hunting, or fishing, the less the likelihood of human catastrophe due to a disaster befalling a particular food species. A most chilling example was the potato famine in Ireland, where an entire human population was excessively dependent on one food species. The situation is fundamentally the same when an Indian tribe depends greatly on salmon at a certain time of year, and then something happens to the salmon population (pollution or modification of the environment in the spawning stream due to a hydroelectric installation, for example). What few people realize is that the entire human population is now setting itself up for the same situation. For example, as we rapidly deplete the stocks of more and more oceanic species through overfishing and pollution, we cut off optional food sources that we might need desperately in the future. The larger the human population becomes and the more the sources of food decline, the more precarious is our situation.

Our great preoccupation with productivity and efficiency and our lack of concern about diversity increase the precariousness of our economic lives, as well as our food. Consider what happens when we try to maximize the manufacturing efficiency of aircraft. We are led, inexorably, to a situation in which a small group of corporations manufacture all aircraft in the United States. Each corporation is so large that it dominates the economies of the communities in which its plants are located. Thus, if a corporation meets with disaster, the community is in deep trouble. This is the case in Seattle, where Boeing sales slackened with saturation of the international aircraft market. Architectural writer Jane Jacobs discovered this principle of relating the economic stability of cities to their corporate diversity when she applied current ecological theories about the relation between diversity and stability to her urban studies.

In a most curious way, diversity appears to affect our economic, social, cultural, and political processes. For example, a slowly growing or nongrowing human population has a greater evenness of numbers in different age classes than a rapidly growing population. In a rapid-growth situation, young people are being added to the population so quickly that their numbers become unusually high relative to the numbers of older people. This strains society's ability to generate adequate educational taxes from the older group for the large younger group. It also is difficult for a rapidly growing society to create new jobs at the rate at which young people want to enter the labor force.

The more even the numbers of people in different age classes, the easier it is to maintain good communication between generations. Thus, all the present discussion about a "generation gap" has its ultimate origin in the lack of diversity in human age classes.

Many similar arguments relating diversity and different forms of stability could be put forth. But the fundamental structure of all such arguments would be the same, whether the subject is a human society or a rare plant. The reason for preserving it is that it may, in some unknown fashion, be important to the maintenance of stability in a part of the planetary ecosystem.

The second class of arguments for maintaining diversity is similar to the argument for buying life insurance. You don't really want or expect to use it, but you buy it just in case. Similarly, a civilization does not expect its acts to harm the world, but just in case they are destructive it would be nice to have at hand other things to fall back on. For example, when we develop new strains of plants and animals, we do not plan on producing lines that will deteriorate in the future. We do not plan on producing strains of collie dogs in which the females will have progressively more difficulty bearing viable offspring, or strains of wheat that will succumb to rust, or berries that after many generations will no longer have much flavor. When these unintended events occur, we fall back on our "insurance policy," either by backcrossing our domestic strains to wild strains or by shifting our attention to new strains or species. But what if there are no new strains or species to replace the unsatisfactory ones?

The insurance value of diversity applies to more than just individual species or strains of plants and animals. Suppose a civilization irrigated farmland in such a fashion that long-term, irreversible destruction of the soil only showed up after a century. Suppose, further, that the entire landscape of this civilization had been managed in an identical fashion. Then when the entire landscape lost its fertility, the civilization would be without land to produce food. Further, it wouldn't even have any unmanaged land to compare with the managed lands for scientific investigations. A simple example of the importance of such comparisons is the few forest areas in Greece from which goats have been excluded.

The contrast between the grazed and ungrazed lands is so startling that no argument from goat-lovers could withstand visual comparison of forested areas with and without goats.

It is tremendously important for any civilization to set aside areas where common cultivation practices are not adopted. If the same techniques are used everywhere, we can never know the long-term results of the practice. Thus, we can never know if intensive annual pesticide sprayings have long-term deleterious effects on orchards, forests, or woodlots unless we have unsprayed areas for comparison.

In short, a prudent civilization maintains the landscape under many different management strategies, including parcels of each soil and climate zone that are not managed at all. This landscape diversity has two values. First, we have a yardstick for determining if something unexpected or odd is gradually showing up in a managed area. Without the unmanaged areas, the odd or unexpected effect could be ascribed to something else, to a change in climate, for example. The unsettled arguments as to whether the changes in the landscape of the Mediterranean basin, the Middle East, North Africa, and northern India were due to climatic change or man's activities show clearly the importance of having unmanaged areas for checking. The second value of landscape diversity is that if a civilization unwittingly destroys its managed lands, it has other places on which to raise food while the destroyed areas are gradually rebuilt to productivity.

A generalization of this argument holds that an extremely prudent civilization would try to maintain other civilizations with different ideas about land use. Over the short term, the ideas of civilization A might appear vastly superior to those of civilization B. But over the long term it could turn out that the apparently "primitive" practices of civilization B were based on millennia of trial and error and incorporated deep wisdom that was unintelligible to civilization A.

The third argument for diversity originates in the theory of modern ecologists that any habitat contains a set of "niches," or functions, that may be filled. If only part of the niches are filled, then the sun's energy that is captured by, and flows through, a system will be less than if all the niches were filled.

Perhaps the best-known and most convincing illustration of this argument comes from Africa. Research shows that a mix of native animal species uses the landscape more economically than imported livestock. Each of the different types of antelope and other game consume slightly different mixes of food plants or parts of plants, so that a whole assemblage of different species uses the landscape more efficiently than, say, beef cattle would by themselves.

The same point has been demonstrated repeatedly in analyses of the fish production per year per acre from different mixes of fish species. The more fish species there are in a body of water, the greater the gross production. Human understanding of this principle reaches its pinnacle in Oriental fish farming, where up to nine different species of carp are grown together in the set of proportions that makes best use of the resources in a pond.

Humanity has given far too little thought to the fourth argument for preserving diversity. How much diversity in the world around us is optimal for the human mind? Might the extent of environmental diversity have any relationship to the average level of mental health in a population? Could a certain level of diversity be most satisfying—emotionally and esthetically—to the human mind because of the conditions during human evolution? Diversity in an environment may have a much deeper significance for man than is generally recognized. We know that human beings tend to hallucinate when kept in confined quarters and deprived of sensory stimuli. This could be interpreted as a protective device by the mind to provide an otherwise unavailable need. Reports have been published indicating that extremely refractory mental patients, who had not spoken to anyone in years, showed an almost miraculous response when taken to wilderness areas.

The recent popularity of skin diving as recreation may convey a deep message. It may be that the rate of incoming sensory stimuli while skin diving is optimal for the human mind. I know that after several hours of constant interruption by the phone and visitors, I almost jump with each new phone call. But I also know that I can become bored amid all this stimuli. The extremely deep satisfaction I derive from exploring the ocean edge of a tropical island may be telling me something important about my mind and all our minds. We have evolved over a very long period so that our minds can cope handily with a certain rate of incoming sensory stimuli. We find the stimuli rate we can cope with in nature because we evolved there. Either sharply higher or sharply lower rates of incoming sensory stimuli are bad for our nervous systems.

This is only anecdotal evidence, but more carefully designed and measured research leads to the same conclusion. For some years, Professor J. Lee Kavanau of UCLA has been conducting experiments on small mammal behavior in heavily instrumented cages. These cages are wired, enabling the animal to change its environment and recording every move the animal makes and every detail of the conditions in the cage. The animals learn to control their environment by pressing levers. Kavanau has discovered that animals will press levers to select other than optimal conditions. In other words, confronted with a choice of living constantly in an optimal world but being bored or of living in a world that is only optimal part of the time and experiencing variety, even a small rodent will opt for variety. It is reasonable to assume that humans would opt even more strongly for variety rather than constant optimality. Perhaps diversity is not merely a luxury for us. It may be something we need.

If, upon reflection, you agree with my general line of argument as to the intrinsic value of diversity, then important implications follow for many aspects of our lives. Particularly, the argument has important political implications.

For example, if diversity breeds stability, then it is worthwhile for a government to regulate the rate at which different interest groups acquire wealth and power. Undue concentration of power and wealth allows a small group of people to change the landscape to suit themselves, even though the change may not suit others. For example, wilderness mountaintops and tropical islands have been overdeveloped for second homes because the prospective profits for developers were very large relative to the total costs for society. Costs were small for the developers because they were not equitably divided within the society. If something went sour with the development—the lots didn't sell after trees were bulldozed—or if subsequent sewage and pollution control costs spiraled, then someone else, not the developer, absorbed the costs. Thus, the developer reaped a great gain from subdividing, and someone else paid the price. Given this situation, it is scarcely surprising that so much of the world is being destroyed or that diversity is diminishing so rapidly.

A comparable situation exists with respect to the oceans, which our culture treats as an international "common property resource." Since no one or no one nation owns the oceans or their contents, no one has a motive for perpetuating the living diversity of the oceans. Consequently, the precious living treasures of two-thirds of the earth may be less diverse or even depleted in a short time. And there are too many links between oceanic and terrestial life for such a loss to occur without profoundly affecting humanity.

Vive la Différence

MARSTON BATES

[1968]

Some people eat with a knife and fork, others with chop-sticks, and still others use their fingers. Among the knife-and-fork people, the British think Americans are funny because of the way they keep shifting the fork from the left to the right hand; Americans, on the other hand, may be fascinated by the British skill in stashing peas in the mashed potatoes on the back of the fork—held always in the left hand. To each of us, of course, our way of doing things is the right way. This would not matter much if it were not for the complications of the "missionary syndrome," which leads us to try to per-suade other people to abandon their ways and take up ours.

The etiquette of eating is trivial; except maybe at diplomatic dinners, where I suppose that an ambassador might seriously compromise the international standing of his country by picking up the wrong fork. But our attitudes toward food—kinds and ways of eating it— illustrate an intolerance that has deeper and far more serious aspects. This is what led me in my book *Gluttons and Libertines* to start with the idea of ridiculing our attitudes toward sex by finding parallels in the less highly charged attitudes toward food. I soon found myself going beyond food and sex and writing a sort of general plea for the tolerance of diversity. Nicholas Samstag, in an amusing notice in *The Saturday Review,* said the title of the book should have been *"Vive la Différence, or The Spice of Variety."*

I still like my own title, although I must admit that

367

Samstag's suggestion is a better indication of the book's actual contents. As time goes on, I become more and more impressed with the positive value of diversity—with the urgent need for learning tolerance—and I cannot resist the temptation to sound off on the subject once more.

There are, of course, many kinds of diversity. In the world of nature we have the possibility of diversity in the gene pool of a given species of organism; diversity in kinds of plants and animals in a biological community; diversity in kinds of communities, from desert to rain forest or from ocean depths to coral reef.

Diversity in the gene pool of a species provides the raw material for evolution, makes possible adaptation to changing environments, and allows for flexibility. Diversity in the biological community, on the other hand, makes for stability and continuity. This can be seen in the contrast between the relatively simple communities of the far north and the complex aggregations of animals and plants that make up a tropical rain forest or a coral reef. The animal populations in the far north fluctuate greatly, though more or less regularly, from year to year, as is shown by the fur records of the Hudson's Bay Company over a period of a hundred years. In the case of showshoe hares and lynx, an increase in the number of hares is followed by an increase in the predatory lynx, until the hare population is again reduced to scarcity, leading, in turn, to a decline in the numbers of lynx. This results in a fairly regular series of cyclic fluctuations at about ten-year intervals. Such cyclic fluctuations are unknown in the rain forest, where the complexity of prey-predator relations makes for flexibility and results in a relatively steady state for all populations. But the various arguments for maintaining diversity in biological systems are well summarized by that great British ecologist Charles Elton in a chapter on "The Conservation of Variety" in *The Ecology of Invasions*, published in 1958.

The diversity in biological communities has enabled life to take advantage of almost all the varied conditions on our planetary surface—the chief exceptions being ice caps and extreme deserts. What variety there is! Somehow we must keep these varied landscapes from being entirely swamped by human alterations so that future generations can, in some degree, share experience with the wilderness.

There is need for diversity among people, too, whether looked at as individuals, as communities, or as large societies. We try to recognize the need of the individual in our educational system, attempting to give everyone, whatever his future specialty, some background in the arts, the sciences, and the humanities: some experience with differing points of view. That we do not succeed very well is no reflection on the soundness of the idea. In another way, the concept of "vacation" expresses our felt need for refreshing change. The cult of hobbies is, again, a manifestation of diversity in the activities of individuals, and as work becomes more monotonous and more specialized, the need to escape with a vacation or a hobby becomes greater.

Beyond this, there is the matter of role diversity within a society—and culture diversity among societies. Contemporary Western civilization must have a greater variety of possible roles than any previous culture, a consequence of our increasing specialization. Yet there is still a great and valid outcry against the pressures for conformity. I think this is because we have many possible occupations, but few permissible styles of life. The monotony shows in the rows of little boxes in the suburbs, in the standardized education, in the multiplying chain stores and shopping centers, in the routine of the assembly line. And monotony, meaninglessness, and frustration are compounded in our ghettos.

The West, in the last few hundred years, has had a bulldozing effect on other cultures. Our power to enforce our ideas is declining, but it still has considerable momentum. I remember reading somewhere that Indonesia, influenced by Western ideas of modesty, has required the dancing girls of Bali to cover their breasts. The Japanese are said to be somewhat worried about Western attitudes toward their abortion laws. And to me it seems particularly odd to see Japanese, Malays, Hindus, and Nigerians dressed up in our silly Western clothing. There is a growing movement to retain indigenous dress, but it is still not quite respectable in diplomatic circles. I sometimes suspect that the chief trouble with Fidel Castro is his beard and windbreaker. It probably ought to be his interminable speeches—but you can hardly carry out diplomatic negotiations with a man wearing a windbreaker.

The opposite of diversity is uniformity. An interesting word—uniform. Standardized dress serves to depersonalize the soldier, the policeman, the waiter, or bellboy. The effect is to convert individuals into abstractions, symbols of some occupation or hierarchial rank, drab units in a "brave new world."

In this connection I find the nonconforming antics of our young fascinating, and there is plenty of chance for observation in a university environment. They are obviously rebelling against the adult world that they are entering—I can't blame them when I look at the mess we have made of things—and they flaunt the inner rebellion with an outer show of diversity in dress. It at least succeeds in upsetting the police, the school authorities, and, probably, the parents; a reaction that I fail to understand except in terms of our unease about anything different. The "beats" of a few years ago seemed pretty uniform—conforming to the standards of the group, however different these might be from the standards of the larger society. But I see no such uniformity in the youth of today. The only uniformity is the effort to be different, to be individual.

The boys may have long hair or short, sideburns, beards, moustaches, or goatees; they may go barefooted, wear boots or (perhaps most commonly) dirty sneakers. Their trousers may be tight or loose, Levi's or corduroys, or shorts made by attacking trousers with a pair of scissors. They may wear an earring and/or a variety of kinds of ornaments hung around the neck. They sometimes manage to look quite dirty, although I suspect most of them bathe often enough; they haven't gone back to the Saturday-night sponging of our ancestors. What is all the fuss about?

Some of the boys, with their neatly trimmed and combed long hair, look as though they might have stepped out of some castle in the Middle Ages; more, I am afraid, look like seventeenth-century pirates, and their beards are often reminiscent of the fashions of the last century, as are some of the "mod" clothes.

A large proportion of the girls have taken to wearing masculine clothing. This is understandable in practical terms—at least they get pockets. I sometimes wonder, though, at the amount of trouble they must take to look so disheveled; the effect seems contrived rather than accidental.

The consequence of these boy-girl tendencies in dress is to minimize the differences between the sexes, which our traditional clothing exaggerates. I am reminded of Geoffrey Gorer's observation that non-aggressive human societies "make very little distinction between the ideal characters of men and women, particularly that they have no ideal of brave, aggressive masculinity." I really think our young are non-aggressive, although they can be obstinate enough. The fierce posturings are made by people of my generation, in no immediate danger of landing on the firing line.

How do we distinguish right from wrong in the puzzling, relative world in which we live? I like the answer given by Philip Wylie—perhaps best known for *Generation of Vipers*—in a recently published book entitled *The Magic Animal*. It is a shrill, almost paranoid book, which sometimes sounds as though only the author clearly understood what a mess we are making of things. The standard of ethics, the "biological imperative," that he proposes would be to judge actions in terms of the needs of posterity. Not in terms of our own family, or of future Americans or Japanese, but in terms of "all the children of mankind." "To evaluate a culture properly," he writes, "one must balance its gains and deficits in relation to the future generations of all human beings."

This would leave most of our daily behavior ethically neutral, whether concerned with work or play, food or sex (unless unduly contributing to the population problem); but it would condemn our wanton exploitation of resources, our damage to the environment of this "spaceship earth" in which those future generations will have to live. What has this got to do with diversity? It leaves a wide range of tolerance for individual and cultural behavior that is not destructive, and it implies a command to maintain the diversity of the biosphere so that our children, too, can enjoy clear trout streams, giant redwoods, deep canyons, and open spaces.

I think there is a corollary: that we should tolerate diversity in behavior to the extent that it does not damage the continuity of society. Antisocial activities should be classified as "crimes." But who is to decide what is antisocial, and how can it be decided? Murder, genocide, and war seem to me clearly evil, but all can be, and have been, justified in terms of the "good" of continuing society. And I am sure there are people in our country who regard boys wearing earrings as a sign of the collapse of all our treasured values, a mark of social disintegration.

The answer probably lies in "common sense." But whose, yours or mine? We can't all think alike—that would be uniformity instead of diversity. So let's argue— but let's not kill each other in the process.

INDEX

Index

About the Authors

MARSTON BATES (1906–1974) was professor of zoology at the University of Michigan 1952–1971; his twelve books on man and nature include *The Forest and the Sea.*

FRANK A. BEACH (1911–   ) was chairman and curator, Department of Animal Behavior, at The American Museum of Natural History 1942–1946 and is still a research associate. He now teaches psychology at the University of California, Berkeley.

ALAN M. BECK (1942–   ), a mammalogist, holds a doctorate in ecology from Johns Hopkins University. He is currently director of the Bureau of Animal Affairs, New York City.

LAURA BOHANNAN (1922–   ) received her Ph.D. in anthropology at Oxford. She was editor of *American Anthropologist* 1970–1973 and is currently associate professor of anthropology at the University of Illinois.

ROY E. BROWN (1931–   ) is a faculty member at Mount Sinai School of Medicine, specializing in community medicine, nutrition, epidemiology, and pediatrics.

ARCHIE CARR (1909–   ) has been professor of zoology at the University of Florida since 1937 and a research associate of the American Museum of Natural History since 1951. His many books on reptiles include *So Excellent a Fishe*; he received the John Burroughs Medal for nature writing for *The Windward Road.*

EDWIN H. COLBERT (1905–   ) was curator of vertebrate paleontology at The American Museum of Natural History 1943–1970 and is now curator emeritus. He is curator of vertebrate paleontology at the Museum of Northern Arizona.

J. FRANK DOBIE (1888–1964) was professor of English at the University of Texas 1933–1947. His numerous books were chiefly focused on the history and fauna of Texas.

PAUL R. EHRLICH (1932–) has been professor of biology at Stanford University since 1966. His specialty is population biology.

ARTHUR W. GALSTON (1920–) is professor of biology at Yale University.

E. THOMAS GILLIARD (1912–1965) was associated with The American Museum of Natural History for thirty-three years, becoming curator of ornithology in 1962.

HARRY F. HARLOW (1905–) is professor of psychology and director of the Primate Laboratory at the University of Wisconsin.

MARVIN HARRIS (1927–) is professor of anthropology at Columbia University and author of several books, including *Culture, Man, and Nature* and *Cows, Pigs, Wars, and Witches*.

RICHARD M. KLEIN (1923–) is professor of botany at the University of Vermont.

G. H. R. VON KOENIGSWALD (1902–), German paleontologist, worked on Java Man at The American Museum of Natural History 1945–1946. He is now curator of paleoanthropology, Senckenberg-Museum, Frankfurt am Main, Germany.

JOSEPH WOOD KRUTCH (1893–1970), critic, essayist, and teacher, wrote a number of books dealing with man's relation to nature and the universe.

OLIVER LA FARGE (1901–1963) specialized in anthropology and archaeology at Harvard University and twice served as president of the American Association on Indian Affairs. His particular interest in the Navajo is reflected in his Pulitzer Prize novel *Laughing Boy* and other books.

RICHARD BORSHAY LEE (1937–), Canadian anthropologist, is associate professor of anthropology at the University of Toronto and author of *Kalahari: Hunter-Gatherers.*

PAUL S. MARTIN (1928–) is professor of paleoenvironmental studies, Department of Geosciences, University of Arizona.

MARGARET MEAD (1901–) has been associated with the Department of Ethnology of The American Museum of Natural History since 1926; she was curator 1965–1969 and is now curator emeritus. Her books include *Coming of Age in Samoa* and *Sex and Temperament in Three Primitive Societies.*

N. SCOTT MOMADAY (1934–), a Kiowa Indian, is professor of English and comparative literature at Stanford University.

OLAUS J. MURIE (1889–1963) was field biologist for the U.S. Fish and Wildlife Service 1920–1946 and director of the Wilderness Society 1946–1963. His books include *The Elk of North America.*

MAXIMILIAN RENNER (1919–), German zoologist on the staff of the Zoologisches Institut in Munich, is principally concerned with the biology and behavior of bees.

THEODORE ROOSEVELT (1858–1919), President of the United States 1901–1909, was also an explorer, big-game hunter, naturalist, pioneer conservationist, and writer.

GEORGE B. SCHALLER (1933–), German zoologist, is research associate, Institute for Animal Behavior Research, New York Zoological Society, and author of books on animals.

VICTOR B. SCHEFFER (1906–) was wildlife biologist with the U.S. Fish and Wildlife Service 1937–1969. His books include *The Year of the Whale,* which won the John Burroughs Medal for nature writing.

T. C. SCHNEIRLA (1902–1968) was curator, Department of Animal Behavior at The American Museum of Natural History 1943–1968.

GEORGE GAYLORD SIMPSON (1902–) was associated with The American Museum of Natural History from 1927 to 1959 and curator of fossil mammals and birds and chairman, Department of Paleontology and Geology, from 1944. He is presently professor of geosciences at the University of Arizona.

PIERRE TEILHARD DE CHARDIN (1881–1955), French Jesuit paleontologist and philosopher, was one of the discoverers of Peking Man.

LEWIS THOMAS (1913–), formerly professor of pathology, Yale University School of Medicine, is now president of Memorial Sloan-Kettering Cancer Institute.

NIKOLAAS TINBERGEN (1907–), Dutch zoologist, has been professor of animal behavior at Oxford University since 1966. He shared the 1973 Nobel Prize in Physiology and Medicine for his pioneering work in ethology.

COLIN M. TURNBULL (1924–), English-American anthropologist, was associate curator, anthropology, at The American Museum of Natural History 1959–1969 and is now professor of anthropology, Virginia Commonwealth University. His books include *The Mountain People*, a study of the Ik.

KENNETH E. F. WATT (1929–), Canadian zoologist, is professor of zoology, University of California at Davis; his special fields are biomathematics and the ecology of fish and insects.

FRANZ WEIDENREICH (1873–1948), German anatomist and anthropologist, became visiting professor of anatomy and acting director of the Cenozoic Research Laboratory, Peking, China, in 1935 and from 1935 to 1941 was concerned with the excavation of Peking Man. He later worked at The American Museum of Natural History with Dr. G. H. R. von Koenigswald on Java Man.

ARTHUR H. WESTING (1928–   ) has been a research forester with the U.S. Forest Service and associate professor of tree physiology at the University of Massachusetts; he is presently chairman, Department of Biology, Windham College.

GEORGE M. WOODWELL (1928–   ) has been senior ecologist at Brookhaven National Laboratory since 1961.

JOE D. WRAY (1926–   ), member of the field staff, Health Sciences, The Rockefeller Foundation, is an adviser to the rural health program of Ramathibodi Teaching Hospital, Bangkok, Thailand.